BE

Jane Messer was born in Melbourne and travelled widely before settling in Sydney. She is a writer and teacher with a special interest in insomnia. Her short stories, reviews and articles have appeared in a range of Australian journals and her first novel, *Night by Night*, was published in 1994.

BEDLAM
an anthology of sleepless nights

Selected and introduced by
Jane Messer

ALLEN & UNWIN

For Michiel,
and Lottie—may you always rest easy

Publication of this title was assisted by the
Australia Council, the Federal Government's
arts funding and advisory body.

First published in 1996 by
Allen & Unwin Pty Ltd
9 Atchison Street, St Leonards, NSW 2065 Australia
Phone: (61 2) 9901 4088
Fax: (61 2) 9906 2218
E-mail: 100252.103@compuserve.com

National Library of Australia
Cataloguing-in-Publication entry:

Bedlam: an anthology of sleepless nights.

 ISBN 1 86448 072 6.

 1. Insomnia—Literary collections. 2. Sleep—Literary
 collections. I. Messer, Jane, 1960– .

808.80353

Set in 9.5/12pt Schoolbook by DOCUPRO, Sydney
Printed by Australian Print Group, Maryborough, Vic.
10 9 8 7 6 5 4 3 2

CONTENTS

ACKNOWLEDGMENTS

My thanks go to the enthusiasts who encouraged me in my obsession, in particular my publisher Sophie Cunningham. Thanks also to Jane Gleeson-White for her helpful comments and the warmth of her interest, my agent Margaret Connolly for her sympathy, Kath Prokhovnik for helpful touches, and to Michiel Gerber who thought it was a great idea from the start and all along. Elizabeth and Craig McIlwain assisted greatly with library searches. Special thanks go to Claine Keily, without whose help the anthology might not have been completed. Her enthusiasm, and editorial and research assistance were invaluable. Many people who have contributed suggestions, always welcome and sometimes used, and I thank them all.

Two articles by Professor Ernest L. Fontana provided insights and leads. They are 'Literary Insomnia', *New Orleans Review*, Volume 17, Number 2, 1990, and 'Insomnia in Raymond Carver's Fiction', *Studies in Short Fiction*, Newberry, 1989, Fall, 26:4, p.447. Italo Calvino is quoted briefly in my introduction to Colette (from *Six Memos for The Next Millennium*, Vintage, 1988). E.M. Forster's remarks in the Introduction are from his *Aspects Of The Novel*, Harcourt Brace Jovanovich, 1955. The biography of Carson McCullers, *The Lonely Hunter*, is by Virginia Spencer Carr, Carroll & Graf Publishers. Remarks by Hanah Arendt are drawn from her foreword to *Daguerreotypes and Other Essays*, The University of Chicago Press, 1979, Copyright of the Rungstedlund Foundation.

Every effort has been made to contact copyright holders; in the event of an inadvertent omission or error, the editor should be notified at Allen & Unwin, PO Box 8500, St Leonards, 2065, NSW Australia. For permission to reprint the poems, stories and excerpts in this anthology, acknowledgment has been sought as follows:

Gaston Bachelard, *The Right to Dream*, translated by J.A. Underwood, © 1988 Dallas Institute Publications. Permission granted by the Dallas Institute Publications.

Phillip K. Dick, *Do Androids Dream of Electric Sheep?*, Granada Publishing, Panther, 1972.

Isak Dinesen, 'Night Walk' from *Last Tales*, translated by Sidste Fortaellinger, © 1957 by Random House and renewed by the Rungstedlund Foundation.

Stephen Dixon, *Quite Contrary—The Mary and Newt Story*, Harper & Row Publishers, © Stephen Dixon.

Fyodor Dostoevsky, *Notes From Underground*, Robert G. Durgy (ed.), translated by Serge Shishkoff, Thomas Y. Crowell Company.

Marguerite Duras, *10:30 On a Summer Night*, translated by Anne Borchardt. Used by permission of Grove/Atlantic, Inc. © 1962 by Marguerite Duras.

Louise Erdrich, *The Blue Jay's Dance—A Birth Year*, HarperCollins Publishers UK, 1996.

Gwen Harwood, *Bone Scan*, HarperCollins Publishers, Australia.

Ernest Hemingway, 'A Clean, Well-Lighted Place' by permission of the Hemingway Foreign Rights Trust. All rights outside US, Hemingway Foreign Rights Trust, by deed of Mary Hemingway 16 March 1962 as widow and sole legatee of the author.

Elizabeth Jolley *The George's Wife*, © Elizabeth Jolley, 1993. Used by permission of Penguin Books Australia.

Franz Kafka, *Diaries of Franz Kafka*, translated by Will and Edwin Muir, published by Martin Secker & Warburg Ltd. Used by permission of Reed Books, UK.

Yasunari Kawabata, *House of the Sleeping Beauties and Other Stories*, translated by Edward Seidensticker, published by Kodansha International Ltd. English © 1969 by Kodansha International Ltd. All rights reserved. Reprinted by permission.

Gilliam Mears, *The Mint Lawn*, Allen & Unwin, © Gillian Mears 1991.

Gabriel García Márquez, *Innocent Eréndira and Other Stories*, Picador, 1981 translated by Gregory Rabassa, © Harper and Row Publishers Inc. 1978, by permission Random House UK.

Haruki Marakami, *The Elephant Vanishes*, translated by Jay Rubin, Alfred A. Knopf, 1993.

When you lie down at night
turning from side to side
and you can't be satisfied no way you do
Old Man Blues got you

Leadbelly

INTRODUCTION

Many of literature's best known characters have spent nights sleepless: Hamlet and Macbeth, Heathcliff and Catherine, Humbert Humbert, Roderick Usher, Don Quixote and Isabel Archer, to name a few.[1] Yet sleeplessness, though key to many narratives, has generally not been regarded as a subject in itself, as for instance, sleep and dreams have been. These other states have enjoyed the favour of critics' and readers' imaginations, and we are familiar with their well-worn metaphors: sleep as death or peace, and dreams as prophesy or freedom.

It is insomnia's ambiguous, threshold qualities that have perhaps caused it to be passed over. Insomnia is a restless state that lies between sleep and wakefulness, insentience and cognisance. It is not clearly one or the other; you can be very sleepy, yet awake, or be half-asleep, yet still awake. Sleep, dreams and waking have time on their side too, because they coincide with night and day. This temporal concurrence helps us recognise them as distinct states.

Why isn't sleeplessness the same as wakefulness? Sleeplessness is vague and troubled: people doze and half-dream, sleep-walk, even act as the undead, as zombies. Insomniacs see and think things that others cannot, since those others are bedded down asleep. Insomniacs unearth secrets. Or, like Jorge Luis Borges's young Funes who can remember everything—even the 'marbled grain in the design of a leather-bound book' seen years earlier—they recall vast pasts. Insomniacs see transgressions, and go places and do things without witnesses. Insomnia can be a private madness. The insomniac's madness is unseen by the sleeping, rational, normal world. Charlotte Perkins Gilman draws a horrifying portrait of the confined wife secretly losing her mind as she watches the yellow, intricately patterned and torn wallpaper: 'He thought I was asleep first, but I wasn't and lay there for hours trying to decide whether that front pattern and the back pattern really did move together or separately'.

Insomnia can also be simple privacy, a time to oneself in which to think and watch and feel what may. Charmian Clift, traveller, writer, mother and wife, wrote, 'Perhaps, in a busy and eventful life, these night-watches are the only times when one can ever be truly alone, and there is a sort of elation in this, a sense of quickened heartbeats, of heightened perceptions, of self-surprise'.

A person who wants to go to sleep, or who ought to be asleep, or who is conscious of their state as insomnia, is separated from other good citizens by the affliction, though we must be careful not to always regard it as suffering. Colette cannot sleep for pleasure in 'Night Without Sleep', a vignette in which she looks upon her lover all night long. Celine's Ferdinand declares proudly, 'My trouble is insomnia. If I had always slept properly, I'd never have written a line.'

Certainly the absence of sleep does not necessarily suggest sleep's desirability. It is like pain, which for the masochist and dominatrix needn't imply its opposite—absence of pain; or hunger, which for the martyr and anorexic doesn't evoke the desirability of food. Those who enjoy pain, hunger or sleeplessness may sometimes be the most marginal of our bedfellows, but those insomniacs do transform insomnia from being a dull problem into a positive idea capable of shaping consciousness. In *Notes from Underground*, Dostoevsky's retired clerk is constantly conscious. He sometimes sleeps, at other times suffers from insomnia, nevertheless his consciousness is unceasing. He is always aware of his thoughts, and is entirely alone and opposed to the world because of this. 'Dostoevsky's Epilepsy' is a disputed disease that describes a state of illumination and omnipotence that comes prior to an epileptic fit; the clerk's consciousness is thoroughly diseased in this way.

Like the distress that can accompany these compulsions, insomnia has its own insistence and despair. Marcel Proust, infamously and amply practised at the art of insomnia, a writer who produced great work during the night, wanted to sleep. He wrote often to his mother saying so. Both a banal and an extraordinary insomniac, Proust accused his mother of colluding with the servants to keep him awake: 'I simply can't understand your behaviour . . . I've spent every night since I came back in weeping, and not without good cause . . . Today, when I had a choking fit [asthma], I was so misguided as to ring for Marie who'd just told me she'd finished her lunch, and you immediately punished me for it, as soon as I'd taken my trional, by seeing to it that there was a noise of hammering and shouting all day.' Of course many other writers have written during insomnia, though we think of Proust first: William Shakespeare, Rainer Maria Rilke, Franz Kafka, Gertrude Stein (the writing was her 'nightly miracle'), Emily Brontë and Lewis Carol to name a few.

Sleep's dreams kept Franz Kafka awake: 'Again it was the power of my dreams, shining forth into wakefulness even before I was asleep, which did not let me sleep'. Thus, another ambiguity and absurdity: sleeplessness speaks of opportunity and deprivation. (Insomnia is *absurd*.) Gaston Bachelard meditates on this ambivalence in shapely terms. Insomnia 'preserves the geometry of day—except that that geometry has of course loosened its stays . . .'. Bachelard figures sleeplessness as a failure of the necessary 'irrational, Schopenhaurian will'. He recognises the extraordinary in sleeplessness, but thinks it comical, that its dreams and nightmares don't have sincerity. Maurice Blanchot argues similarly, that insomniacs are more of less guilty, because sleeping 'with eyes open is an anomaly symbolically indicating something which the general consciousness does not approve of'. We can credit him the guilty Macbeth, and Dante's *Inferno* in which insomnia is a punishment given to the dammed Paolo and Francesca. Buffeted by winds they are constantly restless: only 'the innocent sleep'.

Sometimes, if you are like black-eyed Heathcliff walking the damp moors, you are very much awake. His insomnia is his anguish, and like the beheaded, staring Macbeth in Roman Polanski's film *Macbeth*, Heathcliff literally dies wide awake. In Polanski's film, Macbeth has been beheaded by his enemies, and the hooraying soldiers have impaled his head—eyes open and staring—on a pole. Showing it off, one of the soldiers runs in a circle inside a ring of his cheering comrades. Suddenly, the camera changes its point of view, and we are *inside* Macbeth's head, looking out of his dead, open—insomniac— eyes, seeing what he sees, the blurred rush of craven men.

Polanski and Emily Brontë overturn the conventional metaphor of sleep as death. For Macbeth and Heathcliff, the boundaries between waking and sleeping, life and death, are confounded. Their sleeplessness is their death and so for them sleep cannot be death. Mrs Dean is fascinated as she looks at the dead Heathcliff, because his staring eyes are so atemporal. His insomnia defies the ordinary rigours of time.

Many of the writers included here portray insomnia as beyond time: the insomniac is an immortal being whose reality makes sleep seem sentimental by comparison. During insomnia, one's consciousness can be so extraordinary as to make dreams seem prosaic. Isak Dinesen describes sleepers as the 'living dead'; only insomniacs are truly alive. This bravura of constant, ceaseless consciousness is the hallmark of the tradition of sleeplessness in literature, be it figured literally or symbolically.

There is a tradition of literary insomnia. It has been employed as a literal subject, contributing to plot and characterisation; and as a metaphoric sign, as with Anton Chekhov's 'A Case History' in which the sick girl's 'honourable' insomnia is a consequnce of workers' enslavement. On a more practical level, sleeplessness has also given structure to narratives such as Baldwin's *Giovanni's Room*, where the tale is told over the course of a single sleepless night. Ernest Fontana, an American academic, argues that Raymond Carver's insomnia affected his distinctive minimalist technique. Carver increasingly used the present tense and dramatic monologues, which mimic the individual act of insomnia, rather than the third person discursive narrative.

Women can claim a particular place in the writing of sleeplessness, because it is so private and they have lived, and do still live such privatised lives. Insomnia works as a trope for the perceived impossibility of self-expression. Woman's inability to control her own physical existence, particularly the sexual and moral dangers associated with the night—the hours of insomnia—mark literature about and by women. Dependent on Macbeth, Lady Macbeth is frustrated in her ambitions. But she is also too ambitious, and her sleeplessness is her self-imposed punishment. She sleep-walks, nightly washing the dead King Duncan's blood from her hands, both awake and asleep. Gilman's narrator in *The Yellow Wallpaper* goes mad in the confines of the nursery room, not allowed by her husband, a physician, to go out. Sylivia Plath's Esther Green-wood is overwhelmed, in terms that would be familiar to Virginia Woolf, by her need to be a writer and her fear of what it entails to be a woman. Esther has insomnia for a month and lives beneath her mattress (bettering Kafka who slept with his arms crossed to feel their weight like a soldier with his pack). Emily Holmes Coleman's young mother in *The Shutter of Snow* goes mad after the birth of her child. Sepa-rated from her baby in an asylum, she is sleepless. The child is both the cause of her madness, and the thing she wants most when she is privately, madly, awake. These sleepless women are 'women of the night'; not prostitutes, but insomni-acs.

This is not merely a light pun. Bram Stoker (a celibate, though married) well understood the implications of the night, a woman's sensuality, and sleeplessness. Vampires must be 'bidden' by their victims. Young Lucy is a pretty woman with three suitors—a sensualist and thus susceptible to Dracula's call. By contrast, her friend Mina is demure and already devoted to one man. As Dracula approaches England by ship, Lucy is increasingly wakeful and agitated in her sleep, until the fatal night when she leaves her bed and meets him at the West Cliff and is 'taken' by him. Once bitten, Lucy is essen-tially no longer a virgin.

Vampires, ghouls and zombies are the living dead, and in this way form one far definitional edge of insomnia. They're neither alive nor dead; neither asleep nor awake. There is Mary Shelley's monster who, once he is brought out of the deep sleep of death, is constantly awake by being alive. His life is indeed an affliction. 'Dostoevsky's Epilepsy', whether the disease be real or not, is another boundary, its omniscient consciousness representing the wakefulness of insomnia. Last, and appropriately for this anthology, there is Scheherazade, the great storyteller who saved her own and other virgins' lives by telling her king a thousand and one tales for as many nights. Scheherazade gave readers and writers the experience of never-ending stories within stories. Insomnia is certainly the friend of literature.

In bringing together these works, I once imagined Ernest Hemingway's soldier from 'Now I Lay Me Down' lying in bed with Gilman's wife from *The Yellow Wallpaper*. Are they impossible bedmates or could they go to sleep together? Hemingway metaphorises women as a possible end to insomnia. In 'A Clean Well-Lighted Place' there is the suggestion that a woman would be a cure for insomnia. However, Hemingway's sleeplessness signals unending despair, for which a woman's flesh is no panacea. In fact, this anthology does place these impossible bedmates together between the sheets. It has insomniacs from ancient to modern literature lying down together. What a torment of tossing and turning—and conversation—there might be.

While trying to tuck-in Hemingway and Gilman, I was reading E. M. Forster's *Aspects of the Novel*, where he instructs the reader to visualise a group of novelists from various centuries and schools 'as seated together in a room, a circular room, a sort of British Museum reading-room—all writing their novels simultaneously . . . That is to be our vision of them— an imperfect vision, but it is suited to our power, it will preserve us from a serious danger, the danger of pseudo-scholarship.'

While asserting that there is a tradition of sleeplessness in literature, I do not wish to press too hard upon it as a mould, to insist too exactly upon this tradition's shape. In introducing the pieces I have sometimes suggested an interpretation that if not always scholarly is certainly readerly. I hope these introductions are not too intrusive. They are intended only to set the context, and to give some idea of what caught this anthologist's eye—I can't help but share my enthusiasm. The selections themselves span many years and continents and languages. I chose those which interested if not enthralled me, and searched for insomniacs in the crevices that might be overlooked, such as in prison, or with child.

The idea of *Bedlam* came about through my work as a fiction writer and yes, my experience as an insomniac. I had been an insomniac who was writing a novel about a bookseller who doesn't sleep. The bookseller collects books with passages about sleeplessness, copying out the passages in an old note-book. One day she flippantly describes these notes as an 'anthology of sleepless nights in literature'. Some time after placing those words on the page, I realised that this fictional book could indeed be a real book. I continued to write the novel, and began to collect books and put aside others that I had kept on my shelves for years which had beautifully written, interesting and insightful stories or passages about insomnia. Friends and colleagues came forward with suggestions. I searched databases for writing about literary insomnia, but found them very thin. Ah! Not just a gap in the market, a gap in others' thinking. This is how the book progressed, with my ideas about literary insomnia being formed as I went along, the whole a work of love and obsession.

Note

1 Unfortunately not all the writers mentioned in the Introduction have been able to be included in this anthology.

QUEEN INSOMNIA

SCHEHERAZADE

The First of the Thousand Nights and One Night

With so many sleepless nights ahead of Scheherazade and the King, it seems proper to begin this anthology with the first tales. The Thousand Nights *begins with two kings taking revenge upon their adulterous wives. Having executed his first wife, King Shahryár goes on to take a virgin nightly, beheading each young woman on the following day—until he meets Scheherazade. By leaving her tales unfinished on morning's approach, Scheherazade excites the King's curiosity to hear more the next night, and thus stays his order to behead her. Finally, on the thousand and first night, the King exclaims that she has indeed taught him well with her stories, and that his soul has been changed. And so Scheherazade saves her own life and that of many other women with her storytelling.*

Originating as oral stories in Persia and Arabia, the tales were first introduced into western Europe with a French translation based on a 14th or 15th century Egyptian compilation. The following extract was translated into English by Powys Mathers from the French translation of J. C. Mardrus. (It was possibly the 1888 translation by the English explorer Sir Richard Burton that Isak Dinesen, also included in this anthology, read, the Nights *being much loved by her.)*

The Tale of King Shahryár and of his Brother, King Shahzamán

It is related—But Alláh is all wise and all knowing, all powerful and all beneficent—that there was, in the tide and show of ancient time and the passage of the age and of the moment, a king among the kings of Sásán, in the isles of India and China. He was master of armies and auxiliaries, of slaves and of a great following; and he had two sons, one tall and the other small. Both were heroic horsemen; but the taller was the greater in this exercise and reigned over lands and governed with justice among men, so that the peoples of the land and of the kingdom loved him. His name was King Shahryár. The smaller brother was called King Shahzamán and ruled over Samarkand al-Ajam.

Both lived in their countries and were just rulers of the people for a space of twenty years; by the end of which time each was at the height of his splendour and his growth.

This was the way with them until the tall king was seized by a violent longing to see his brother. Then he commanded his wazír to depart and return with him: and the wazír answered: 'I hear and I obey.'

The wazír set out and, arriving in all security by the grace of Alláh, entered the presence of the brother, wished him peace, and told him the purpose of his journey.

King Shahzamán answered: 'I hear and I obey.' Then he made preparations for his departure and for the going out of his tents, his camels, and mules; his slaves and fighting-men. Lastly he raised his own wazír to the governorship, and departed to seek the lands of his brother.

But, in the middle of the night, he recalled a thing which he had left forgotten at the palace. Returning and entering, he found his wife stretched on her bed and being embraced by a black slave. At this sight, the world darkened before his face and he said within his soul: 'If such a thing has come to pass when I have hardly left the city, what would the conduct of this wanton be if I were absent for long at my brother's house?' So he drew his sword and with one stroke killed them upon the carpets of the bed. Then he returned, ordering his camp to move forward, journeyed through the night till he came to his brother's city.

His brother rejoiced at his approach, went out to meet him and greeting him, wished him peace; also he adorned the city for him, and began to speak with him jovially. But King Shahzamán remembered the affair of his wife, and a cloud of grief veiled him; his cheeks became sallow and his body frail.

King Shahryár, seeing him in this pass and thinking it was due to his exile from lands and kingdom, questioned him no further on the subject and let him be. But, on a later day, he said: 'My brother, I know not! and yet I see your body grow frail and your cheeks sallow.' Shahzamán answered: 'My brother, I am stricken in the heart of my heart.' But he did not reveal what he had seen happen to his wife. So King Shahryár continued: 'Then come hunting and coursing with me, for in that pursuit perhaps your breast may throw off this trouble.' King Shahzamán had no wish to do so; and his brother went out to hunt alone.

Now there were in the King's palace certain windows that looked on to the garden, and, as King Shahzamán leaned there and looked out, the door of the palace opened and twenty women slaves with twenty men slaves came from it; and the wife of the King, his brother, was among them and walked there in all her bright beauty. When they came to the pool of a fountain they all undressed and mingled one with another. Suddenly, on the King's wife crying: 'O Masud! Yá Masud!', a gigantic negro ran towards her, embraced her, and turning her upon her back, enjoyed her. At this signal, all the other men slaves did the same with the women and they continued thus a long while, not ceasing their kisses and embraces and goings in and the like until the approach of dawn.

At this sight the King's brother said within himself: 'By Alláh, mine is even a lighter misfortune than his.' So he let his grief and discontent slip from him, saying to himself: 'Truly, this is more terrible than all which happened to me.' And from that moment he began to drink again and to eat without pause.

Meanwhile the King, his brother, came back from hunting, and the two wished each other peace. Then King Shahryár, observing his brother Shahzamán, saw that colour and life had come back to him and further that he, who had so long dealt sparingly with his food, now ate abundantly. So, in his astonishment, he asked him the explanation of this; and the other answered: 'Listen and I will tell you the cause of my former pallor. When you sent your wazír to me to require my presence at your side, I made my preparation for departure and left my city. But afterwards, remembering the present which I destined for you and which I gave you at the palace,

I went back and found my wife lying with a black slave, the two sleeping upon the carpets of my bed. I killed the pair of them and made my way to you, thrice wretched in my thought for what had happened. That was the cause of my former paleness and loss of strength. As for the return of colour to my cheeks, spare me, I pray, from speaking of it.'

When his brother heard these words, he said: 'By Alláh, I conjure you to tell me the other half of the matter!' So King Shahzamán told him all he had seen. And King Shahryár exclaimed: 'First must I see this with my own eyes!' To this his brother answered: 'Make it appear, then, that you are going out to hunt and course; but hide instead with me, and you shall be witness of the sight and see the truth of it!'

Immediately the King proclaimed his departure by the public crier and the soldiers went out beyond the city with their tents. The King went forth also and, settling himself in his tents, said to his young slaves: 'Let no one enter!' Then he disguised himself and, leaving secretly, went towards the palace where his brother was. On his arrival he stationed himself at the window giving on to the garden. Scarcely had an hour passed when the women slaves, circling about their mistress, came into the garden with the men slaves; and they did all that Shahzamán had told of them and passed the time in these diversions until asr, the beginning of the sun's decline.

When King Shahryár saw these things, reason fled from her seat in his mind and he said to his brother Shahzamán: 'Let us go hence and fare forth to seek our destiny upon the road of Alláh; for we have no right in royalty, nor shall have, until we have found someone who has met a fate like ours: without that, in truth, death would be better than our lives.' To this his brother made the fitting answer and both went out by a secret door of the palace. They travelled night and day until they came to a tree in the middle of a lonely meadow near the salt sea. In this meadow there was an eyelet of fresh water at which they drank and afterwards sat down to rest. An hour had hardly passed when the sea began to be troubled and suddenly a column of black smoke came up out of it which rose to the sky and moved towards the meadow. Seeing this, they became afraid and climbed as high as they were able into the tall tree, and began to consider what this might mean.

Then, behold! the smoke column changed to a Jinní of great size, vast-shouldered, gigantically-breasted, and carrying on his head a box. He put foot to the earth, came towards the tree in which they were, and stopped below it. Then he lifted the lid of the box and took from it a large coffer which he also opened; and thereupon appeared a desirable young girl, bright in her beauty, shining like the sun. As the poet says:

> She comes, a torch in the shadows, and it is day;
> Her light more brightly lights the dawn.
> Suns leap from out her beauty
> And moons are born in the smiling of her eyes.
> Ah, that the veils of her mystery might be rent
> And the folk of the world lie ravished at her feet.
> Forced by the great light of her sweet glancing
> Wet tears smart forth from every watching eye.

When the Jinní had looked long at the beauty of the girl, he said to her: 'O Queen of every silky thing! O you whom I ravished away upon your bridal night! I would sleep a little.' And the Jinní, resting his head upon the knees of the young girl, went to sleep.

Then the child raised her head and saw the two kings hidden in the tree-top. At once she lifted the head of the Jinní from her knees, rested it upon the ground, and stood up beneath the tree, saying to them by signs: 'Come down. Have no fear of this Ifrít.' They also answered by signs: 'Alláh be with you! Pray excuse us from such a dangerous undertaking!' She said: 'I conjure you by Alláh! Come down quickly, or I will warn the Ifrít and he shall kill you with the worst of deaths!' Then they were afraid and came down beside her; and she said at once: 'Come, pierce me violently with your lances; if not, I will wake the Ifrít.' Then Shahryár said fearfully to Shahzamán: 'You, my brother, do first what she requires!' To which the other answered: 'I will do nothing until you have given me an example, my elder brother!' And each began to coax the other, making with their eyes gestures of coupling. Then she said: 'Why do I see you working your eyes in this way? If you do not come forward and do it to me at once, I will wake the Ifrít.' So, in their fear of the Jinní, they both did to her as she had commanded, and when they were well wearied, she said: 'You are indeed experienced riders!' Then, drawing from her pocket a little bag, she took from it a necklace of five hundred and seventy seal-rings, saying: 'Know you what these are?' And they answered: 'We do not know.' Then she said: 'The givers of these seal-rings have all coupled with me on the unwitting horns of this Ifrít. So now, O brothers, give me yours!' Then they gave her their seal-rings, taking them off their hands. Whereon she said: 'Know that this Ifrít carried me off on the night of my marriage, imprisoned me in a coffer and placed that coffer in a box and fastened about the box seven chains, yes, and then laid me at the bottom of the moaning sea that wars and dashes with its waves. But he did not know that whenever any one of us women desires a thing, nothing can prevent her from it. And the poet said, besides:

Friend, trust not at all in women, smile at their promising,
For they lower or they love at the caprice of their parts.
Filled to the mouth with deceit, they lavish a lying love
Even while the very floss fringing their silks is faithless.
Respect and remember the words of Yúsuf. Forget not
Ibíls worked all Adam's woe with one woman.
Rail not, my friend. At this house, at whom you are railing,
Mild love tomorrow will give place to madness.
Say not: 'If I love, I'll escape the follies of loving,'
But rather: 'Only a miracle brings a man safe from among them.'

At these words the brothers marvelled even to the limits of marvelling and said to each other: 'If this be a Jinní and in spite of his power much more terrible things have happened to him than to us, it is an adventure which ought to console us!'

So at that same hour they left the young woman and returned each to his own city.

When King Shahryár entered his palace, he caused his wife's head to be cut off at the neck, and in the same way the heads of the slaves, both men and women. Then he ordered his wazír to bring him every night a young and virgin girl, whom he ravished and when the night had passed, caused to be slain. This he did for three long years; so that the people were all one cry of grief, one tumult of horror. They fled away with such daughters as remained to them and in all the city there remained not one girl who retained the state to serve for this assault.

At last the King, as was his custom, ordered the wazír to bring him a young girl; and the wazír went forth and hunted, but found no girl at all. So he returned to his own home, dejected and wretched and with his soul full of his fear of the King.

Now this wazír had himself two daughters who in the matters of beauty, charm, brilliance, perfection, and delicate taste, were each unrivalled save by the other. The name of the elder was Shahrazád, and that of the younger Dunyazád. Shahrazád had read the books, the annals, and the legends of old kings, together with the histories of past peoples. Also she was credited with possessing a thousand books of stories telling of the peoples, the kings, and the poets of bygone ages and of past time. She was sweetly eloquent of speech and to listen to her was music.

When she had looked at her father, she said: 'Why do I see you so bowed and changed with care and sorrow? Know, my father, that the poet says: "Thou who art sad, oh be comforted; for nothing endures and as every joy vanishes away so also vanishes every sorrow!" '

When the wazír heard these words, he told his daughter from beginning to end all that had happened concerning the King. Then Shahrazád said: 'By Alláh, father, you must marry me to this king; for either I shall live or, dying, I shall be a ransom for the daughters of the Mussulmáns and the cause of their deliverance out of the hands of the King.' Then said he: 'Alláh be with you! You shall never expose yourself to such a danger.' And she answered: 'It is necessary that I do this.' So he said to her: 'Take care that the fate of the ass with the bull and the husbandman befall not you also. Listen':

The Fable of the Ass, the Bull and the Husbandman

Know, my daughter, that there was once a merchant, master of riches and cattle, married and the father of children; to whom Alláh had also given understanding of the tongues of beasts and birds. The place of this merchant's house was in a fertile land on the bank of a river, and in his farm there were an ass and a bull.

One day the bull came to the stable where the ass was lodged and found it well swept and watered, with well-winnowed barley in the manger and on the ground well-sifted straw, and the ass lying there at his ease. (For when his master mounted him it would only be for some short ride that chance demanded, and the ass would quickly return to his rest.) Now on that day the merchant heard the bull say to the ass: 'Give you joy of your food, and may you find it healthy, profitable, and of a good digestion! I myself am weary; but you are rested. You eat well-winnowed barley and are catered for; and if, on occasion, your master mounts you, he brings you quickly back. As for me I am but used to labour and to work the mill.' And the ass said: 'When you go out into the field and they put the yoke upon your neck, throw yourself to the earth and do not rise, even if they beat you; also, when you do get up, fall down again immediately. And after, if they let you back to the byre and give you beans to eat, leave them, as if you were ill. Force yourself in this way not to eat or drink for a day or two or even three. Thus you will rest from your labour and your weariness.'

Remember that the merchant was there and heard their words.

When the husbandman came to give forage to the bull, he saw that he ate very little; and when in the morning he took him out to work he found him to be ill. Then the merchant said to the husbandman: 'Take the ass and make him work in the bull's place for the whole day!' So the man returned and took the ass in place of the bull and made it labour during the whole day.

When the ass came back to the stable at the end of the day, the bull thanked him for his goodness of heart and for having let him rest from his fatigue. But the ass answered nothing and, instead, repented very bitterly.

Next day the husbandman came and took the ass again and made him work till the fall of day; so that the ass returned with a galled neck and broken by fatigue. Then the bull, seeing

the state he was in, began to thank him with effusion and
load him with praises. To which the ass replied: 'How restful
were the days before this, when nothing but luxury was my
lot,' and added: 'Meanwhile I will give you a piece of good
advice; I heard our master say: "If the bull does not get up
from his place, we must hand him over to the slaughterer to
kill and to make a leather cloth for the table!" I am much
afraid for your safety.'

When the bull heard the ass's words, he thanked him and
said: 'To-morrow I will go with them freely and attend to my
labours.' With that he began to eat and swallowed all the
forage and even licked the bushel clean with his tongue.

Remember their master saw and heard all this.

When the day came the merchant went out with his wife
towards the byres and both of them sat down. Then the
husbandman came and took out the bull who, at the sight of
his master, began to frisk his tail and loudly break wind and
gallop wildly in all directions. The merchant was seized with
such a laughter that he rolled on his back. His wife asked:
'What are you laughing at?' He answered: 'At a thing which I
have seen and heard, but of which I may not tell you without
dying.' And she said: 'You must tell me the reason of your
laughter, even if you have to die for it.' He said: 'I cannot tell
you, because I fear to die.' Then said she: 'I know, you are
laughing at me.' After this she did not cease to quarrel and
confound him with wilful words until she drove him into great
perplexity. Finally, he made his children come to him and sent
to call the kádí and witnesses, wishing to make his will before
he should tell the secret to his wife and die. For he greatly
loved his wife, since she was the daughter of his father's
brother and the mother of his children, and since he had lived
with her for one hundred and twenty years. Further, he invited
all his wife's relatives and the folk of the district and, relating
the story, told them how he would die on the instant of
revealing his secret. Then all who were present said to the
wife: 'Allåh be with you! Leave this matter on one side lest
your husband, the father of your children, die.' But she
answered: 'I will never leave him in peace until he tells me,
even if he has to die for it.' So they stopped reasoning with
her; and the merchant rose from among them and went, by

the side of the stable, towards the garden, in order that he might first make his death ablution there and then return to tell his secret and to die.

Now the merchant had a valiant cock which could satisfy fifty hens, and also a dog. And he heard the dog calling to the cock and scolding it, saying: 'Are you not ashamed of being so gay when our master is on the point of death?' Then the cock asked the dog how this was so, and, when the dog had told him the story, he exclaimed: 'By Alláh, our master is extraordinarily lacking in intelligence! I myself have fifty wives, and I succeed very well by contenting one and scolding another, while he, who has only one wife, does not know the way of dealing even with her. It is quite simple; he has but to cut himself some good mulberry twigs, go back in strength to his private room, and beat her until she either dies or repents. She will not importune him with any questions on any subject after that, I do assure you.' So the cock spoke, and when the merchant heard him, light returned to his reason and he resolved to beat his wife.

Here the wazír paused in his story and said to his daughter Shahrazád: 'It may be I shall do to you as the merchant did to his wife.' She asked him: 'What did he do?' And the wazír continued:

The merchant entered his wife's chamber, after having cut and hidden about him certain mulberry twigs, and called to her saying: 'Come into my private room that I may tell you my secret, out of the sight of all, and then die.' So she entered with him and he shut the door of the private room and fell upon her with redoubled blows until she swooned away. Finally, when she could speak, she cried: 'I repent! I repent!' and, beginning to caress her husband's hands and feet, did repent in very truth. Afterwards she walked out with him, and all the relatives and those gathered there rejoiced. Happy and prosperous were the fortunes of them all until their deaths.

Thus he spoke, and when Shahrazád, the wazír's daughter, heard her father's story, she said: 'Even so, my father, I wish you to do what I have asked you.' So the wazír, without insisting further, had the wedding garments of his daughter Shahrazád made ready, and then went to tell the matter to King Shahryár.

Meanwhile, Shahrazád gave these instructions to her young sister: 'When I am with the King I will send to fetch you; then when you have come and when you see the King finish his act with me, you must say: "Tell me, my sister, some of your stories of marvel that the night may pass pleasantly." Then will I tell you tales which, if Alláh wills, shall be the deliverance of the daughters of the Mussulmáns.'

After this the wazír, her father, came to take her and went up with her into the presence of the King. And the King, being overborne with happiness, said to him: 'Is the needful thing indeed present?' And respectfully the wazír answered: 'Yes!'

But when the King wished to take the young girl, she began to weep, so that he asked: 'What ails you?' She answered: 'O my King, I have a little sister and I would say my farewells to her.' So the King sent for the little sister, who came and threw herself upon the neck of Shahrazád, and lastly cowered down beside the bed.

Then the King rose and, taking the maiden Shahrazád, ravished her virginity.

Afterwards they spoke together and Dunyazád said to Shahrazád: 'Alláh be with you! Tell us, my sister, some of your tales of marvel, that the night may pass pleasantly.' And Shahrazád answered: 'Gladly and as a duty, if the great and courteous King permits.' When the King heard these words, and being moreover unable to sleep, he was in no way averse to listening to the tale of Shahrazád.

And Shahrazád, this first night, began the following tale . . .

A Woman's Flesh

ERNEST HEMINGWAY

Hemingway has written a number of stories that could be included here. For instance, in 'Now I Lay Me' the wounded soldier Nick Adams is afraid to go to sleep. To pass the time he recounts all the fishing trips he has made and the people he has known. His attempt to remember all the women he has known intimately doesn't succeed in putting him to sleep either. In the story below, two men discuss how best one might sleep.

Born in 1899, Hemingway committed suicide in 1961.

A Clean, Well-Lighted Place

It was late and everyone had left the café except an old man who sat in the shadow the leaves of the tree made against the electric light. In the daytime the street was dusty, but at night the dew settled the dust and the old man liked to sit late because he was deaf and now at night it was quiet and he felt the difference. The two waiters inside the café knew that the old man was a little drunk, and while he was a good client they knew that if he became too drunk he would leave without paying, so they kept watch on him.

'Last week he tried to commit suicide,' one waiter said.

'Why?'

'He was in despair.'

'What about?'

'Nothing.'

'How do you know it was nothing?'

'He has plenty of money.'

They sat together at a table that was close against the wall near the door of the café and looked at the terrace where the tables were all empty except where the old man sat in the shadow of the leaves of the tree that moved slightly in the wind. A girl and a soldier went by in the street. The street light shone on the brass number on his collar. The girl wore no head covering and hurried beside him.

'The guard will pick him up,' one waiter said.

'What does it matter if he gets what he's after?'

'He had better get off the street now. The guard will get him. They went by five minutes ago.'

The old man sitting in the shadow rapped on his saucer with his glass. The younger waiter went over to him.

'What do you want?'

The old man looked at him. 'Another brandy,' he said.

'You'll be drunk,' the waiter said. The old man looked at him. The waiter went away.

'He'll stay all night,' he said to his colleague. 'I'm sleepy now. I never get to bed before three o'clock. He should have killed himself last week.'

The waiter took the brandy bottle and another saucer from the counter inside the café and marched out to the old man's table. He put down the saucer and poured the glass full of brandy.

'You should have killed yourself last week,' he said to the deaf man. The old man motioned with his finger. 'A little more,' he said. The waiter poured on into the glass so that the brandy slopped over and ran down the stem into the top saucer of the pile. 'Thank you,' the old man said. The waiter took the bottle back inside the café. He sat down at the table with his colleague again.

'He's drunk now,' he said.

'He's drunk every night.'

'What did he want to kill himself for?'

'How should I know?'

'How did he do it?'

'He hung himself with a rope.'

'Who cut him down?'

'His niece.'

'Why did they do it?'

'Fear for his soul.'

'How much money has he got?'

'He's got plenty.'

'He must be eighty years old.'

'Anyway I should say he was eighty.'

'I wish he would go home. I never get to bed before three o'clock. What kind of hour is that to go to bed?'

'He stays up because he likes it.'

'He's lonely. I'm not lonely. I have a wife waiting in bed for me.'

'He had a wife once too.'

'A wife would be no good to him now.'

'You can't tell. He might be better with a wife.'

'His niece looks after him.'

'I know. You said she cut him down.'

'I wouldn't want to be that old. An old man is a nasty thing.'

'Not always. This old man is clean. He drinks without spilling. Even now, drunk. Look at him.'

'I don't want to look at him. I wish he would go home. He has no regard for those who must work.'

The old man looked from his glass across the square, then over at the waiters.

'Another brandy,' he said, pointing to his glass. The waiter who was in a hurry came over.

'Finished,' he said, speaking with that omission of syntax stupid people employ when talking to drunken people or foreigners. 'No more tonight. Close now.'

'Another,' said the old man.

'No. Finished.' The waiter wiped the edge of the table with a towel and shook his head.

The old man stood up, slowly counted the saucers, took a leather coin purse from his pocket and paid for the drinks, leaving half a peseta tip.

The waiter watched him go down the street, a very old man walking unsteadily but with dignity.

'Why didn't you let him stay and drink?' the unhurried waiter asked. They were putting up the shutters. 'It is not half past two.'

'I want to go home to bed.'

'What is an hour?'

'More to me than to him.'

'An hour is the same.'

'You talk like an old man yourself. He can buy a bottle and drink at home.'

'It's not the same.'

'No, it is not,' agreed the waiter with a wife. He did not wish to be unjust. He was only in a hurry.

'And you? You have no fear of going home before your usual hour?'

'Are you trying to insult me?'

'No, hombre, only to make a joke.'

'No,' the waiter who was in a hurry said, rising from pulling down the metal shutters. 'I have confidence. I am all confidence.'

'You have youth, confidence, and a job,' the older waiter said. 'You have everything.'

'And what do you lack?'

'Everything but work.'

'You have everything I have.'

'No. I have never had confidence and I am not young.'

'Come on. Stop talking nonsense and lock up.'

'I am of those who like to stay late at the café,' the older waiter said. 'With all those who do not want to go to bed. With all those who need a light for the night.'

'I want to go home and into bed.'

'We are of two different kinds,' the older waiter said. He was dressed now to go home. 'It is not only a question of youth and confidence, although those things are very beautiful. Each night I am reluctant to close up because there may be someone who needs the café.'

'Hombre, there are bodegas open all night long.'

'You do not understand. This is a clean and pleasant café. It is well lighted. The light is very good and also, now, there are shadows of leaves.'

'Good night,' said the younger waiter.

'Good night,' the other said. Turning off the electric light he continued the conversation with himself. It is the light of course but it is necessary that the place be clean and pleasant. You do not want music. Certainly you do not want music. Nor can you stand before a bar with dignity although that is all that is provided for these hours. What did he fear? It was not fear or dread. It was a nothing that he knew too well. It was all a nothing and a man was nothing too. It was only that and light was all it needed and a certain cleanness and order. Some lived in it and never felt it but he knew it all was nada y pues nada y nada y pues nada. Our nada who art in nada, nada be thy name thy kingdom nada thy will be nada in nada as it is in nada. Give us this nada our daily nada and nada us our nada as we nada our nadas and nada us not into nada but deliver us from nada; pues nada. Hail nothing full of nothing, nothing is with thee. He smiled and stood before a bar with a shining steam pressure coffee machine.

'What's yours?' asked the barman.

'Nada.'

'Otro loco mas,' said the barman and turned away.

'A little cup,' said the waiter.

The barman poured it for him.

'The light is very bright and pleasant but the bar is unpolished,' the waiter said.

The barman looked at him but did not answer. It was too late at night for conversation.

'You want another copita?' the barman asked.

'No, thank you,' said the waiter and went out. He disliked bars and bodegas. A clean, well-lighted café was a very different thing. Now, without thinking further, he would go home to his room. He would lie in the bed and finally, with daylight, he would go to sleep. After all, he said to himself, it is probably only insomnia. Many must have it.

*Mothers, lovers, husbands and wives, these are the
people insomniacs share their beds with: this vignette
is unusual because the lover enjoys her insomnia.
Daylight transforms insomnia into reluctant wakefulness, 'the night so soon over'.*

*The two selections included in this anthology are
drawn from Colette's extensive autobiographical writings. These include essays, memoirs, observations
and portraits, such as the one of Marcel Proust later
on. Italo Calvino has written of his own work that
he 'tried to remove weight . . . from the structure of
stories and from language'. Colette's writing certainly
achieves the deft lightness that he sought.*

*She was born Sidonie-Gabrielle Colette in 1873,
dying in 1954.*

Night Without Sleep

In our house there is only one bed, too big for you, a little
narrow for us both. It is chaste, white, completely exposed; no
drapery veils its honest candour in the light of day. People who
come to see us survey it calmly and do not tactfully look aside,
for it is marked, in the middle, with but one soft valley, like
the bed of a young girl who sleeps alone.

They do not know, those who enter here, that every night
the weight of our two united bodies hollows out a little more,
beneath its voluptuous winding sheet, that valley no wider
than a tomb.

O our bed, completely bare! A dazzling lamp, slanted above
it, denudes it even more. We do not find there, at twilight, the
well-devised shade of a lace canopy or the rosy shell-like glow
of a night lamp. Fixed star, never rising or setting, our bed
never ceases to gleam except when submerged in the velvety
depths of night.

Rigid and white, like the body of a dear departed, it is

haloed with a perfume, a complicated scent that astounds, that one inhales attentively, in an effort to distinguish the blond essence of your favourite tobacco from the still lighter aroma of your extraordinarily white skin, and the scent of sandalwood that I give off; but that wild odour of crushed grasses, who can tell if it is mine or thine?

Receive us tonight, O our bed, and let your fresh valley deepen a little more beneath the feverish torpor caused by a thrilling spring day spent in the garden and in the woods.

I lie motionless, my head on your gentle shoulder. Surely, until tomorrow, I will sink into the depths of a dark sleep, a sleep so stubborn, so shut off from the world, that the wings of dream will come to beat in vain. I am going to sleep . . . Wait only until I find, for the soles of my feet that are tingling and burning, a cool place . . . You have not budged. You draw in long drafts of air, but I feel your shoulder still awake and careful to provide a hollow for my cheek . . . Let us sleep . . . The nights of May are so brief. Despite the blue obscurity that bathes us, my eyelids are still full of sunshine, and I contemplate the day that has passed with closed eyes, as one peers, from behind the shelter of a Persian blind, into a dazzling summer garden . . .

How my heart throbs! I can also hear yours throb beneath my ear. You're not asleep? I raise my head slightly and sense rather than see the pallor of your upturned face, the tawny shadow of your short hair. Your knees are like two cool oranges . . . Turn toward me, so that mine can steal some of that smooth freshness.

Oh! Let us sleep . . . My skin is tingling, there is a throbbing in the muscles of my calves and in my ears, and surely our soft bed, tonight, is strewn with pine needles! Let us sleep! I command sleep to come.

I cannot sleep. My insomnia is a kind of gay and lively palpitation, and I sense in your immobility the same quivering exhaustion. You do not budge. You hope I am asleep. Your arm tightens at times around me, out of tender habit, and your charming feet clasp mine between them . . . Sleep approaches, grazes me, and flees . . . I can see it! Sleep is exactly like that heavy velvety butterfly I pursued in the garden aflame with iris . . . Do you remember? What youthful impatience glorified this entire sunlit day! A keen and insistent breeze flung over the sun a smoke screen of rapid clouds and withered the too tender leaves of the linden trees; the flowers of the butternut tree fell like brownish caterpillars upon our hair, with the flowers of the catalpas, their colour the rainy mauve of the Parisian sky. The shoots of the black-currant bush that you brushed against, the wild sorrel dotting the grass with its rosettes, the fresh young mint, still brown, the sage as downy as a hare's ear—everything overflowed with a powerful and spicy sap which became on my lips mingled with the taste of alcohol and citronella.

I could only shout and laugh, as I trod the long juicy grass that stained my frock . . . With tranquil pleasure you watchfully regarded my wild behaviour, and when I stretched out my hand to reach those wild roses—you remember, the ones of such a tender pink—your hand broke the branch before I could, and you took off, one by one, the curved little thorns, coral-hued, claw-shaped . . . And then you gave me the flowers disarmed . . .

You gave me the flowers, disarmed . . . You gave me, so I could rest my panting self, the best place in the shade, under the Persian lilacs with their ripe bunches of flowers. You picked the big cornflowers in the round flower beds, enchanted flowers whose hairy centres smell of apricot . . . You gave me the cream in the small jug of milk, at teatime, when my ravenous appetite made you smile . . . You gave me the bread with the most golden crust, and I can still see your translucent hand in the sunshine raised to shoo away the wasp that sizzled, entangled in my curls . . . You threw over my shoulders a light mantle when a cloud longer than usual slowly passed, toward the end of the day, when I shivered, in a cold sweat, intoxicated with the pleasure that is nameless among mankind, the innocent pleasure of happy animals in the springtime . . . You told me: 'Come back . . . Stop . . . We must go in!' You told me . . .

Oh! If I think of you, then it's goodbye to sleep. What hour struck just then? Now the windows are growing blue. I hear a murmuring in my blood, or else it is the murmur of the gardens down there . . . Are you asleep? No. If I put my cheek against yours, I feel your eyelashes flutter like the wings of a captive fly . . . You are not asleep. You are spying upon my excitement. You protect me against bad dreams; you are thinking of me as I am thinking of you, and we both feign, out of a strange sentimental shyness, a peaceful sleep. All my body yields itself up to sleep, relaxed, and my neck weighs heavily on your gentle shoulder; but our thoughts unite in love discreetly across this blue dawn, so soon increasing.

In a short while the luminous bar between the curtains will brighten, redden . . . In a few more minutes I will be able to read, on your lovely forehead, your delicate chin, your sad mouth and closed eyelids, the determination to appear to be sleeping . . . It is the hour when my fatigue, my nervous insomnia can no longer remain mute, when I will throw my arms outside this feverish bed, and my naughty heels are already preparing to give a mischievous kick.

Then you will pretend to wake up! Then I shall be able to take refuge in you, with confused and unjust complaints, exasperated sighs, with clenched hands cursing the daylight that has already come, the night so soon over, the noises in the street . . . For I know quite well that you will then tighten your arms about me and that, if the cradling of your arms is not enough to soothe me, your kiss will become more clinging, your hands more amorous, and that you will accord me the sensual satisfaction that is the surcease of love, like a sovereign exorcism that will drive out of me the demons of fever, anger, restlessness . . . You will accord the sensual pleasure bending over me voluptuously, maternally, you who seek in your impassioned loved one the child you never had.

Yasunari Kawabata

*At the end of Yasunari Kawabata's 1960 novella,
extracted below, old Eguchi finally sleeps beside two
girls. One of them, the 'dark girl', dies beside him.
Despite her death, the cycle can immediately continue; after removing the dead girl the mistress of the
house suggests to Eguchi that he return to his room
and go to sleep. 'There is another girl,' she says—
another girl to 'sleep' with.*

*Born in 1899 (the same year as Hemingway and
Borges), Kawabata was in 1968 the first Japanese
writer to be awarded the Nobel laureate for literature.
The following pages come at the beginning of the
novella.*

House of the Sleeping Beauties

He was not to do anything in bad taste, the woman of the inn
warned old Eguchi. He was not to put his finger into the mouth
of the sleeping girl, or try anything else of that sort.

There were this room, some four yards square, and the one
next to it, but apparently no other rooms upstairs; and, since
the downstairs seemed too restricted for guest rooms, the place
could scarcely be called an inn at all. Probably because its
secret allowed none, there was no sign at the gate. All was
silence. Admitted through the locked gate, old Eguchi had seen
only the woman to whom he was now talking. It was his first
visit. He did not know whether she was the proprietress or a
maid. It seemed best not to ask.

A small woman perhaps in her mid-forties, she had a
youthful voice, and it was as if she had especially cultivated
a calm, steady manner. The thin lips scarcely parted as she
spoke. She did not often look at Eguchi. There was something
in the dark eyes that lowered his defences, and she seemed
quite at ease herself. She made tea from the iron kettle on
the bronze brazier. The tea leaves and the quality of the

brewing were astonishingly good, for the place and the occasion—to put old Eguchi more at ease. In the alcove hung a painting by Kawai Gyokudō, probably a reproduction, of a mountain village warm with autumn leaves. Nothing suggested that the room had unusual secrets.

'And please don't try to wake her. Not that you could, whatever you did. She's sound asleep and knows nothing.' The woman said it again: 'She'll sleep on and on and know nothing at all, from start to finish. Not even who's been with her. You needn't worry.'

Eguchi said nothing of the doubts that were coming over him.

'She's a very pretty girl. I only take guests I know I can trust.'

As Eguchi looked away his eye fell on his wrist watch.

'What time is it?'

'A quarter to eleven.'

'I should think so. Old gentlemen like to go to bed early and get up early. So whenever you're ready.'

The woman got up and unlocked the door to the next room. She used her left hand. There was nothing remarkable about the act, but Eguchi held his breath as he watched her. She looked into the other room. She was no doubt used to looking through doorways, and there was nothing unusual about the back turned toward Eguchi. Yet it seemed strange. There was a large, strange bird on the knot of her obi. He did not know what species it might be. Why should such realistic eyes and feet have been put on a stylised bird? It was not that the bird was disquieting in itself, only that the design was bad; but if disquiet was to be tied to the woman's back, it was there in the bird. The ground was a pale yellow, almost white.

The next room seemed to be dimly lighted. The woman closed the door without locking it, and put the key on the table before Eguchi. There was nothing in her manner to suggest that she had inspected a secret room, nor was there in the tone of her voice.

'Here is the key. I hope you sleep well. If you have trouble getting to sleep, you will find some sleeping medicine by the pillow.'

'Have you anything to drink?'

'I don't keep spirits.'

'I can't even have a drink to put myself to sleep?'

'No.'

'She's in the next room?'

'She's asleep, waiting for you.'

'Oh?' Eguchi was a little surprised. When had the girl come into the next room? How long had she been asleep? Had the woman opened the door to make sure that she was asleep? Eguchi had heard from an old acquaintance who frequented the place that a girl would be waiting, asleep, and that she would not awaken; but now that he was here he seemed unable to believe it.

'Where will you undress?' She seemed ready to help him. He was silent. 'Listen to the waves. And the wind.'

'Waves?'

'Good night.' She left him.

Alone, old Eguchi looked around the room, bare and without contrivance. His eye came to rest on the door to the next room. It was of cedar, some three feet wide. It seemed to have been put in after the house was finished. The wall too, upon examination, seemed once to have been a sliding partition, now sealed over to make the secret chamber of the sleeping beauties. The colour matched that of the other walls but seemed fresher.

Eguchi picked up the key. Having done so, he should have gone into the next room; but he remained seated. It was as the woman had said: the sound of the waves was violent. It was as if they were beating against a high cliff, and as if this little house were at its very edge. The wind carried the sound of approaching winter, perhaps because of the house itself, perhaps because of something in old Eguchi. Yet it was quite warm enough with only the single brazier. The district was a warm one. The wind did not seem to be driving leaves before it. Having arrived late, Eguchi had not seen what sort of country the house lay in; but there had been the smell of the sea. The garden was large for the size of the house, with a considerable number of large pines and maples. The needles of the pines lay strong against the sky. The house had probably been a country villa.

The key still in his hand, Eguchi lighted a cigarette. He

took a puff or two and put it out; but a second one he smoked to the end. It was less that he was ridiculing himself for the faint apprehension than that he was aware of an unpleasant emptiness. He usually had a little whisky before going to bed. He was a light sleeper, given to bad dreams. A poetess who had died young of cancer had said in one of her poems that for her, on sleepless nights, 'the night offers toads and black dogs and corpses of the drowned'. It was a line Eguchi could not forget. Remembering it now, he wondered whether the girl asleep—no, put to sleep—in the next room might be like a corpse from a drowning; and he felt some hesitation about going in to her. He had not heard how the girl had been put to sleep. She would in any case be in an unnatural stupor, not conscious of events around her, and so she might have the muddy, leaden skin of one racked by drugs. There might be dark circles under her eyes, her ribs might show through a dry, shrivelled skin. Or she might be cold, bloated, puffy. She might be snoring lightly, her lips parted to show purplish gums. In his sixty-seven years, old Eguchi had passed ugly nights with women. Indeed the ugly nights were the hardest ones to forget. The ugliness had had to do not with the appearance of the women but with their tragedies, their warped lives. He did not want to add another such episode, at his age, to the record. So ran his thoughts, on the edge of the adventure. But could there be anything uglier than an old man lying the night through beside a girl put to sleep, unwaking? Had he not come to this house seeking the ultimate in the ugliness of old age?

The woman had spoken of guests she could trust. It seemed that everyone who came here could be trusted. The man who had told Eguchi of the house was so old that he was no longer a man. He seemed to think that Eguchi had reached the same stage of senility. Probably because the woman of the house was accustomed only to making arrangements for such old men, she had turned upon Eguchi a look neither of pity nor of inquiry. Still able to enjoy himself, he was not yet a guest to be trusted; but it was possible to make himself one, because of his feelings at that moment, because of the place, because of his companion. The ugliness of old age pressed down upon him. For him too, he thought, the dreary circumstances of the other guests were not far off. The fact that he was here surely indicated as much. And so he had no intention of breaking the ugly restrictions, the sad restrictions imposed upon the old men. He did not intend to break them, and he would not. Though it might be called a secret club, the number of old men who were members seemed to be few. Eguchi had come neither to expose its sins nor to pry into its secret practices. His curiosity was less than strong, because the dreariness of old age lay already upon him too.

'Some gentlemen say they have good dreams when they come here,' the woman had said. 'Some say they remember how it was when they were young.'

Not even then did a wry smile come over his face. He put his hands to the table and stood up. He went to the cedar door.

'Ah!'

It was the crimson velvet curtains. The crimson was yet deeper in the dim light. It was as if a thin layer of light hovered before the curtains, as if he were stepping into a phantasm. There were curtains over the four walls. The door was curtained too, but the edge had been tied back. He locked the door, drew the curtain, and looked down at the girl. She was not pretending. Her breathing was of the deepest sleep. He caught his breath. She was more beautiful than he had expected. And her beauty was not the only surprise. She was young too. She lay on her left side, her face toward him. He could not see her body—but she would not yet be twenty. It was as if another heart beat its wings in old Eguchi's chest.

Her right hand and wrist were at the edge of the quilt. Her left arm seemed to stretch diagonally under the quilt. Her right thumb was half hidden under her cheek. The fingers on the pillow beside her face were slightly curved in the softness of sleep, though not enough to erase the delicate hollows where they joined the hand. The warm redness was gradually richer from the palm to the fingertips. It was a smooth, glowing white hand.

'Are you asleep? Are you going to wake up?' It was as if he were asking so that he might touch her hand. He took it in his, and shook it. He knew that she would not open her eyes. Her hand still in his, he looked into her face. What kind of girl might she be? The eyebrows were untouched by cosmetics, the closed eyelashes were even. He caught the scent of maidenly hair. After a time the sound of the waves was higher, for his heart had been taken captive. Resolutely he undressed. Noting that the light was from above, he looked up. Electric light came through Japanese paper at two skylights. As if with more composure than was his to muster, he asked himself whether it was a light that set off to advantage the crimson of the velvet, and whether the light from the velvet set off the girl's skin like a beautiful phantom; but the colour was not strong enough to show against her skin. He had become accustomed to the light. It was too bright for him, used to sleeping in the dark, but apparently it could not be turned off. He saw that the quilt was a good one.

He slipped quietly under, afraid that the girl he knew would sleep on might awaken. She seemed to be quite naked. There was no reaction, no hunching of the shoulders or pulling in of the hips, to suggest that she sensed his presence. There should be in a young girl, however soundly she slept, some sort of quick reaction. But this would not be an ordinary sleep, he knew. The thought made him avoid touching her as he stretched out. Her knee was slightly forward, leaving his legs in an awkward position. It took no inspection to tell him that she was not on the defensive, that she did not have her right knee resting on her left. The right knee was pulled back, the leg stretched out. The angle of the shoulders as she lay on her left side and that of the hips seemed at variance, because of the inclination of her torso. She did not appear to be very tall.

The fingers of the hand old Eguchi had shaken gently were also in deep sleep. The hand lay as he had dropped it. As he pulled his pillow back the hand fell away. One elbow on the pillow, he gazed at it. As if it were alive, he muttered to himself. It was of course alive, and he meant only to say how very pretty it was; but once he had uttered them the words took on an ominous ring. Though this girl lost in sleep had not put an end to the hours of her life, had she not lost them, had them sink into bottomless depths? She was not a living doll, for there could be no living doll; but, so as not to shame an old man no longer a man, she had been made into a living toy. No, not a toy: for the old men, she could be life itself. Such life was, perhaps, life to be touched with confidence. To

Eguchi's farsighted old eyes the hand from close up was yet smoother and more beautiful. It was smooth to the touch, but he could not see the texture.

It came to the old eyes that in the earlobes was the same warm redness of blood that grew richer toward the tips of the fingers. He could see the ears through the hair. The flush of the earlobes argued the freshness of the girl with a plea that stabbed at him. Eguchi had first wandered into this secret house out of curiosity, but it seemed to him that men more senile than he might come to it with even greater happiness and sorrow. The girl's hair was long, possibly for old men to play with. Lying back on his pillow, Eguchi brushed it aside to expose her ear. The sheen of the hair behind the ear was white. The neck and the shoulder too were young and fresh. They did not yet have the fullness of woman. He looked around the room. Only his own clothes were in the box. There was no sign of the girl's. Perhaps the woman had taken them away, but he started up at the thought that the girl might have come into the room naked. She was to be looked at. He knew that she had been put to sleep for the purpose, and that there was no call for this new surprise; but he covered her shoulder and closed his eyes. The scent of a baby came to him in the girl's scent. It was the milky scent of a nursing baby, and richer than that of the girl. Impossible—that the girl should have had a child, that her breasts should be swollen, that milk should be oozing from the nipples. He gazed afresh at her forehead and cheeks, and at the girlish line from the jaw down over the neck. Although he knew well enough already, he slightly raised the quilt that covered the shoulder. The breast was not one that had given milk. He touched it softly with his finger. It was not wet. The girl was approaching twenty. Even if the expression babyish was not wholly inappropriate, she should no longer have the milky scent of a baby. In fact it was a womanish scent. And yet it was very certain that old Eguchi had this very moment smelled a nursing baby. A passing spectre? However much he might ask why it had come to him, he did not know the answer; but probably it had come through the opening left by a sudden emptiness in his heart. He felt a surge of loneliness tinged with sorrow. More than sorrow or loneliness, it was the bleakness of old age, as if frozen to him.

And it changed to pity and tenderness for the girl who sent out the smell of young warmth. Possibly only for purposes of turning away a cold sense of guilt, the old man seemed to feel music in the girl's body. It was a music of love. As if he wanted to flee, he looked at the four walls, so covered with velvet that there might have been no exit. The crimson velvet, taking its light from the ceiling, was soft and utterly motionless. It shut in a girl who had been put to sleep, and an old man.

'Wake up. Wake up.' Eguchi shook at the girl's shoulder. Then he lifted her head. 'Wake up. Wake up.'

BRAM STOKER

Dracula

Why does Dracula choose Lucy over her friend Mina? Once reason might be that Lucy is portrayed as the more sensual of the two women, and her latent eroticism makes her susceptible to Dracula, the vampire 'lover'. She can be tempted where the earnest Mina cannot (well, at least not until after her wedding night, when Mina understands the vampire's desire).

Dracula sails to England, killing the crew one by one and the captain last of all. As the ship draws closer Lucy sleeps badly, her desire conjured and manipulated by him. She certainly gives Mina some sleepless nights. What follows is Lucy's first meeting with Dracula as recorded by Mina in her diary.

Born in Dublin in 1847, Stoker published Dracula *when he was thirty. He is also the author of* Lair of the Whiteworm.

Mina Murray's Journal

8 August Lucy was very restless all night, and I, too, could not sleep. The storm was fearful and as it boomed loudly among the chimney-pots, it made me shudder. When a sharp puff came it seemed to be like a distant gun. Strangely enough, Lucy did not wake, but she got up twice and dressed herself. Fortunately, each time I awoke in time and managed to undress her without waking her, and got her back to bed. It is a very strange thing, this sleep-walking, for as soon as her will is thwarted in any physical way, her intention, if there be any, disappears, and she yields herself almost exactly to the routine of her life.

Early in the morning we both got up and went down to the harbour to see if anything had happened in the night. There were very few people about, and though the sun was bright, and the air clear and fresh, the big, grim-looking waves, that seemed dark themselves because the foam that topped them was like snow, forced themselves in through the narrow mouth of the harbour—like a bullying man going through a crowd. Somehow I felt glad that Jonathan was not on the sea last night, but on land. But, oh, is he on land or sea? Where is he, and how? I am getting fearfully anxious about him. If I only knew what to do, and could do anything!

10 August The funeral of the poor sea-captain today was most touching. Every boat in the harbour seemed to be there, and the coffin was carried by captains all the way from Tate Hill Pier up to the churchyard. Lucy came with me, and we went early to our old seat, whilst the cortège of boats went up the river to the Viaduct and came down again. We had a lovely view, and saw the procession nearly all the way. The poor fellow was laid to rest quite near our seat so that we stood on it when the time came and saw everything. Poor Lucy seemed much upset. She was restless and uneasy all the time, and I cannot but think that her dreaming at night is telling on her. She is quite odd in one thing: she will not admit to me that there is any cause for restlessness; or if there be, she does not understand it herself. There is an additional cause in that poor old Mr Swales was found dead this morning on our seat, his neck being broken. He had evidently, as the doctor said, fallen back in the seat in some sort of fright, for there was a look of fear and horror on his face that the men said made them shudder. Poor dear old man! Perhaps he had seen Death with his dying eyes! Lucy is so sweet and sensitive that she feels influences more acutely than other people do. Just now she was quite upset by a little thing which I did not much heed, though I am myself very fond of animals. One of the men who came up here often to look for the boats was followed by his dog. The dog is always with him. They are both quiet persons, and I never saw the man angry, nor heard the dog bark. During the service the dog would not come to its master, who was on the seat with us, but kept a few yards off, barking and howling.

Its master spoke to it gently, and then harshly, and then angrily; but it would neither come nor cease to make a noise. It was in a sort of fury, with its eyes savage, and all its hairs bristling out like a cat's tail when puss is on the war-path. Finally the man, too, got angry, and jumped down and kicked the dog, and then took it by the scuff of the neck and half dragged and half threw it on the tombstone on which the seat is fixed. The moment it touched the stone the poor thing became quiet and fell all into a tremble. It did not try to get away, but crouched down, quivering and cowering, and was in such a pitiable state of terror that I tried, though without effect, to comfort it. Lucy was full of pity, too, but she did not attempt to touch the dog, but looked at it in an agonised sort of way. I greatly fear that she is too super-sensitive a nature to go through the world without trouble. She will be dreaming of this tonight, I am sure. The whole agglomeration of things— the ship steered into port by a dead man; his attitude, tied to the wheel with a crucifix and beads; the touching funeral; the dog, now furious and now in terror—will all afford material for her dreams.

I think it will be best for her to go to bed tired out physically, so I shall take her for a long walk by the cliffs to Robin Hood's Bay and back. She ought not to have much inclination for sleep-walking then.

Same day, 11 o'clock p.m. Oh, but I am tired! If it were not that I had made my diary a duty I should not open it tonight. We had a lovely walk. Lucy, after a while, was in gay spirits, owing, I think, to some dear cows who came nosing towards us in a field close to the lighthouse, and frightened the wits out of us. I believe we forgot everything except, of course, personal fear, and it seemed to wipe the slate clean and give us a fresh start. We had a capital 'severe tea' at Robin Hood's Bay in a sweet little old-fashioned inn, with a bow-window right over the seaweed-covered rocks of the strand. I believe we should have shocked the 'New Woman' with our appetites. Men are more tolerant, bless them! Then we walked home with some, or rather many, stoppages to rest, and with our hearts full of a constant dread of wild bulls. Lucy was really tired, and we intended to creep off to bed as soon as we could. The

young curate came in, however, and Mrs Westenra asked him
to stay for supper. Lucy and I had both a fight for it with the
dusty miller; I know it was a hard fight on my part, and I am
quite heroic. I think that some day the bishops must get
together and see about breeding up a new class of curates,
who don't take supper, no matter how they may be pressed to,
and who will know when girls are tired. Lucy is asleep and
breathing softly. She has more colour in her cheeks than usual,
and looks, oh, so sweet. If Mr Holmwood fell in love with her
seeing her only in the drawing-room, I wonder what he would
say if he saw her now. Some of the 'New Women' writers will
some day start an idea that men and women should be allowed
to see each other asleep before proposing or accepting. But I
suppose the New Woman won't condescend in future to accept;
she will do the proposing herself. And a nice job she will make
of it, too! There's some consolation in that I am so happy
tonight, because dear Lucy seems better. I really believe she
has turned the corner, and we are over her troubles with
dreaming. I should be quite happy if I only knew if Jonathan . . . God bless and keep him.

11 August, 3 a.m. Diary again. No sleep now, so I may as well
write. I am too agitated to sleep. We have had such an
adventure, such an agonising experience. I fell asleep as soon
as I had closed my diary . . . Suddenly I became broad awake,
and sat up, with a horrible sense of fear upon me, and of some
feeling of emptiness around me. The room was dark, so I could
not see Lucy's bed; I stole across and felt for her. The bed was
empty. I lit a match, and found that she was not in the room.
The door was shut, but not locked, as I had left it. I feared to
wake her mother, who has been more than usually ill lately,
so threw on some clothes and got ready to look for her. As I
was leaving the room it struck me that the clothes she wore
might give me some clue to her dreaming intention. Dressing-
gown would mean house; dress, outside. Dressing-gown and
dress were both in their places. 'Thank God,' I said to myself,
'she cannot be far, as she is only in her nightdress.' I ran
downstairs and looked in the sitting-room. Not there! Then I
looked in all the other open rooms of the house, with an
ever-growing fear chilling my heart. Finally I came to the

hall-door and found it open. It was not wide open, but the catch of the lock had not caught. The people of the house are careful to lock the door every night, so I feared that Lucy must have gone out as she was. There was no time to think of what might happen; a vague, overmastering fear obscured all details. I took a big, heavy shawl and ran out. The clock was striking one as I was in the Crescent, and there was not a soul in sight. I ran along the North Terrace, but could see no sign of the white figure which I expected. At the edge of the West Cliff above the pier I looked across the harbour to the East Cliff, in the hope or fear—I don't know which—of seeing Lucy in our favourite seat. There was a bright full moon, with heavy black, driving clouds, which threw the whole scene into a fleeting diorama of light and shade as they sailed across. For a moment or two I could see nothing, as the shadow of a cloud obscured St Mary's Church and all around it. Then as the cloud passed I could see the ruins of the abbey coming into view; and as the edge of a narrow band of light as sharp as a sword-cut moved along, the church and the churchyard became gradually visible. Whatever my expectation was, it was not disappointed, for there, on our favourite seat, the silver light of the moon struck a half-reclining figure, snowy white. The coming of the cloud was too quick for me to see much, for shadow shut down on light almost immediately; but it seemed to me as though something dark stood behind the seat where the white figure shone, and bent over it. What it was, whether man or beast, I could not tell; I did not wait to catch another glance, but flew down the steep steps to the pier and along by the fish-market to the bridge, which was the only way to reach the East Cliff. The town seemed as dead, for not a soul did I see; I rejoiced that it was so, for I wanted no witness of poor Lucy's condition. The time and distance seemed endless, and my knees trembled and my breath came laboured as I toiled up the endless steps to the Abbey. I must have gone fast, and yet it seemed to me as if my feet were weighted with lead, and as though every joint in my body were rusty. When I got almost to the top I could see the seat and the white figure, for I was now close enough to distinguish it even through the spells of shadow. There was undoubtedly something, long and black, bending over the half-reclining white figure. I called in fright, 'Lucy! Lucy!' and something raised a head, and from where I was I could see a white face and red, gleaming eyes. Lucy did not answer, and I ran on to the entrance of the church-yard. As I entered, the church was between me and the seat, and for a minute or so I lost sight of her. When I came in view again the cloud had passed, and the moonlight struck so brilliantly that I could see Lucy half reclining with her head lying over the back of the seat. She was quite alone, and there was not a sign of any living thing about.

When I bent over her I could see that she was still asleep. Her lips were parted, and she was breathing—not softly as usual with her, but in long, heavy gasps, as though striving to get her lungs full at every breath. As I came close, she put up her hand in her sleep and pulled the collar of her nightdress close around her throat. Whilst she did so there came a little shudder through her, as though she felt the cold. I flung the warm shawl over her, and drew the edges tight round her neck, for I dreaded lest she should get some deadly chill from the night air, unclad as she was. I feared to wake her all at once, so, in order to have my hands free that I might help her, I fastened the shawl at her throat with a big safety-pin; but I must have been clumsy in my anxiety and pinched or pricked her with it, for by-and-by, when her breathing became quieter, she put her hand to her throat again and moaned. When I had her carefully wrapped up I put my shoes on her feet, and then began very gently to wake her. At first she did not respond; but gradually she became more and more uneasy in her sleep, moaning and sighing occasionally. At last, as time was passing fast, and, for many other reasons, I wished to get her home at once, I shook her more forcibly, till finally she opened her eyes and awoke. She did not seem surprised to see me, as, of course, she did not realise all at once where she was. Lucy always wakes prettily, and even at such a time, when her body must have been chilled with cold, and her mind somewhat appalled at waking unclad in a churchyard at night, she did not lose her grace. She trembled a little, and clung to me; when I told her to come at once with me home she rose without a word, with the obedience of a child. As we passed along, the gravel hurt my feet, and Lucy noticed me wince. She stopped and wanted to insist upon my taking my shoes;

but I would not. However, when we got to the pathway outside the churchyard, where there was a puddle of water remaining from the storm, I daubed my feet with mud, using each foot in turn on the other, so that as we went home, no one, in case we should meet any one, should notice my bare feet.

MIGUEL DE CERVANTES SAAVEDRA

A Spaniard, Cervantes worked as a soldier, slave and tax-man before writing Don Quixote, *which had been conceived in prison 'where every misery is lodged and every doleful sound makes its dwelling'. The popular tale was first published in 1605. Cervantes (and his contemporary, William Shakespeare) died in April 1616.*

What Befell our Imaginative Gentleman in the Inn he Supposed to be a Castle

'Don Quixote of La Mancha,' answered Sancho Panza; 'he's a knight-errant and one of the finest and strongest that the world has seen these many years.'

'What is a knight-errant?' asked the wench.

'Are you so fresh in the world that you don't know?' answered Sancho Panza. 'Know then, sister, that a knight-errant is something that, in two words, is cudgelled and an emperor. Today he is the most wretched creature in the world, but tomorrow you'll find him handing out two or three crowns of kingdoms to his squire.'

'How is it, then,' said the landlady, 'that you haven't got an earldom at least, seeing that you're the squire of this good gentleman?'

'It's early yet,' answered Sancho, 'for it's only about a month since we have been gallivanting in search of adventures. Up to the present we haven't bumped into any adventure worth the naming, but perhaps indeed we look for one thing and light on another. But, believe me, if my master Don Quixote recovers from this wound or fall, and I be not crippled by it. I wouldn't barter my hopes for the best title in Spain.'

Then Don Quixote, who had been listening attentively to this conversation, sat up in his bed as best he could and, taking the landlady by the hand, said: 'Believe me, beautiful lady, you may call yourself fortunate in having harboured my person in your castle. For I am such a person that if I say little about myself, it is because men hold that self-praise debases a man; but my squire will tell you who I am. Let me just say that I shall keep engraved for all time in my memory the service you have done me, and I shall be grateful to you as long as I live. Would to high heaven that Love had not enthralled me and subjected me to his laws and to the eyes of the beautiful, ungrateful Dulcinea, whose name I whisper to myself, else would the eyes of this beauteous damsel here bereave me of my freedom.'

The landlady, her daughter and the good Maritornes stood bewildered by the words of our knight-errant, which they understood as well as if he had spoken in Greek, although they realised that they were compliments and offers of service. Not being accustomed to such language, they gazed at him wonderingly and thought he must be a far different kind of man from those now in fashion. And so, thanking him in their rough pot-house phrases for his offers, they left. The Asturian Maritornes rubbed down Sancho, for he needed her care no less than his master.

Now, the carrier and she had agreed to spend the night together, and she had given him her word that, as soon as the people in the inn were all quiet and her master and mistress were asleep, she would come to him and satisfy his desires as much as he pleased. And it is said of this good-natured wench that she never gave her word without keeping it, even though she had given it in the woods without any witness; for she prided herself on being of gentle birth, and thought it no disgrace to be in service in an inn. In fact she would maintain that misfortunes and unhappy accidents had brought her to that state.

Don Quixote's hard, narrow, niggardly and rickety bed stood first in order in the middle of the dilapidated star-lit cock-loft, and next to it Sancho had placed his own, consisting only of a rush mat and a coverlet that seemed to be rather of napless linen than wool. Beyond those two beds was that of the carrier, made, as we have said, of the pack-saddles and the trappings of his two best mules out of the twelve he owned; sleek, fat and goodly beasts they were, for he was one of the rich carriers of Arévalo, according to the author of this story, who makes special mention of him because he knew him well. Now this carrier, after he had visited his mules and given them their second feed, laid himself down on his pack-saddles and waited patiently for the coming of his most punctual Maritornes. Sancho was already plastered and in bed, but though he tried to sleep, he could not do so owing to the pain in his ribs. Don Quixote for the same reason had both his eyes wide open like a hare. All the inn was sunk in silence, and there was no other light but that of a lantern that hung in the middle of the gateway. This wonderful stillness and our knight's thoughts, which unceasingly reverted to the adventures described at every step in the books of chivalry (the true authors of his misfortune), brought to his imagination one of the strangest follies that can be conceived. He fancied that he was now in a famous castle (for, as we have said, all the inns where he lodged seemed to him to be castles) and that the landlord's daughter (daughter of the lord of the castle), captivated by his gallant presence, had fallen in love with him and had promised to lie with him that night for a good space of time without her parents being any the wiser. Then, taking as gospel truth all this fancy which he had created, he began to feel anxious as he reflected on the perils which his honour would suffer, but he resolved in his heart not to be guilty of the least infidelity to his Lady Dulcinea del Toboso, even though Queen Guinevere herself should appear before him.

While he lay thinking of these follies, the hour approached (that was unlucky for him) when the Asturian wench, faithful to her promise, entered the room. Clad in her shift, barefoot, with her hair trussed up in a fustian net, she stole in with soft and wary steps, feeling her way towards her carrier. But scarcely had she reached the door when Don Quixote heard her, and, sitting up in his bed, despite plasters and pain, stretched out his arms to receive his fair damsel; but the Asturian, crouching and holding her breath, kept groping her way in search of her lover. Suddenly she encountered Don Quixote's arms, who seized her first tightly by one of her wrists and then, pulling her towards him (not a word did she dare to utter), made her sit down on the bed. Then he felt her shift, and though it was of sackcloth he thought it was made of the finest and most delicate lawn. She wore on her wrists bracelets of glass beads, but he fancied they were precious pearls from the Orient; her hair, which was almost as coarse as a horse's mane, he took to be threads of the most glittering gold of Arabia, whose brightness obscured that of the sun; her breath, reeking of last night's stale meat-salad, seemed to him to shed a sweet and aromatic fragrance: in short, he transformed her in his fantasy into the likeness of one of the princesses he had read about in his books, who came thus adorned to see the grievously wounded knight, being overcome with love of him. And such was the infatuation of the poor gentleman that neither touch, nor breath, nor other idiosyncrasies of the good damsel undeceived him, though they would have made anyone else save a carrier vomit. He thought he held in his arms the goddess of beauty herself, and clasping her fast he began to court her in a low, tender voice, saying: 'I wish, fair and noble lady, I were in a state to repay so great a boon as thou hast given me by disclosing thy beauty; but Fortune, never weary of persecuting the virtuous, has seen fit to lay me in this bed, where I lie so bruised and battered that, even though were I ready to satisfy thy wish, 'twere impossible for me to do so, for there is a still more invincible obstacle, namely, the faith I have plighted to the peerless Dulcinea del Toboso, sole mistress of my most hidden thoughts. Had this obstacle not intervened, I should not be so doltish a knight as to let slip the happy opportunity thy great bounty has bestowed upon me.'

Maritornes all this while sweated in mortal fear at finding herself locked in Don Quixote's arms, and without attending or even hearing what he said, wriggled silently to free herself.

The carrier, whose lustful desires had kept him awake, as soon as he heard his moll enter the door, listened attentively to all that Don Quixote said. Full of jealous suspicions lest the Asturian wench might play him false, he crept forward towards Don Quixote's bed and stood still, waiting to see the outcome of the knight's discourse, which, however, he could not fathom. When he saw the wench struggling to get free and Don Quixote trying to detain her, he no longer relished the jest. So he raised his fist and discharged such a terrific blow on the lantern jaws of the enamoured knight that he bathed his whole mouth in blood, and not content with this he mounted upon his ribs and, using his feet like a trotting horse, paced up and down from one end to the other. Now the bed was unsteady and its foundations were not of the strongest, so, being unable to endure the additional load of the carrier, it collapsed to the ground with such a crash that it woke up the innkeeper. He as once suspected that it was one of Maritornes' nightly skirmishes, seeing that she did not answer when he called her. Nursing this suspicion, he rose, and, lighting a lamp, went towards the place whence he had heard the scuffle. The wench, seeing her master coming, and knowing full well his ferocious temper, was scared out of her wits and rushed for safety to the bed of Sancho, who was now asleep, where she rolled herself up like a ball.

The innkeeper came in, shouting: 'Where are you, you damned whore? I'll swear these are your doings.'

Just then Sancho awoke, and feeling such a bulk on top of him, fancied he had got the nightmare, and began to lay about him on all sides with his fists. Not a few of those blows descended upon Maritornes, and, at last, stung by sheer pain, she cast aside all decorum and paid him back with such stiff interest that she soon roused him from sleep, whether he would or no. And he, finding himself pummelled in that manner by one whom he could not see, raised himself up as best he could, caught hold of Maritornes, and the two of them began the most obstinate and droll skirmish in the world. The carrier, perceiving by the light of the innkeeper's lamp the dismal condition of his lady, left Don Quixote and ran to her assistance. The landlord did likewise but with different intention, for his was to chastise the wench, thinking that she was certainly the sole cause of all this harmony. And so, just as the proverb says, 'The cat began to bite the rat, the rat began to gnaw the rope, the rope began to bind the stick', so the carrier drubbed Sancho, Sancho Maritornes, Maritornes Sancho, and the innkeeper Maritornes: all of them minced it with such expedition that they gave themselves no rest: and the best of all was that the innkeeper's lamp went out, and as they were in the dark they flogged one another so unmercifully that wherever a blow fell it left its bruise.

EUGENE ZAMIATIN

Born in 1884 in central Russia, Zamiatin was a writer of essays, short stories, plays and novels. He worked for the revolution until it was achieved, but he soon came to feel that there were great problems with the new order. In the 1920s We *was published in translations outside of Russia, but only read in manuscript at home. It is set in a future society where the ruling principle is that freedom and happiness are incompatible. People are given numbers not names, and live in glass houses where they can be monitored. Work, clothes, food, reading, even sexual partners and times of congress are assigned, and all the aspects of the totalitarian state which we abhor are present: infiltration, surveillance and informing.*

In the extract below, the narrator of We *is deeply troubled by a mysterious female Number who seems to want him to follow her in her disobedience.*

We

She was sitting in a low armchair. In front of her on a small square table I noticed a bottle filled with something poisonously green, and two small glasses with thin stems. In the corner of her mouth she had a very thin paper tube; she was ejecting smoke formed by the burning of that ancient smoking substance whose name I do not now remember.

The membrane was still vibrating. Within, the sledge hammer was pounding the red-hot iron bars of my chest. I heard distinctly every blow of the hammer, and . . . What if she, too, heard it?

But she continued to produce smoke very calmly; calmly she looked at me; and nonchalantly she flicked ashes on the pink check!

With as much self-control as possible I asked, 'If you still feel that way, why did you have me assigned to you? And why did you make me come here?'

As if she had not heard at all, she poured some of the green liquid from the bottle into one of the small glasses, and sipped it.

'Wonderful liqueur! Want some?'

Then I understood: alcohol! Like lighting there came to memory what I had seen yesterday: the stony hand of the Well-Doer, the unbearable blade of the electric ray; there on the Cube, the head thrown back, the stretched-out body! I shivered.

'Please listen,' I said. 'You know, do you not, that anyone who poisons himself with nicotine, and more particularly with alcohol, is severely treated by the United State?'

Dark brows raised high to the temples, the sharp mocking triangle.

'"It is more reasonable to annihilate a few than to allow many to poison themselves . . . And degeneration," . . . etc. . . . This is true to the point of indecency.'

'Indecency?'

'Yes. To let out into the street such a group of bald-headed, naked little truths. Only imagine, please. Imagine, say, that persistent admirer of mine—S-, well, you know him. Then imagine: if he should discard the deception of clothes and appear in public in his true form . . . Oh!' She laughed. But I clearly saw her lower, sorrowful triangle: two deep grooves from the nose to the mouth. And for some reason these grooves made me think: that double-curved being, half-hunched, with winglike ears—he embraced her? Her, such . . . Oh!

Naturally, I try now merely to express my abnormal feelings of that moment. Now, as I write, I understand perfectly that all this is as it should be; that he, S-4711, like any other honest Number, has a perfect right to the joys of life, and that it would be unjust . . . But I think the point is quite clear.

I-330 laughed a long, strange laugh. Then she cast a look at me, into me.

'The most curious thing is that I am not in the least afraid of you. You are such a dear, I am sure of it! You would never think of going to the Bureau and reporting that I drink liqueurs and smoke. You will be sick or busy, or I don't know what . . . Furthermore, I am sure you will drink this charming poison with me.'

What an impertinent, mocking tone! I felt definitely that in a moment I would hate her. (Why in a moment? In fact, I hated her all the time.)

I-330 tilted the little glass of green poison straight into her mouth. Then she stood up, and all rosy through the translucent saffron-yellow tissue, she made a few steps and stopped behind my chair . . . Suddenly her arms were about my neck . . . her lips grew into mine, no, even somewhere much deeper, much more terribly . . . I swear all this was very unexpected for me. That is why perhaps . . . for I could not—at this moment I see clearly—I could not myself have the desire to . . .

Unbearably sweet lips. (I suppose it was the taste of the liqueur.) It was as though burning poison were being poured into me, and more, and more . . .

I tore away from the earth and began revolving as an independent planet, down, down, following an incalculable curve . . .

What happened next I am able to describe only in an approximate way, only by way of more or less suitable analogies.

It never occurred to me before but it is true: we who live on the earth, we are always walking over a seething red sea of fire which is hidden in the womb of the earth. We never think of it. But imagine the ground under our feet suddenly transformed into a thin glass shell; suddenly we should behold . . . !

I became glass-like and saw within myself. There were two selves in me. One, the former D-503, Number D-503; and the other . . . Before, that other used only to show his hairy paws from time to time, but now that whole other self left his shell. That shell was breaking, and in a moment . . .

Grasping the last straw (the arms of the chair) with all my strength, I asked loudly (so as to hear my first self), 'Where, where did you get this poison?'

'Oh, this? A physician, one of my . . . '

' "One of my! one of my" what?' And my other self jumped up suddenly and yelled: 'I won't allow it! I want no one but

me . . . I shall kill anyone who . . . Because I . . . You . . . ' I
saw my other self grasp her rudely with his hairy paws, tear
the silk, and put his teeth in her flesh! . . . I remember
exactly, his teeth! . . .

I do not remember how, but I-330 slipped away and I saw
her straighten, her head raised high, her eyes overlaid by that
cursed, impenetrable curtain. She stood leaning with her back
against the closet door and listening to me.

I remember I was on the floor; I embraced her limbs, kissed
her knees, and cried supplicatingly, 'At once, right away, right
away.'

Sharp teeth . . . The sharp, mocking triangle of the
brows . . . She bent over and in silence unbuttoned my badge.

'Yes, yes, dear—dear.'

I began to hastily to remove my unif. But I-330, silent as
before, lifted my badge to my eyes, showing me the clock upon
it. It was twenty-two-twenty-five.

I became cold. I knew what it meant to be out in the street
after twenty-two-thirty. My insanity disappeared at once. I was
again I. I saw clearly one thing: I hated her, hated her,
hated . . . Without saying goodbye, without looking back, I ran
out of the room. Hurriedly trying to fasten the badge back in
its place, I ran down the stairs (I was afraid lest someone
notice me in the elevator), and tore out into a deserted street.

Everything was in its place; life so simple, ordinary, orderly.
Glittering glass houses, pale glass sky, a greenish, motionless
night. But under that cool glass something wild, something
red and hairy, was silently seething. I was grasping for breath,
but I continued to run so as not to be late.

Suddenly I felt that my badge which I had hurriedly pinned
on was detaching itself; it came off and fell to the sidewalk. I
bent over to pick it up and in the momentary silence I heard
somebody's steps. I turned. Someone small and hunched was
disappearing around the corner. At least so it seemed. I started
to run as fast as I could. The wind whistled in my ears. At
the entrance to my house I stopped and looked at the clock;
one minute to twenty-two-thirty! I listened; nobody behind. It
was my foolish imagination, the effect of the poison.

The night was full of torture. My bed seemed to lift itself
under me, then to fall again, then up again! I used auto-

suggestion: 'At night all the Numbers must sleep; sleeping at night is a duty just like working during the day. To sleep at night is necessary for the next day's work. Not to sleep at night is criminal.' Yet I could not sleep—I could not. I was perishing! I was unable to fulfil my duties to the United State! I . . .

Angela Carter

Angela Carter was a fabulist and a feminist, drawing on fables, old wives' tales, fairy tales and myth in her writing. The charms of the dead edge this short extract from the novel The Infernal Desire Machines of Doctor Hoffman, *originally published in 1972.*
Born in 1940, Carter died too soon in 1992.

Infernal Desire Machines

Now the moon had fully risen and shone straight into my room through the screen of ivy and roses so that dappled shadows fell with scrupulous distinction on the bed, the walls and the floor. Inside looked like the negative of a photograph of outside and the moon had already taken a black and white picture of the garden. I woke instantly and completely, with no residue of sleep in my mind, as though this was the proper time for me to wake although it could only have been a little past midnight. I was too wakeful to stay in my bed and got restlessly up to look out of the window. The grounds were far more extensive than I had at first thought and those behind the house were even further on the way to wilderness than those through which I had passed. The moon shone so brightly there was not a single dark corner and I could see the dried-up bed of a large pond or small lake which was now an oval of flat-petalled lilies while the roses had entirely engulfed in their embrace a marble Undine who reclined on her side in a touching attitude of provincial gracefulness. Delineated with the precision of a woodcut in the moonlight, a family of young foxes rolled and tumbled with one another on a clearing which had been a lawn. There was no wind. The night sighed beneath the languorous weight of its own romanticism.

I do not think she made a sound to startle me but all at once I grew conscious of a presence in the room and cold sweat pricked the back of my neck. Slowly I turned from the window. She lived on the crepuscular threshold of life and so I remember her as if standing, always, hesitantly in a doorway like an unbidden guest uncertain of her welcome. Her eyes were open but blind and she held a rose in her outstretched fingers. She had taken off her plain, black dress and wore a white calico nightgown such as convent schoolgirls wear. As I went towards her, so she came to me and I took the rose because she seemed to offer it to me. A thorn under the leaves pierced my thumb and I felt the red rose throb like a heart and saw it emit a single drop of blood as if like a sin-eater it had taken on the pain of the wound for me. She wound her insubstantial arms around me and put her mouth on mine. Her kiss was like a draught of cold water and yet immediately excited my desire for it was full of an anguished yearning.

I led her to the bed and, in the variegated shadows, penetrated her sighing flesh, which was as chill as that of a mermaid or of the marmoreal water-maiden in her own garden. I was aware of a curiously attenuated response, as if she were feeling my caresses through a veil, and you must realise that all this time I was perfectly well aware she was asleep, for, apart from the evidence of my senses, I remembered how the peep-show proprietor had talked of a beautiful somnambulist. Yet, if she was asleep, she was dreaming of passion and afterwards I slept without dreaming for I had experienced a dream in actuality. When I woke in the commonplace morning, nothing was left of her in the bed but some dead leaves and there was no sign she had been in the room except for a withered rose in the middle of the floor.

STEPHEN DIXON

Stephen Dixon is a prolific short story writer and novelist. His books include Interstate, No Relief, Work, Too Late, Garbage *and* Frog. *This short story is taken from* Quite Contrary—the Mary and Newt Story. *His stories often combine the humorous and the irritating, as in the one below.*

Born in 1936, he lives in Baltimore.

Mary Wants to Sleep

She starts upstairs. It's around ten. I'm reading downstairs.

'Should I shampoo tonight or early tomorrow morning?' she says, halfway up.

'Tonight, so I can nuzzle into your hair when you're sleeping.'

'No, tomorrow morning. I just don't have the strength.'

'You going right to sleep then?'

'I'll read for a while first.'

She continues upstairs. I want to follow her, but I stay where I am. Give her time to wash, undress, get in bed and involved with her book. I don't want her to think I'm running up right after her. That because she said she was going to sleep soon, I have to get in bed and talk and try to make love with her before she's too tired to or asleep. I want my going upstairs to look natural, in other words.

I read for about ten minutes more. Then I yawn. An unnatural yawn—forced, like a couple of my loud page turnings, so she could hear it—till it becomes natural. I shut off the downstairs lights. Another glass of wine? I'd like to, and ordinary nights I'd take it upstairs with me, offer her some to sip, which she might say will make her sleep better. But the wine will put her off. She'll think I drink too much. I might say something about need. Mine on the wine, which might lead to mine on hers, hers on no one, how she didn't want anyone except her children needing her and then maybe only when they had to be listened to or were pushing or pressing too hard and needed someone to react against.

I go upstairs. Light's on. She's in bed reading. Middle of the bed. Scarf around her head. It means she thinks her hair's filthy. She'll move when I climb in. Mary: hold out your arms, ask for one of my hug-a-bugs. She's wearing a nightgown. Usually she wears nothing. It's an old gown, an ankle-length muslin one that's not pleasant to touch. Her mother's and before that her paternal grandmother's and a relative's even before that, a great-grandaunt's. It's fairly warm spring night. But maybe she is cold or it's to serve as a reminder of her mother or her American ancestry or as some sort of physical or psychological protection against me when I get in bed, and maybe all five or was that four? She knows I'm coming to bed. I came up with my book. I put it on the floor next to what has come to be called my side of the bed. Nine out of ten times I'll sleep there. One of the things I once found on my street and wanted to give to her was an old oak table for that side. She said, 'No room, keep it for your place.' She looks up from her book. Smiles, I smile, I go in the bathroom right outside the bedroom, brush my teeth, wash my face, urinate, squeeze the last drops free, put some water on the glans in case it smells unclean, dry it with a toilet tissue, wash my hands. I go in the bedroom and start to undress. Linetta talks in her sleep from the next room. I listen. Garbled words. Then recognisable ones and silence.

'You hear what Linetta just said in her sleep?' I say.

'No, what?'

'Dandy lions, Tiger's milk.'

'All there is?' She thinks. 'The puffballs she was blowing about the back today to give us more flowers and you salad leaves. And the tiger's milk I think Cindy might have tried to feed her today because she thinks Linnie's a little languid and growing too fast and thin.'

She reads, turns a page, frowns and goes back to the bottom of the previous page, then to the top of the unread page she turned to before and laughs and shakes her head, impressed at what she's read.

'Anything funny?' I say.

'Not everyone might think so.'

'Are those huge grapefruits downstairs Martha's big Bahamian surprise?'

'Yes, did you have one?'

'There were only two. I thought you and Linetta might want them.'

'You can have half of one or even a whole. You want one now, go and take it.'

'They didn't look that ripe.'

'She said to get them she had to stand on Cy's shoulders and stretch over an electric fence on the road and club them off a tree.'

'Maybe that's why they don't look ripe. Big as they are, not ready yet and no body-building and colouring ethylene for the trip north. Stolen grapefruits. Hate to be a prude, but do you approve?'

Only now, since she started reading again, does she look up. 'She picked them, so what do you want from me?'

'But you got the booty.'

'Snooty booty. Rich man's citrus land, she said, so no great loss.' Back to her book.

'Something about that woman reminds me of someone.'

'Sounds like she reminds you of someone you don't like.'

'It's just she's so vague, frivolous and almost vacuous, and not even the least concerned about her unconcernedness about all of this. Running on about skinnydipping in her pater's bedroom pool there, sunbathing all day and later inside at night with special infrared pool lights. All those rings on her fingers and necklaces on her breasts and sparkles on her toenails, and everytime I see her, wearing a new pair of the most up-to-date eye and lip finishers and shoes. She in fact does remind me of my cousin Blondie and most of her parvenu to old-time well-to-do friends.'

'Martha's okay. She feels, has a generous heart and good mind. I wouldn't put her down.'

'I'm not saying I don't like or disapprove of her.'

'You're not?' She looks up. 'Then that's your behemothian surprise about Martha to me. So she has money, does different things and has a good time. What of it?'

'But that's it. She doesn't do different things, only original repeats or exploitative feats that nobody else could afford, to shock us. Oh, I don't know why I feel like this about her. I'm probably only railing at her in place of something I got against myself. But that pet seal in her bathtub. Those rare macaws encaged in a space big enough for a single baby peewee, because it's an antique. Though you're right. I should at least appreciate her for her theatrical and topical value, get to know her better and give her her due as she no doubt does to me.'

'No, I don't think you two would hit it off.' Back to her book.

I get in bed. 'Was it really only last night that I broke down like that and cried?'

'You mean because it seems so long ago?'

'I can hardly believe it. I suppose that's typical of someone after a long volcanic cry. Or maybe it's just another thing I don't want to reflect on and for the same reason that I dumped on Martha, so I'm pushing it days out of the way. What do you think?'

'Let me finish the page. It's the end of the story.'

We read. It's a short page. Last story of a collection. She holds the book. In it, a man comes through a forest after a week's journey by foot, sees his house, doesn't know how he could be there since by his calculations he should still be a few hundred miles from it, knocks, nobody answers, calls out, nobody comes, opens the door, sees the woman he loved and who he was taken from years before by the ruler's men and who he'd thought dead, whispers her name, she walks to him with her arms out, he sees a child coming out of their bedroom, asks who it is, she says hers and his, he holds her, she puts her head on his shoulder, he kisses her neck, she says yes, he says for what? she says to his marriage proposal several years before which she couldn't answer then because simultaneously he was suddenly blindfolded and bound and she gagged and held down, he says, 'I forgot, but of course, darling, yes.'

'Seems like a very nice sort of story,' I say. 'Medieval romance?'

'Bizarre. Absolutely A to Izzard weird. I don't understand it. That couple and child were never in the story till the top of this page.'

'I want to read it.' She gives me the book. 'Tomorrow, I mean. It's been a full day.'

'Very full. And nice. Teaching. Being observed. Good confer-
ence with my assistant principal. Driving home along the
burgeoning and blooming river route. Walking with you. That
was a nice walk. Transplanting. Gardening. Grading papers
and seeing my and their hard-earned results. Linetta in a
delicious mood for a change. Hurray! And super supper, Newt.
Thank you for that. And now blotto in bed. That's why I
couldn't shampoo. Too full a day. I'm one-third after-dinner
wined, perfectly contented and bushed.'

'I kept you from a lot of sleep last night with my fleeting
breakdown.'

'Well now I'm going to get myself some sleep.'

'You're not feeling romantic?'

'No chance.' She takes off the scarf and nightgown and drops
them on the floor. 'You want to read?'

I kiss her arm. 'No.'

'Good. Mind if I shut off the light?'

'Shut it.'

She shuts off the light, turns her back to me, moves a few
inches further away from me and says, 'Goodnight, lovey.'

'Christ.'

'What?'

'I'm not that sleepy.'

'And I'm not feeling that way. I can't manufacture it and I
won't be forced.'

'At least give me a kiss.'

'I don't like it when you beg.'

'Then don't make me beg.'

'You make you beg. But I don't even like to talk about it
this way and I'm too tired to tell you why.'

'Then let's drop it.'

'Good idea. Now I really have to get some sleep, Newt. It's
been a long and I now see exhausting two days.'

It's dark. No moon. Stars? No stars. I can barely see the
trees against the sky. She turns over and her face comes down
near mine. I can tell by her breath. Her mouth must be only
a couple inches away. Our knees touch. Accident on her part?
I put my left foot on one of hers, bend over her and kiss her
lips.

'Night, lovey,' she says. The knees stay.

If she'd just snuggle up to me now. Rest her head on my shoulder and chest. Let me hold her. That would suffice. We wouldn't need words. Best nights and morning afters were the ones where we fell asleep and held each other till dawn like that. 'Snuggle up a—'

'What?' She jumped. I'd startled her. 'What? I was almost asleep.'

'I'm sorry. All I was saying was snuggle up a little closer, will ya, huh?'

'I don't want to. I'm comfortable where I am.' She pulls her foot out from under mine. Our knees came apart when she jumped. I get out of bed.

'I guess I'm not tired enough for sleep after all and do want to read,' I say.

'Not here, please?'

'Wasn't going to. Goodnight.'

I put on my pants and shirt and go downstairs and turn on the light and sit in the rocking chair and rock and roll till I realise the rocking squeaks might be keeping her from sleep. I stand and go upstairs and get my book off the floor and go downstairs and sit on the couch and read. The cat leaps on my lap out of nowhere, terrifying me. I throw it off, say 'Say you're sorry.' It licks its landing paws. I don't want to read. Book: cultural psychology. Interesting in a self-analytical way during the day, but now trying. Maybe I should read her book—that story. But I don't want to read. Even an Elizabethan poem? No. I go upstairs, get my wallet, pop into my moccasins, go downstairs, turn off the light and open the door. The cowbell on the door's outside makes a long clang and then keeps clinging. I grab the bell to hush it and it clangs again. I'll remember to sneak up and grab the clapper next time I'm walking in, and if I walk out again tonight, to open the door very slowly. I'm sure, if she's not asleep, she thinks I'm making this noise to draw attention to my leaving. If we get in another spat soon, she'll mention the bell. 'You deliberately . . . so I'd know how mad you were . . . out of bitterness to me . . . spoiled child,' etcetera, though probably not. Why do I project so much? That could be what's ruining or ruined this relationship, besides my flashflood temper, petulance and jealousy, and other things. I start down the hill. Maybe when I return, projectionless, she'll snuggle up to me. Put her head—yes. Knees click-click. Feet on feet or foot, bodies aligned, occasionally a kiss and hair sniff before we're sleeping dreamily, no words, none, not that we couldn't use many.

Down the steep hill. We walked down it around this same time a few months ago when we couldn't sleep. Too much coffee for her (one demitasse at dinner), not enough wine or beer or too early for me (ten). On our backs then: 'Yes?' 'Yes.' Got out of bed, dressed. After making love? I don't remember. But we saw fireworks across the river that night, in the sky a police helicopter's spotlight probing our shore and river road for something amiss, on our side of the river, a visiting American warship docked at the end of a pleasure-craft harbour, festoonery of bra-like lights stem to stern or is it port to starboard? our favourite local bar filled with lit sailors.

Still braking myself down this steep hill. 'You remember just about everything,' she'd say now, things being different. Next night we broke. Also outside that night a sousing cracking thunderstorm. Morning after the drench I went home by bus and underground. Two weeks ago we came together by chance on a city street. Looked like her, from the back: same black hair brushed smoothly down to her shoulder blades, sort of stocky legs, pinched waist, height, arms, shoulders, shoulder bag, size of head and backside all the same it seemed, though uncustomary clothes never before seen by me: a skirt and Dr Scholl's shoes. 'Howdy, Ms?' I said, taking a slight chance for I still hadn't seen her face. 'Newt. I don't know if I like this.' Wary. Thought I might have been following her. Wasn't. We walked. Bench sat. Fukienese feast. Went home with her that night. That's when I started my unnatural act of not pushing myself on her. Of disappearing several times a day when I didn't need or want to and often without warning but which I felt she'd like. She did. Letting her do things for me that I usually refused, such as making my breakfast and morning coffee and putting my soiled clothes in her and Linetta's wash. I bused back to the city three days later, leaving behind a bogus note chalked on the kitchen blackboard in rainbow colours explaining I wanted to work in my flat as there were some things I had to do that could only be done there. Called the next day and she said I was right to go and that she kind of missed me last night. Returned the following day and developed my new role: impassiveness in place of passion and perturbation, making myself readily unavailable most of the day, often pretending she wasn't there and making her repeat things to me as if I didn't hear or was too engrossed in something at the time to listen, not swivelling around in my chair when I was reading and she was coming downstairs, and being a bit staid, logical and straightforward to her daughter rather than playful, digressive and unserious, and also to her son Timon who arrived last Friday from where he lived with his father and called himself our weekend houseguest. Then returning to the city on my own again. Same thing: devious note, day later I called, Mary saying she liked our recent inter-independence and lack of tension together, back I bused, ho-hum, and I thought she was really warming up to the new cool me. Taking my hand or arm or both when we walked. Smoothing out my forehead furrows. Asking me to do the shopping and laundry with her. Suddenly throwing her arms around me in front of our spinning clothes. Treating me to seaside lobster. Lovey-dovey every night with no prompting from me. Till a party two nights ago when I noticed a man there deep in solemn conversation with her and then I saw him tailing her from room to room and when I looked for his female companion I found he hadn't come with one or left any home. And then I saw Mary and him playing one of Linetta's games which required them to press and slap each other's hands while in turns calling out countries alphabetically and then the man perched on Mary's knees while both of them were having their palms read simultaneously by hired professional readers. And I later said 'Who's the man?' and she said 'Which one?' and I said 'The tall curly-haired handsome one with the thick moustache and beige suede jacket' and she said 'An old friend' and I said 'Someone you were pretty close to when we were split up?' and she said 'Yes, I've slept with Michael once or twice though not in the last few weeks' and I said 'That's not what I asked' and she said 'I thought it was implicitly implied' and I said 'Look it, if you want to be or sleep with him tonight or anything, don't let me stop you, I'll just ride back to the city with one of the guests' and she said 'Memory keeps failing me, but have I ever asked you before if

I could leave the room to take a pee?' and I said 'I don't think your analogy works' and she said 'Maybe by implication or rigorous thought or some mnemonic device on your part it might' and I said 'Just wanted you to know how I feel about you two, that's all' and she said 'Very cavalier of you, sir, but how can I believe you?' and I walked away and later saw them lying on a mattress on the floor with several other people, all of them sharing glasses of different-coloured wine and a single cigarette, though I'd never seen Mary smoke before, Michael's head on her belly and his body perpendicular to hers and Mary with her head up against someone's bare feet, and I walked out of the room and stumped back and said 'Mary?' and they both looked up but the lively talk around us continued and she said 'What?' and I said 'What is this?' and she said 'What is this what?' and looked at Michael and shrugged and he, holding a filled glass in one hand, put another glass down and closed his eyes and dragged on the cigarette and then tried passing it to her and she shook her head but he continued to hold it out for her as his eyes were still closed. I left the room and waited for her to come out and then went back in and said a little louder 'Mary?' and she said 'What, Newt, what?' and the conversation and laughter around us all but stopped and I said 'I'd like to speak to you' and she said 'About what?' and I said 'The hors d'oeuvres' and she got up, Michael's head sliding off her to the pillow she quickly provided for it, and met me in the next room and I said 'Your attachment or growing closeness to this man and just that you admitted to once or twice making love to him and that I didn't know about it before is beginning to bug me and I think we have to take a long walk now to talk it all out' and she said 'You're the one I came here with and expect to leave with and who for the past weeks I thought everything was beginning to revolve around again for me, but I can now see that possibility was impossible and it's all falling to pieces again, isn't it?' and I said 'I'll stop, let's go back inside' and she said 'Lovey, it's too late' and I said 'It was all very dumb and unfair of me and I guess I better find a ride back to the city now' and she said 'Dumb, yes, and also yes that I liked you much better in the nonhassling and uninterfering way you've recently been, but I should have known no personality can change like that in a

month and that you were faking it all, right?' and I said 'In
my attitude to you, almost everything' and she said 'I wish for
Christsakes you would have told me and saved us both a bag
of soap bubbles' and grabbed the hand of a mutual friend
flitting past and started gabbing with him about their daughters' science teacher, and later we went home and cooked
separate snacks and never touched one another and slept in
different rooms, despite my repeated mentioning that as fierce
as my folks' arguments were, they always ended them for the
interim when they went to bed together, and Michael wound
up sleeping in the gazebo with the hostess, and the host, we
learned the next day, in a motel with his daughter's college
roommate, and the daughter in her parents' bedroom with the
bartender, who was the roommate's brother and had known
the daughter for a week and proposed and got engaged to her
that night.

Next day I awoke with a note on my chest saying 'Though
you can sleep in my bed tonight if you like, please, though not
out of any fakery, try and stay away from me for the day, as
I've a lot of conclusions to come to and decisions to make.'

Last night, about an hour into bed, I woke up and started
to shake and then cry uncontrollably and continued to cry long
after Mary asked me if this was just another conniving game
I was playing to keep her awake and then held me and kept
patting my back as if trying to burp me, but I could give no
sensible explanation why I continued to cry. I said things like
'Suddenly I was seeing myself with all my masks off and
maybe that's what's making me cry' (and after each of my
explanations I'd blubber and weep) . . . ' 'But it could also be
my dead parents and brother and sister whose faces I still see
passing through my head as if on the same rotating slow-
motion tape . . . But I also feel it's somehow tied in with some
sudden realisation of my own mortality and repressed fear of
severe sickness and death . . . And also what a sonofabitch
and fraud I've been to you and Timon and Lin and just about
everyone I know including all my good friends . . . That I
suddenly feel I really have no friends, good, bad, strong or
weak . . . And that I'm actually a foolish ludicrous loner and
mope without any pride in my past and hope for myself and
future associations and work at thirty-eight . . . But I also feel

it could be just the contrary to all of those and that I'm bawling because I can't take seriously anything I or anyone says or does and that I haven't for twenty years . . . ' and on and on the explanations and crying went, till she said after about an hour of this 'I'm exhausted, Newt. You must be too. Crying can be very enervating. So let's call it a night now and talk about it some more tomorrow if you want, okay?' and she flipped over the wet pillows, shut off the light, patted my back a last time and said 'Sleep, Newt—now I said to sleep' and we both soon fell asleep.

Now I'm in a bar, one of the three on the one store street in her town. The people at the bar are mostly watching a television program called *Shaft*. Several other customers are at the pool table playing for cheeseburgers and pitchers of beer. A commercial cuts into *Shaft* just as it appears he's about to get shot by a multimillionaire loanshark's private firing squad composed of robots. The young woman next to me says 'Is this the movie *Shaft* or the TV show?'

'I don't know,' I say. 'Till tonight I didn't know there was either.'

'Did you see *The Sting*?'

'No.'

'You didn't see *The Sting*?'

'No.'

'It won all the awards. It's fantastic.'

'I plan to.'

'Did you see *The Sting*?' she says to the man on the other side of me.

'Great,' he says.

'Did the ending completely fool you too?'

'Sure did.'

'Is this the TV program *Shaft* or the original movie?'

'TV,' he says, trying to watch the end of it.

I have a couple more beers. Shaft escaped. The news is on. I've been here a half hour. I want to wait for the weather. I leave. I climb the hill. At one point I get so tired I have to sit on the ground. I go to her house, hold the cowbell clapper as I open the door, close the door slowly, go to her room, take off my clothes, get in bed. She stirs.

'Couldn't sleep,' I say.

'What?'

'And now I can't sleep.'

'I can if you don't talk anymore.'

'Come on, Em, don't give me that.'

'Newt. I'm tired. Can't you tell? What's the time?'

'I don't know.'

'You know. It's late.'

I get out of bed and go to the bathroom, though I don't have to. I look for the moon, go into Linetta's room and try and make out what she's saying in her sleep. 'Morons . . . brick balls . . . ' I get back in bed, facing Mary's back, and curl up with her. She moves away.

'Love,' I say. If she heard me, she doesn't say anything.

Tomorrow morning before she leaves for work we'll have another argument. I know what I'll say. She'll say 'You know I hate arguing before I go to work. It kills my whole day. Please don't make a mountain out of a molehill. I told you once I was going to see other men. As friends. And if it turns out, as lovers. You should see other women. Just other people then. But don't put it all on me. It's too much.' She's said things like that before. I'll then say something I'll regret and she'll get very upset with me and maybe cry and then she'll say 'No, this will never work, it can't' and she'll ask me to leave for good and then she'll go to work and I'll have to get on the bus back to the city and I'll leave a note that I'm going because she wants me to and that I don't know when I'll ever see her again if I ever again see her again. It's so complicated. The note, sealed in an envelope, will read a little differently than that. She's right. I do depend too much on her for affection and attention. I shouldn't. I have to try not to. But I see no way how.

I close my eyes and try to sleep. I can't. I go downstairs and try to read. I can't. I drink several glasses of wine and feel much sleepier now and go back to bed, but I can't sleep. I move around. It's the last thing I should do. But I want her to hear me and say 'Something must be really disturbing you, Newt—what's wrong?' I want her to hold me and say 'Lovey, it's all right. I love you and everything still only revolves around you.'

But she says 'Newt. I'm not going to give you much of a

choice. You have to either fall asleep immediately or not move an inch around in bed or just leave this room and sleep somewhere else tonight. If you insist on making noises in whatever room you move to, then you'll have to leave the house.'

I say 'Screw off' and she says 'Will you get lost?' and I push her off the bed with my feet. From the floor she says 'That's it. That's the last time. Now I don't want to have to get crazy or angrier than I am and have Linetta hear another word of this, so please get the hell out of here for good' and I get dressed and leave the house.

'Lessons' in Sleep

64

CHARLES DICKENS

'Lying Awake' reads like a dashed-off piece of non-sense—and is the better for it. It is taken from The Uncommercial Traveller and Reprinted Pieces, *etc. Dickens was born in 1812, lived in England, America and Italy, and died in 1870.*

Lying Awake

'My uncle lay with his eyes half closed, and his nightcap drawn almost down to his nose. His fancy was already wandering, and began to mingle up the present scene with the crater of Vesuvius, the French Opera, the Colosseum at Rome, Dolly's Chop-house in London, and all the farrago of noted places with which the brain of a traveller is crammed; in a word, he was just falling asleep.'

Thus, that delightful writer, WASHINGTON IRVING, in his Tales of a Traveller. But, it happened to me the other night to be lying: not with my eyes half closed, but with my eyes wide open; not with my nightcap drawn almost down to my nose, for on sanitary principles I never wear a nightcap: but with my hair pitchforked and tousled all over the pillow; not just falling asleep by any means, but glaringly, persistently, and obstinately, broad awake. Perhaps, with no scientific intention or invention, I was illustrating the theory of the Duality of the Brain; perhaps one part of my brain, being wakeful, sat up to watch the other part which was sleepy. Be that as it may, something in me was as desirous to go to sleep as it possibly could be, but something else in me *would not* go to sleep, and was as obstinate as George the Third.

Thinking of George the Third—for I devote this paper to my train of thoughts as I lay awake: most people lying awake sometimes, and having some interest in the subject—put me in mind of BENJAMIN FRANKLIN, and so Benjamin Franklin's paper on the art of procuring pleasant dreams, which would seem necessarily to include the art of going to sleep, came into my head. Now, as I often used to read that paper when I was a very small boy, and as I recollect everything I read then as perfectly as I forget everything I read now, I quoted 'Get out of bed, beat up and turn your pillow, shake the bed-clothes well with at least twenty shakes, then throw the bed open and leave it to cool; in the meanwhile, continuing undrest, walk about your chamber. When you begin to feel the cold air unpleasant, then return to your bed, and you will soon fall asleep, and your sleep will be sweet and pleasant.' Not a bit of it! I performed the whole ceremony, and if it were possible for me to be more saucer-eyed than I was before, that was the only result that came of it.

Except Niagara. The two quotations from Washington Irving and Benjamin Franklin may have put it in my head by an American association of ideas; but there I was, and the Horse-shoe Fall was thundering and tumbling in my eyes and ears, and the very rainbows that I left upon the spray when I really did last look upon it, were beautiful to see. The night-light being quite as plain, however, and sleep seeming to be many thousand miles further off than Niagara, I made up my mind to think a little about Sleep; which I no sooner did than I whirled off in spite of myself to Drury Lane Theatre, and there saw a great actor and dear friend of mine (whom I had been thinking of in the day) playing Macbeth, and heard him apostrophising 'the death of each day's life', as I have heard him many a time, in the days that are gone.

But, Sleep. I *will* think about Sleep. I am determined to think (this is the way I went on) about Sleep. I must hold the word Sleep tight and fast, or I shall be off at a tangent in half a second. I feel myself unaccountably straying already, into Clare Market. Sleep. It would be curious, as illustrating the equality of sleep, to inquire how many of its phenomena are common to all classes, to all degrees of wealth and poverty, to every grade of education and ignorance. Here, for example, is her Majesty Queen Victoria in her palace, this present blessed night, and here is Winking Charley, a sturdy vagrant, in one of her Majesty's jails. Her Majesty has fallen, many thousand of times, from that same Tower, which *I* claim a right to tumble off now and then. So has Winking Charley. Her Majesty in her sleep has opened or prorogued Parliament, or has held a

Drawing Room, attired in some very scanty dress, the deficiencies and improprieties of which have caused her great uneasiness. I, in my degree, have suffered unspeakable agitation of mind from taking the chair at a public dinner at the London Tavern in my night-clothes, which not all the courtesy of my kind friend and host MR BATHE could persuade me were quite adapted to the occasion. Winking Charley has been repeatedly tried in a worse condition. Her Majesty is no stranger to a vault or firmament, of a sort of floorcloth, with an indistinct pattern distantly resembling eyes, which occasionally obtrudes itself on her repose. Neither am I. Neither is Winking Charley. It is quite common to all three of us to skim along with airy strides a little above the ground; also to hold, with the deepest interest, dialogues with various people, all represented by ourselves, and to be at our wit's end to know what they are going to tell us; and to be indescribably astonished by the secrets they disclose. It is probable that we have all three committed murders and hidden bodies. It is pretty certain that we have all desperately wanted to cry out, and have had no voice; that we have all gone to the play and not been able to get in; that we have all dreamed much more of our youth than of our later lives; that—I have lost it! The thread's broken.

Up the Great Saint Bernard

And up I go. I, lying here with the night-light before me, up I go, for no reason on earth that I can find out, and drawn by no links that are visible to me, up the Great Saint Bernard! I have lived in Switzerland, and rambled among the mountains; but why I should go there now, and why up the Great Saint Bernard in preference to any other mountain, I have no idea. As I lie here broad awake, and with every sense so sharpened that I can distinctly hear distant noises inaudible to me at another time, I make that journey, as I really did, on the same summer day, with the same happy party—ah! two since dead, I grieve to think—and there is the same track, with the same black wooden arms to point the way, and there are the same storm-refuges here and there; and there is the same snow falling at the top, and there are the same frosty mists, and there is the same intensely cold convent with its ménagerie smell, and the same breed of dogs fast dying out, and the same breed of jolly young monks whom I mourn to know as humbugs, and the same convent parlour with its piano and the sitting round the fire, and the same supper, and the same lone night in a cell, and the same bright fresh morning when going out into the highly rarefied air was like a plunge into an icy bath. Now, see here what comes along; and why does this thing stalk into my mind on the top of a Swiss mountain!

It is a figure that I once saw, just after dark, chalked upon a door in a little back lane near a country church—my first church. How young a child I may have been at the time I don't know, but it horrified me so intensely—in connexion with the churchyard, I suppose, for it smokes a pipe, and has a big hat with each of its ears sticking out in a horizontal line under the brim, and is not in itself more oppressive than a mouth from ear to ear, a pair of goggle eyes, and hands like two bunches of carrots, five in each, can make it—that it is still vaguely alarming to me to recall (as I have often done before, lying awake) the running home, the looking behind, the horror, of its following me; though whether disconnected from the door, or door and all, I can't say, and perhaps never could. It lays a disagreeable train. I must resolve to think of something on the voluntary principle.

The balloon ascents of this last season. They will do to think about, while I lie awake, as well as anything else. I must hold them tight though, for I feel them sliding away, and in their stead are the Mannings, husband and wife, hanging on the top of Horsemonger Lane Jail. In connexion with which dismal spectacle, I recall this curious fantasy of the mind. That, having beheld that execution, and having left those two forms dangling on the top of the entrance gateway—the man's, a limp, loose suit of clothes as if the man had gone out of them; the woman's, a fine shape, so elaborately corseted and artfully dressed, that it was quite unchanged in its trim appearance as it slowly swung from side to side—I never could, by my uttermost efforts, for some weeks, present the outside of that prison to myself (which the terrible impression I had received continually obliged me to do) without presenting it with the two figures still hanging in the morning air. Until, strolling past the gloomy place one night, when the street was deserted and quiet, and actually seeing that the bodies were not there, my fancy was persuaded, as it were, to take them down and bury them within the precincts of the jail, where they have lain ever since.

Dangerous exhibitions

The balloon ascents of last season. Let me reckon them up. There were the horse, the bull, the parachute, and the tumbler hanging on—chiefly by his toes, I believe—below the car. Very wrong, indeed, and decidedly to be stopped. But, in connexion with these and similar dangerous exhibitions, it strikes me that that portion of the public whom they entertain, is unjustly reproached. Their pleasure is in the difficulty overcome. They are a public of great faith, and are quite confident that the gentleman will not fall off the horse, or the lady off the bull or out of the parachute, and that the tumbler has a firm hold with his toes. They do not go to see the adventurer vanquished, but triumphant. There is no parallel in public combats between men and beasts, because nobody can answer for the particular beast—unless it were always the same beast, in which case it would be a mere stage-show, which the same public would go in the same state of mind to see, entirely believing in the brute being beforehand safely subdued by the man. That they are not accustomed to calculate hazards and dangers with any nicety, we may know from their rash exposure of themselves in overcrowded steamboats, and unsafe conveyances and places of all kinds. And I cannot help thinking that instead of railing, and attributing savage motives to a people naturally well disposed and humane, it is better to teach them and lead them argumentatively and reasonably—for they are very reasonable, if you will discuss a matter with them—to more considerate and wise conclusions.

This is a disagreeable intrusion! Here is a man with his throat cut, dashing towards me as I lie awake! A recollection of an old story of a kinsman of mine, who, going home one foggy winter night to Hampstead, when London was much smaller and the road lonesome, suddenly encountered such a figure rushing past him, and presently two keepers from a madhouse in pursuit. A very unpleasant creature indeed, to come into my mind unbidden, as I lie awake.

The balloon ascents of last season. I must return to the balloons. Why did the bleeding man start out of them? Never mind; if I inquire, he will be back again. The balloons. This particular public have inherently a great pleasure in the contemplation of physical difficulties overcome; mainly as I take it, because the lives of a large majority of them are exceedingly monotonous and real, and further, are a struggle against continual difficulties, and further still, because anything in the form of accidental injury, or any kind of illness or disability is so very serious in their own sphere. I will explain this seeming paradox of mine. Take the case of a Christmas Pantomime. Surely nobody supposes that the young mother in the pit who falls into fits of laughter when the baby is boiled or sat upon, would be at all diverted by such an occurrence off the stage. Nor is the decent workman in the gallery, who is transported beyond the ignorant present by the delight with which he sees a stout gentleman pushed out of a two pair of stairs window, to be slandered by the suspicion that he would be in the least entertained by such a spectacle in any street in London, Paris or New York. It always appears to me that the secret of this enjoyment lies in the temporary superiority to the common hazards and mischance of life; in seeing casualties, attended when they really occur with bodily and mental suffering, tears and poverty, happen through a very rough sort of poetry without the least harm being done to any one—the pretence of distress in a pantomime being so broadly humorous as to be no pretence at all. Much as in the comic fiction I can understand the mother with a very vulnerable baby at home, greatly relishing the invulnerable baby on the stage, so in the Cremorne reality I can understand the mason who is always liable to fall off a scaffold in his working jacket and to be carried to the hospital, having an infinite admiration of the radiant personage in spangles who goes into the clouds upon a bull, or upside down, and who, he takes it for granted—not reflecting upon the thing—has, by uncommon skill and dexterity, conquered such mischance as those to which he and his acquaintance are continually exposed.

I wish the Morgue in Paris would not come here as I lie awake, with its ghastly beds, and the swollen saturated clothes hanging up, and the water dripping, dripping all day long, upon that other swollen saturated something in the corner, like a heap of crushed over-ripe figs that I have seen in Italy! And this detestable Morgue comes back again at the head of a procession of forgotten ghost stories. This will never do. I must think of something else as I lie awake; or, like that sagacious animal in the United States who recognised the colonel who was such a dead shot, I am a gone 'Coon. What shall I think of? The late brutal assaults. Very good subject. The late brutal assaults.

(Though whether, supposing I should see, here before me as I lie awake, the awful phantom described in one of those ghost stories, who, with a head-dress of shroud, was always seen looking in through a certain glass door at a certain dead hour—whether in such a case it would be the least consolation to me to know on philosophical grounds that it was merely my imagination, is a question I can't help asking myself by the way.)

The whipping panacea

The late brutal assaults. I strongly question the expediency of advocating the revival of whipping for those crimes. It is a natural and generous impulse to be indignant at the perpetration of inconceivable brutality, but I doubt the whipping panacea gravely. Not in the least regard or pity for the criminal, whom I hold in far lower estimation than a mad wolf, but in consideration for the general tone and feeling, which is very much improved since the whipping times. It is bad for a people to be familiarised with such punishments. When the whip went out of Bridewell, and ceased to be flourished at the cart's tail and at the whipping-post, it began to fade out of madhouses, and workhouses, and schools and families, and to give place to a better system everywhere, than cruel driving. It would be hasty, because a few brutes may be inadequately punished, to revive, in any aspect, what, in so many aspects, society is hardly yet happily rid of. The whip is a very contagious kind of thing, and difficult to confine within one set of bounds. Utterly abolish punishment by fine—a barbarous device, quite as much out of data as wager by battle, but particularly connected in the vulgar minds with this class of offence—at least quadruple the term of imprisonment for aggravated assaults—and above all let us, in such cases, have no Pet Prisoning, vain glorifying, strong soup, and roasted meats, but hard work, and one unchanging and uncompromising dietary of bread and water, well or ill; and we shall do much better than by going down into the dark to grope for the whip among the rusty fragments of the rack, and the branding iron, and the chains and gibbet from the public roads, and the weights that pressed men to death in the cells of Newgate.

I had proceeded thus far, when I found I had been lying awake so long that the very dead began to wake too, and to crowd into my thoughts most sorrowfully. Therefore, I resolved to lie awake no more, but to get up and go out for a night walk—which resolution was an acceptable relief to me, as I dare say it may prove now to a great many more.

Djuna Barnes

What do People Talk About When They Can't Sleep?

In his introduction to Nightwood, *T. S. Eliot wrote,
'When the question is raised of writing an introduction to a book of creative order, I always feel that the
few books worth introducing are exactly those which
it is an impertinence to introduce'. 'Watchman, What
of the Night?' is the title of the fifth part of Barnes's
novel, first published in 1936. In this extract, Doctor
Matthew O'Connor's fantastic monologue on the night
is directed at Nora, one of the two women who love
Robin Vote, the novel's protagonist.*

*Barnes was born in New York in 1892 and died
in 1982.*

Watchman, What of the Night?

About three in the morning, Nora knocked at the little glass
door of the *concierge*'s loge, asking if the doctor was in. In the
anger of broken sleep the *concierge* directed her to climb six
flights, where at the top of the house, to the left, she would
find him.

Nora took the stairs slowly. She had not known that the
doctor was so poor. Groping her way she rapped, fumbling for
the knob. Misery alone would have brought her, though she
knew the late hours indulged in by her friend. Hearing his
'come in' she opened the door and for one second hesitated, so
incredible was the disorder that met her eyes. The room was
so small that it was just possible to walk sideways up to the
bed; it was as if being condemned to the grave the doctor had
decided to occupy it with the utmost abandon.

A pile of medical books, and volumes of a miscellaneous
order, reached almost to the ceiling, water-stained and covered
with dust. Just above them was a very small barred window,
the only ventilation. On a maple dresser, certainly not of

European make, lay a rusty pair of forceps, a broken scalpel, half a dozen odd instruments that she could not place, a catheter, some twenty perfume bottles, almost empty, pomades, creams, rouges, powder boxes and puffs. From the half-open drawers of this chiffonier hung laces, ribands, stockings, ladies' underclothing and an abdominal brace, which gave the impression that the feminine finery had suffered venery. A swill-pail stood at the head of the bed, brimming with abominations. There was something appallingly degraded about the room, like the rooms in brothels, which give even the most innocent a sensation of having been accomplice; yet this room was also muscular, a cross between a *chambre à coucher* and a boxer's training camp. There is a certain belligerence in a room in which a woman has never set foot; every object seems to be battling its own compression—and there is a metallic odour, as of beaten iron in a smithy.

In the narrow iron bed, with its heavy and dirty linen sheets, lay the doctor in a woman's flannel nightgown.

The doctor's head, with its over-large black eyes, its full gun-metal cheeks and chin, was framed in the golden semi-circle of a wig with long pendent curls that touched his shoulders, and falling back against the pillow, turned up the shadowy interior of their cylinders. He was heavily rouged and his lashes painted. It flashed into Nora's head: 'God, children know something they can't tell; they like Red Riding Hood and the wolf in bed!' But this thought, which was only the sensation of a thought, was of but a second's duration as she opened the door; in the next, the doctor had snatched the wig from his head, and sinking down in the bed drew the sheets up over his breast. Nora said, as quickly as she could recover herself: 'Doctor, I have come to ask you to tell me everything you know about the night.' As she spoke, she wondered why she was so dismayed to have come upon the doctor at the hour when he had evacuated custom and gone back into his dress.

The doctor said, 'You see that you can ask me anything,' thus laying aside both their embarrassments.

She said to herself: 'Is not the gown the natural raiment of extremity? What nation, what religion, what ghost, what dream, has not worn it—infants, angels, priests, the dead; why should not the doctor, in the grave dilemma of his alchemy, wear his dress?' She thought: 'He dresses to lie beside himself, who is so constructed that love, for him, can be only something special; in a room that giving back evidence of his occupancy, is as mauled as the last agony.'

'Have you ever thought of the night?' the doctor inquired with a little irony; he was extremely put out, having expected someone else, though his favourite topic, and one which he talked on whenever he had a chance, was the night.

'Yes,' said Nora, and sat down on the only chair. 'I've thought of it, but thinking about something you know nothing about does not help.'

'Have you,' said the doctor, 'ever thought of the peculiar polarity of times and times; and of sleep? Sleep the slain white bull? Well, I, Dr Matthew-Mighty-grain-of-salt-Dante-O'Connor, will tell you how the day and the night are related by their division. The very constitution of twilight is a fabulous reconstruction of fear, fear bottom-out and wrong side up. Every day is thought upon and calculated, but the night is not premeditated. The Bible lies the one way, but the night-gown the other. The night, 'Beware of that dark door!'''

'I used to think,' Nora said, 'that people just went to sleep, or if they did not go to sleep that they were themselves, but now—' she lit a cigarette and her hands trembled— 'now I see that the night does something to a person's identity, even when asleep.'

'Ah!' exclaimed the doctor. 'Let a man lay himself down in the Great Bed and his "identity" is no longer his own, his "trust" is not with him, and his "willingness" is turned over and is of another permission. His distress is wild and anonymous. He sleeps in a Town of Darkness, member of a secret brotherhood. He neither knows himself nor his outriders; he berserks a fearful dimension and dismounts, miraculously, in bed!

'His heart is tumbling in his chest, a dark place! Though some go into the night as a spoon breaks easy water, others go head foremost against a new connivance; their horns make a dry crying, like the wings of the locust, late come to their shedding.

'Have you thought of the night, now, in other times, in foreign countries—in Paris? When the streets were gall high with things you wouldn't have done for a dare's sake, and the way it was then; with the pheasants' necks and the goslings' beaks dangling against the hocks of the gallants, and not a pavement in the place, and everything gutters for miles and miles, and a stench to it that plucked you by the nostrils and you were twenty leagues out! The criers telling the price of wine to such effect that the dawn saw good clerks full of piss and vinegar, and blood-letting in side streets where some wild princess in a night-shift of velvet howled under a leech; not to mention the palaces of Nymphenburg echoing back to Vienna with the night trip of late kings letting water into plush cans and fine woodwork! no,' he said, looking at her sharply, 'I can see you have not! You should, for the night has been going on for a long time.'

She said, 'I've never known it before—I thought I did, but it was not knowing at all.'

'Exactly,' said the doctor. 'You thought you knew, and you hadn't even shuffled the cards—now the nights of one period are not the nights of another. Neither are the nights of one city the nights of another. Let us take Paris for an instance, and France for a fact. *Ah, mon dieu! La nuit effroyable! La nuit, qui est une immense plaine, et le coeur qui est une petite extremite!* Ah, good Mother mine, *Notre Dame-de-bonne-Garde!* Intercede for me now, while yet I explain what I'm coming to! French nights are those which all nations seek the world over—and have you noticed that? Ask Dr Mighty O'Connor; the reason the doctor knows everything is because he's been everywhere at the wrong time and has now become anonymous.'

'But,' Nora said, 'I never thought of the night as a life at all—I've never lived it—why did she?'

'I'm telling you of French nights at the moment,' the doctor went on, 'and why we all go into them. The night and the day are two travels, and the French—gut-greedy and fist-tight though they often are—alone leave testimony of the two in the dawn; we tear up the one for the sake of the other; not so the French.'

DOROTHY PARKER

Parker's soliloquies impressed her readers and fellow writers; they looked easy, but few could imitate her. 'The Little Hours', in which the narrator is plagued by La Rochefoucauld's rather useless 17th century maxims, was first collected by Parker herself in The Original Portable *in 1944.*

Dorothy Parker was born in 1893, dying in 1967 in Manhattan.

The Little Hours

Now what's this? What's the object of all this darkness all over me? They haven't gone and buried me alive while my back was turned, have they? Ah, now would you think they'd do a thing like that! Oh, no, I know what it is. I'm awake. That's it. I've waked up in the middle of the night. Well, isn't that nice. Isn't that simply ideal. Twenty minutes past four, sharp, and here's Baby wide-eyed as a marigold. Look at this, will you? At the time when all decent people are just going to bed, I must wake up. There's no way things can ever come out even, under this system. This is as rank as injustice is ever likely to get. This is what brings about hatred and bloodshed, that's what *this* does.

Yes, and you want to know what got me into this mess? Going to bed at ten o'clock, that's what. That spells ruin. T-e-n-space-o-apostrophe-c-l-o-c-k: ruin. Early to bed, and you'll wish you were dead. Bed before eleven, nuts before seven. Bed before morning, sailors give warning. Ten o'clock after a quiet evening of reading. Reading—there's an institution for you. Why, I'd turn on the light and read, right this minute, if reading weren't what contributed toward driving me here. I'll show it. God, the bitter misery that reading works in this world! Everybody knows that—everybody who *is* everybody. All the best minds have been off reading for years. Look at the swing La Rochefoucauld took at it. He said that if nobody had ever learned to read, very few people would be in love. There was a man for you, and that's what *he* thought of it. Good for you, La Rochefoucauld; nice going, boy. I wish I'd never learned to read. I wish I'd never learned to take off my clothes. Then I wouldn't have been caught in this jam at half-past four in the morning. If nobody had ever learned to undress, very few people would be in love. No, his is better. Oh, well, it's a man's world.

La Rochefoucauld, indeed, lying quiet as a mouse, and me tossing and turning here! This is no time to be getting all steamed up about La Rochefoucauld. It's only a question of minutes before I'm going to be pretty darned good and sick of La Rochefoucauld, once and for all. La Rochefoucauld this and La Rochefoucauld that. Yes, well, let me tell you that if nobody had ever learned to quote, very few people would be in love with La Rochefoucauld. I bet you I don't know ten souls who read him without a middleman. People pick up those scholarly little essays that start off 'Was it not that lovable old cynic, La Rochefoucauld, who said . . . ' and then they go around claiming to know the master backwards. Pack of illiterates, that's all they are. All right, let them keep their La Rochefoucauld, and see if I care. I'll stick to La Fontaine. Only I'd be better company if I could quit thinking that La Fontaine married Alfred Lunt.

I don't know what I'm doing mucking about with a lot of French authors at this hour, anyway. First thing you know, I'll be reciting *Fleurs du Mal* to myself, and then I'll be little more good to anybody. And I'll stay off Verlaine too; he was always chasing Rimbauds. A person would be better off with La Rochefoucauld, even. Oh, damn La Rochefoucauld. The big Frog. I'll thank him to keep out of my head. What's he doing there, anyhow? What's La Rochefoucauld to me, or he to Hecuba? Why, I don't even know the man's first name, that's how close I ever was to *him*. What am I supposed to be, a hostess to La Rochefoucauld? That's what *he* thinks. Sez he. Well, he's wasting his time, hanging around here. I can't help him. The only other thing I can remember his saying is that there is always something a little pleasing to us in the misfortunes of even our dearest friends. That cleans me all up with Monsieur La Rochefoucauld. *Maintenant c'est fini, ça.*

Dearest friends. A sweet lot of dearest friends *I've* got. All of them lying in swinish stupors, while I'm practically up and about. All of them stretched sodden through these, the fairest hours of the day, when man should be at his most productive. Produce, produce, produce, for I tell you the night is coming. Caryle said that. Yes, and a fine one *he* was, to go shooting off his face on production. *Oh*, Thomas Car*li*-yil, what *I* know about *you*-oo! No, that will be enough of that. I'm not going to start fretting about Carlyle, at this stage of the game. What did he ever do that was so great, besides founding a college for Indians? (That one ought to make him spin.) Let him keep his face out of this, if he knows what's good for him. I've got enough trouble with that lovable old cynic, La Rochefoucauld— him and the misfortunes of his dearest friends!

The first thing I've got to do is to get out and whip me up a complete new set of dearest friends; that's the first thing. Everything else can wait. And will somebody please kindly be so good as to inform me how I am ever going to meet up with any new people when my entire scheme of living is out of joint—when I'm the only living being awake while the rest of the world lies sleeping? I've got to get this thing adjusted. I must try to get back to sleep right now. I've got to conform to the rotten little standards of this sluggard civilisation. People needn't feel that they have to change their ruinous habits and come my way. Oh, no, no; no, indeed. Not at all. I'll go theirs. If that isn't the woman of it for you! Always having to do what somebody else wants, like it or not. Never able to murmur a suggestion of her own.

And what suggestion has anyone to murmur as to how I am going to drift lightly back to slumber? Here I am, awake as high noon what with all this milling and pitching around with La Rochefoucauld. I really can't be expected to drop everything and start counting sheep, at my age. I hate sheep. Untender it may be in me, but all my life I've hated sheep. It amounts to a phobia, the way I hate them. I can tell the minute there's one in the room. They needn't think that I am going to lie here in the dark and count their unpleasant little faces for them; I wouldn't do it if I didn't fall asleep again until the middle of next August. Suppose they never get counted—what's the worst that can happen? If the number of imaginary sheep in this world remains a matter of guesswork, who is richer or poorer for it? No, sir; *I'm* not their scorekeeper. Let them count themselves, if they're so crazy mad after mathematics. Let them do their own dirty work. Coming around here, at this time of day, and asking me to count them! And not even *real* sheep, at that. Why, it's the most preposterous thing I ever heard in my life.

But there must be *something* I could count. Let's see. No, I already know by heart how many fingers I have. I could count my bills, I suppose. I could count the things I didn't do yesterday that I should have done. I could count the things I should do today that I'm not going to do. I'm never going to accomplish anything; that's perfectly clear to me. I'm never going to be famous. My name will never be writ large on the roster of Those Who Do Things. I don't do anything. Not one single thing. I used to bite my nails, but I don't even do that any more. I don't amount to the powder to blow me to hell. I've turned out to be nothing but a bit of flotsam. Flotsam and leave 'em—that's me from now on. Oh, it's all terrible.

Well. This way lies galloping melancholia. Maybe it's because this is the zero hour. This is the time the swooning soul hangs pendant and vertiginous between the new day and the old, nor dares confront the one or summon back the other. This is the time when all things, known and hidden, are iron to weight the spirit; when all ways, travelled or virgin, fall away from the stumbling feet, when all before the straining eyes is black. Blackness now, everywhere is blackness. This is the time of abomination, the dreadful hour of the victorious dark. For it is always darkest—Was it not that lovable old cynic, La Rochefoucauld, who said it is always darkest before the deluge?

There. Now you see, don't you? Here we are again, practically back where we started. La Rochefoucauld, we are here. Ah, come on, son—how about your going your way and letting me go mine? I've got my work cut out for me right here; I've got all this sleeping to do. Think how I am going to look by daylight if this keeps up. I'll be a seamy sight for all those rested, clear-eyed, fresh-faced dearest friends of mine—the rats! My *dear*, whatever have you been doing; I thought you were so good lately. Oh, I was helling around with La

Rochefoucauld till all hours; we couldn't stop laughing about
your misfortunes. No, this is getting too thick, really. It isn't
right to have this happen to a person, just because she went
to bed at ten o'clock once in her life. Honest, I won't ever do
it again. I'll go straight, after this. I'll never go to bed again,
if I can only sleep now. If I can tear my mind away from a
certain French cynic, *circa* 1650, and slip into lovely oblivion.
1650. I bet I look as if I'd been awake since then.

How do people go to sleep? I'm afraid I've lost the knack. I
might try busting myself smartly over the temple with the
night-light. I might repeat to myself, slowly and soothingly, a
list of quotations beautiful from minds profound; if I can
remember any of the damn things. That might do it. And it
ought effectually to bar that visiting foreigner that's been
hanging around ever since twenty minutes past four. Yes, that's
what I'll do. Only wait till I turn the pillow; it feels as if La
Rochefoucauld had crawled inside the slip.

Now let's see—where shall we start? Why—er—let's see. Oh,
yes, I know one. This above all, to thine own self be true and
it must follow, as the night the day, thou canst not then be
false to any man. Now they're off. And once they get started,
they ought to come like hot cakes. Let's see. Ah, what avail
the sceptred race and what the form divine, when every virtue,
every grace, Rose Aylmer, all were thine. Let's see. They also
serve who only stand and wait. If Winter comes, can Spring
be far behind? Lilies that fester smell far worse than weeds.
Silent upon a peak in Darien. Mrs Porter and her daughter
wash their feet in soda-water. And Agatha's Arth is a hug-the-
hearth, but my true love is false. Why did you die when lambs
were cropping, you should have died when apples were drop-
ping. Shall be together, breathe and ride, so one day more am
I deified, who knows but the world will end tonight. And he
shall hear the stroke of eight and not the stroke of nine. They
are not long, the weeping and the laughter; love and desire
and hate I think will have no portion in us after we pass the
gate. But none, I think, do there embrace. I think that I shall
never see a poem lovely as a tree. I think I will not hang
myself today. Ay tank Ay go home now.

Let's see. Solitude is the safeguard of mediocrity and the
stern companion of genius. Consistency is the hob-goblin of

little minds. Something is emotion remembered in tranquillity. A cynic is one who knows the price of everything and the value of nothing. That lovable old cynic is one who—oops, there's King Charles's head again. I've got to watch myself. Let's see. Circumstantial evidence is a trout in the milk. Any stigma will do to beat a dogma. If you would learn what God thinks about money, you have only to look at those to whom He has given it. If nobody had ever learned to read, very few people—

All right. That fixes it. I throw in the towel right now. I know when I'm licked. There'll be no more of this nonsense; I'm going to turn on the light and read my head off. Till the next ten o'clock, if I feel like it. And what does La Rochefoucauld want to make of that? Oh, he *will*, eh? Yes, he will! He and who else? La Rochefoucauld and *what* very few people?

RECALLING VAST PASTS

JORGE LUIS BORGES

The ability to sleep—to be a 'blind, deaf-mute somnambulist'—is lost to insomnia and a prodigious memory in Borges' story. Funes needs not to sleep so that he will have enough time to remember—everything. Young when he gains his ability to remember, a long life without sleep is not sufficient to take account of even half his childhood.

Ficciones, from which this story is taken, was first published in Spanish in 1944. Borges was born in 1899 and died in 1986.

Funes, the Memorious

I remember him (I scarcely have the right to use this ghostly verb; only one man on earth deserved the right, and he is dead), I remember him with a dark passionflower in his hand, looking at it as no one has ever looked at such a flower, though they might look from the twilight of day until the twilight of night, for a whole life long. I remember him, his face immobile and Indian-like, and singularly *remote*, behind his cigarette. I remember (I believe) the strong delicate fingers of the plainsman who can braid leather. I remember, near those hands, a vessel in which to make maté tea, bearing the arms of the Banda Oriental*; I remember, in the window of the house, a yellow rush mat, and beyond, a vague marshy landscape. I remember clearly his voice, the deliberate, resentful, nasal voice of the old Eastern Shore man, without the Italianate syllables of today, I did not see him more than three times; the last time, in 1887 . . .

That all those who knew him should write something about him seems to me a very felicitous idea; my testimony may perhaps be the briefest and without doubt the poorest, and it will not be the least impartial. The deplorable fact of my being

---

* The Eastern Shore (of the Uruguay River); now the Orient Republic of Uruguay.

an Argentinian will hinder me from falling into a dithyramb—
an obligatory form in the Uruguay, when the theme is an
Uruguayan.

Littérateur, slicker, Buenos Airean: Funes did not use these
insulting phrases, but I am sufficiently aware that for him I
represented these unfortunate categories. Pedro Leandro Ipuche
has written that Funes was a precursor of the superman, 'an
untamed and vernacular Zarathustra'; I do not doubt it, but one
must not forget, either, that he was a countryman from the town
of Fray Bentos, with certain incurable limitations.

My first recollection of Funes is quite clear, I see him at
dusk, sometime in March or February of the year '84. That
year, my father had taken me to spend the summer at Fray
Bentos. I was on my way back from the farm at San Francisco
with my cousin Bernardo Haedo. We came back singing, on
horseback; and this last fact was not the only reason for my
joy. After a sultry day, an enormous slate-gray storm had
obscured the sky. It was driven on by a wind from the south;
the trees were already tossing like madmen; and I had the
apprehension (the second hope) that the elemental downpour
would catch us out in the open. We were running a kind of
race with the tempest. We rode into a narrow lane which
wound down between two enormously high brick footpaths. It
had grown black of a sudden; I now heard rapid almost secret
steps above; I raised my eyes and saw a boy running along
the narrow, cracked path as if he were running along a narrow,
broken wall. I remember the loose trousers, tight at the
bottom, the hemp sandals; I remember the cigarette in the
hard visage, standing out against the by now limitless darkness. Bernardo unexpectedly yelled to him: 'What's the time,
Ireneo?' Without looking up, without stopping, Ireneo replied:
'In ten minutes it will be eight o'clock, child Bernardo Juan
Francisco.' The voice was sharp, mocking.

I am so absentminded that the dialogue which I have just
cited would not have penetrated my attention if it had not
been repeated by my cousin, who was stimulated, I think by
a certain local pride and by a desire to show himself indifferent
to the other's three-sided reply.

He told me that the boy above us in the pass was a certain
Ireneo Funes, renowned for a number of eccentricities, such

as that of having nothing to do with people and of always knowing the time, like a watch. He added that Ireneo was the son of María Clementina Funes, an ironing woman in the town, and that his father, some people said, was an 'Englishman' named O'Connor, a doctor in the salting fields, though some said the father was a horse-breaker, or scout, from the province of El Salto. Ireneo lived with his mother, at the edge of the country house of the Laurels.

In the years '85 and '86 we spent the summer in the city of Montevideo. We returned to Fray Bentos in '87. As was natural, I inquired after all my acquaintances, and finally, about 'the chronometer Funes'. I was told that he had been thrown by a wild horse at the San Francisco ranch, and that he had been hopelessly crippled. I remember the impression of uneasy magic which the news provoked in me: the only time I had seen him we were on horseback, coming from San Francisco, and he was in a high place; from the lips of my cousin Bernardo the affair sounded like a dream elaborated with elements out of the past. They told me that Ireneo did not move now from his cot, but remained with his eyes fixed on the backyard fig tree, or on a cobweb. At sunset he allowed himself to be brought to the window. He carried pride to the extreme of pretending that the blow which had befallen him was a good thing . . . Twice I saw him behind the iron grate which sternly delineated his eternal imprisonment: unmoving, once, his eyes closed; unmoving also, another time, absorbed in the contemplation of a sweet-smelling sprig of lavender cotton.

At the time I had begun, not without some ostentation, the methodical study of Latin. My valise contained the *De viris illustribus* of Lhomond, the *Thesaurus* of Quicherat, Caesar's *Commentaries*, and an odd-numbered volume of the *Historia Naturalis* of Pliny, which exceeded (and still exceeds) my modest talents as a Latinist. Everything is noised around in a small town; Ireneo, at his small farm on the outskirts, was not long in learning of the arrival of these anomalous books. He sent me a flowery, ceremonious letter, in which he recalled our encounter, unfortunately brief, 'on the seventh day of February of the year '84', and alluded to the glorious services which Don Gregorio Haedo, my uncle, dead the same year, 'had rendered to the Two Fatherlands in the glorious campaign of Ituzaingó', and he solicited the loan of any one of the volumes,

to be accompanied by a dictionary 'for the better intelligence
of the original text, for I do not know Latin as yet.' He
promised to return them in good condition, almost immediately. The letter was perfect, very nicely constructed; the
orthography was of the type sponsored by Andrés Bello: *i* for
y, *j* for *g*. At first I naturally suspected a jest. My cousins
assured me it was not so, that these were the ways of Ireneo.
I did not know whether to attribute to impudence, ignorance,
or stupidity, the idea that the difficult Latin required no other
instrument than a dictionary; in order fully to undeceive him
I sent the *Gradus ad Parnassum* of Quicherat, and the Pliny.

On February 14, I received a telegram from Buenos Aires
telling me to return immediately, for my father was 'in no way
well.' God forgive me, but the prestige of being the recipient
of an urgent telegram, the desire to point out to all of Fray
Bentos the contradiction between the negative form of the
news and the positive adverb, the temptation to dramatise my
sorrow as I feigned a virile stoicism, all no doubt distracted
me from the possibility of anguish. As I packed my valise, I
noted that I was missing the *Gradus* and the volume of the
Historia Naturalis. The 'Saturn' was to weigh anchor on the
morning of the next day; that night, after supper, I made my
way to the house of Funes. Outside, I was surprised to find
the night no less oppressive than the day.

Ireneo's mother received me at the modest ranch.

She told me that Ireneo was in the back room and that I
should not be disturbed to find him in the dark, for he knew
how to pass the dead hours without lighting the candle. I
crossed the cobblestone patio, the small corridor; I came to the
second patio. A great vine covered everything, so that the
darkness seemed complete. Of a sudden I heard the high-
pitched, mocking voice of Ireneo. The voice spoke in Latin; the
voice (which came out of the obscurity) was reading, with
obvious delight, a treatise or prayer or incantation. The Roman
syllables resounded in the earthen patio; my suspicion made
them seem undecipherable, interminable; afterwards in the
enormous dialogue of that night, I learned that they made up
the first paragraph of the twenty-fourth chapter of the seventh
book of the *Historia Naturalis*. The subject of this chapter is

memory; the last words are *ut nihil non iisdem verbis redderetur auditum*.

Without the least change in his voice, Ireneo bade me come in. He was lying on the cot, smoking. It seems to me that I did not see his face until dawn; I seem to recall the momentary glow of the cigarette. The room smelled vaguely of dampness. I sat down, and repeated the story of the telegram and my father's illness.

I come now to the most difficult point in my narrative. For the entire story has no other point (the reader might as well know it by now) than this dialogue of almost a half-century ago. I shall not attempt to reproduce his words, now irrecoverable. I prefer truthfully to make a résumé of the many things Ireneo told me. The indirect style is remote and weak; I know that I sacrifice the effectiveness of my narrative; but let my readers imagine the nebulous sentences which clouded that night.

Ireneo began by enumerating, in Latin and Spanish, the cases of prodigious memory cited in the *Historia Naturalis*: Cyrus, king of the Persians, who could call every soldier in his armies by name; Mithridates Eupator, who administered justice in the twenty-two languages of his empire; Simonides, inventor of mnemotechny; Metrodorus, who practiced the art of repeating faithfully what he heard once. With evident good faith Funes marvelled that such things should be considered marvellous. He told me that previous to the rainy afternoon when the blue-tinted horse threw him, he had been—like any Christian—blind, deaf-mute, somnambulistic, memoryless. (I tried to remind him of his precise perception of time, his memory for proper names; he paid no attention to me.) For nineteen years, he said, he had lived like a person in a dream: he looked without seeing, heard without hearing, forgot everything—almost everything. On falling from the horse, he lost consciousness; when he recovered it, the present was almost intolerable it was so rich and bright; the same was true of the most ancient and most trivial memories. A little later he realised that he was crippled. This fact scarcely interested him. He reasoned (or felt) that immobility was a minimum price to pay. And now, his perception and his memory were infallible.

We, in a glance, perceive three wine glasses on the table;

Funes saw all the shoots, clusters, and grapes of the vine. He remembered the shapes of the clouds in the south at dawn on the 30th of April of 1882, and he could compare them in his recollection with the marbled grain in the design of a leather-bound book which he had seen only once, and with the lines in the spray which an oar raised in the Rio Negro on the eve of the battle of the Quebracho. These recollections were not simple; each visual image was linked to muscular sensations, thermal sensations, etc. He could reconstruct all his dreams, all his fancies. Two or three times he had reconstructed an entire day. He told me: *I have more memories in myself alone than all men have had since the world was a world*. And again: *My dreams are like your vigils*. And again, toward dawn: *My memory, sir, is like a garbage disposal*.

A circumference on a blackboard, a rectangular triangle, a rhomb, are forms which we can fully intuit; the same held true with Ireneo for the tempestuous mane of a stallion, a herd of cattle in a pass, the ever-changing flame or the innumerable ash, the many faces of a dead man during the course of a protracted wake. He could perceive I do not know how many stars in the sky.

These things he told me; neither then nor at any time later did they seem doubtful. In those days neither the cinema nor the phonograph yet existed; nevertheless, it seems strange, almost incredible, that no one should have experimented on Funes. The truth is that we all live by leaving behind; no doubt we all profoundly know that we are immortal and that sooner or later every man will do all things and know everything.

The voice of Funes, out of the darkness, continued. He told me that toward 1886 he had devised a new system of enumeration and that in a very few days he had gone beyond twenty-four thousand. He had not written it down, for what he once meditated would not be erased. The first stimulus to his work, I believe, had been his discontent with the fact that 'thirty-three Uruguayans' required two symbols and three words, rather than a single word and a single symbol. Later he applied his extravagant principle to the other numbers. In place of seven thousand thirteen, he would say (for example) *Máximo Perez*; in place of seven thousand fourteen, *The Train*; other numbers were *Luis Melián Lafinur, Olimar, Brimstone,*

*Clubs, The Whale, Gas, The Cauldron, Napoleon, Agustín de
Vedia.* In lieu of five hundred, he would say *nine*. Each word
had a particular sign, a species of mark; the last were very
complicated . . . I attempted to explain that this rhapsody of
unconnected terms was precisely the contrary of a system of
enumeration. I said that to say three hundred and sixty-five
was to say three hundreds, six tens, five units: an analysis
which does not exist in such numbers as *The Negro Timoteo*
or *The Flesh Blanket*. Funes did not understand me, or did
not wish to understand me.

Locke, in the seventeenth century, postulated (and rejected)
an impossible idiom in which each individual object, each
stone, each bird and branch had an individual name; Funes
had once projected an analogous idiom, but he had renounced
it as being too general, too ambiguous. In effect, Funes not
only remembered every leaf on every tree of every wood, but
even every one of the times he had perceived or imagined it.
He determined to reduce all of his past experience to some
seventy thousand recollections, which he would later define
numerically. Two considerations dissuaded him: the thought
that the task was interminable and the thought that it was
useless. He knew that at the hour of his death he would
scarcely have finished classifying even all the memories of his
childhood.

The two projects I have indicated (an infinite vocabulary for
the natural series of numbers, and a usable mental catalogue
of all the images of memory) are lacking in sense, but they
reveal a certain stammering greatness. They allow us to make
out dimly, or to infer, the dizzying world of Funes. He was, let
us not forget, almost incapable of general, platonic ideas. It
was not only difficult for him to understand that the generic
term *dog* embraced so many unlike specimens of differing sizes
and different forms; he was disturbed by the fact that a dog
at three-fourteen (seen in profile) should have the same name
as the dog at three-fifteen (seen from the front). His own face
in the mirror, his own hands, surprised him on every occasion.
Swift writes that the emperor of Lilliput could discern the
movement of the minute hand; Funes could continuously make
out the tranquil advances of corruption, of caries, of fatigue.
He noted the progress of death, of moisture. He was the

solitary and lucid spectator of a multiform world which was instantaneously and almost intolerably exact. Babylon, London and New York have overawed the imagination of men with their ferocious splendour; no one, in those populous towers or upon those surging avenues, has felt the heat and pressure of a reality as indefatigable as that which day and night converged upon the unfortunate Ireneo in his humble South American farmhouse. It was very difficult for him to sleep. To sleep is to be abstracted from the world; Funes, on his back in his cot, in the shadows, imagined every crevice and every moulding of the various houses which surrounded him. (I repeat, the least important of his recollections was more minutely precise and more lively than our perception of physical pleasure or a physical torment.) Toward the east, in a section which was not yet cut into blocks of homes, there were some new unknown houses. Funes imagined them black, compact, made of a single obscurity, he would turn his face in this direction in order to sleep. He would also imagine himself at the bottom of the river, being rocked and annihilated by the current.

Without effort, he had learned English, French, Portuguese, Latin. I suspect, nevertheless, that he was not very capable of thought. To think is to forget a difference, to generalise, to abstract. In the overly replete world of Funes there were nothing but details, almost contiguous details.

The equivocal clarity of dawn penetrated along the earthen patio.

Then it was that I saw the face of the voice which had spoken all through the night. Ireneo was nineteen years old; he had been born in 1868; he seemed as monumental as bronze, more ancient than Egypt, anterior to the prophecies and the pyramids. It occurred to me that each one of my words (each one of my gestures) would live on in his implacable memory; I was benumbed by the fear of multiplying superfluous gestures.

Ireneo Funes died in 1889, of a pulmonary congestion.

ITALO CALVINO

This page is taken from Calvino's Invisible Cities.
*Old Kublai Khan sits in his garden with the young
Marco Polo. Kublai Khan's empire is reaching its end
and Marco Polo tells him tales of cities that he has
seen within its borders. Memory and insomnia coincide in the city of Zora; the place is explored
imaginatively through memories induced by sleeplessness.*

*Born in Cuba in 1928, Italo Calvino grew up in
Italy, dying in 1985.*

Cities & Memory 4

Beyond six rivers and three mountain ranges rises Zora, a
city that no one, having seen it, can forget. But not because,
like other memorable cities, it leaves an unusual image of
your recollections. Zora has the quality of remaining in your
memory point by point, in its succession of streets, of houses
along the streets, and of doors and windows in the houses,
though nothing in them possesses a special beauty or rarity.
Zora's secret lies in the way your gaze runs over patterns
following one another as in a musical score where not a note
can be altered or displaced. The man who knows by heart
how Zora is made, if he is unable to sleep at night, can
imagine he is walking along the streets and he remembers
the order by which the copper clock follows the barber's
striped awning, then the fountain with the nine jets, the
astronomer's glass tower, the melon vendor's kiosk, the statue
of the hermit and the lion, the Turkish bath, the café at the
corner, the alley that leads to the harbour. This city which
cannot be expunged from the mind is like an armature, a
honeycomb in whose cells each of us can place the things he
wants to remember: names of famous men, virtues, numbers,
vegetable and mineral classifications, dates of battles, con-
stellations, parts of speech. Between each idea and each

point of the itinerary an affinity or a contrast can be established, serving as an immediate aid to memory. So the world's most learned men are those who have memorised Zora.

But in vain I set out to visit the city: forced to remain motionless and always the same, in order to be more easily remembered. Zora has languished, disintegrated, disappeared. The earth has forgotten her.

ISAK DINESEN

The Lonely Hunter—a Biography of Carson McCullers *includes a photograph of McCullers, Marilyn Monroe and Isak Dinesen lunching together at McCullers' house. The year is 1959. Monroe is laughing and of course looks gorgeous; McCullers is kissing Monroe's cheek but appears weak from illness; while Dinesen sits at the end of the table sipping champagne and looking positively spectral, her gaunt long face topped with the kind of turban favoured by Simone de Beauvoir.*

She is now well-known as the author of Out of Africa, *a book about her life on her coffee plantation in Kenya. There she entertained her lover Denys Finch-Hatton with many of her own tales on his returns between safaris. Hannah Arendt records that she called herself 'Scheherazade' and speculates that the tales were told to keep him returning to her; that Dinesen was as anxious to entertain as Scheherazade, for if her tales failed so might their romance.*

The narrator's opening question in the story below is an interesting one: will we other insomniacs believe that Angelo Santasilia chose to be an insomniac? Others in this anthology such as Borges, Pinera and Marquez would answer 'yes'. Insomnia offers a greatness of consciousness not known by dull sleepers.

Isak Dinesen was the pen name of Baroness Karen Blixen of Rungstedlund, born in 1885 in Denmark. She died in 1962.

Night Walk

After Leonidas Allori's death a sad misfortune came upon his disciple Angelo Santasilia: he could not sleep.

Will the narrator be believed by such people as have themselves experience of sleeplessness, when he tells them that from the beginning this affliction was the victim's own choice? Yet it was so. Angelo walked out through the prison gate, behind which he had for twelve hours been hostage for his condemned master, into a world which to him contained no direction whatsoever. He was totally isolated, an absolutely lonely figure in this world, and he felt that the man whose grief and shame—like his own—exceeded that of all others must at the same time be exempt from the laws which governed those others. He made up his mind not to sleep any more.

On this day he had no feeling of time, and he took fright when he realised that darkness had fallen, and the day was over. He was aware that his friends, other pupils of the dead artist, were tonight keeping watch together, but on no account would he join them, for they would be talking of Leonidas Allori and would greet him as the chosen disciple, upon whom the eye of the master had last dwelt. *Yes*, he thought, and laughed, *as if I were Elisha, the follower of the great prophet Elijah, on whom the passenger of the chariot of fire threw his mantle!* So he betook himself to the taverns and inns of the town, where casually collected people roared and rioted and where the air was filled with strumming and song, and was heavy with vapours of wine and the smell of the clothes and sweat of strangers. But he would not drink like the others. He left one inn to proceed to another, and both in the taprooms and in the streets he told himself, *All this does not concern me. I myself will not sleep any more.*

In such a tavern, on the night between Monday and Tuesday, he met Giuseppino, or Pino, Pizzuti, the philosopher, a small man shrunken and dark of hue as if he had been hung up in a chimney to be smoked. Pizzuti had once, many years ago, owned the noble marionette theatre in Naples, but later on his luck had left him. In prison, and in chains, three fingers of his right hand had withered, so that he could no longer manoeuvre his puppets. He now wandered from place to place, the poorest of the poor, but luminous, as if phosphorescent, with love of humanity in general and with a knowing and mellifluous compassion for the one human being with whom he just happened to be talking. In this man's company Angelo passed the next day and night, and while he looked at him and listened to him he had no difficulty in keeping awake.

The philosopher at once realised that he had a desperate man before him. To give the boy confidence he for a time spoke about himself. He described his puppets one by one, faithfully and with enthusiasm, as if they had been real friends and fellow artists, and with tears in his eyes, because they were now lost to him. 'Alas, the beloved ones,' he moaned, 'they were devoted to me and they trusted me. But they are dispersed now, limp of arms and legs, with mouldering strings; they are thrown away from the stage to the uttermost parts of the sea. For my hand could no longer lead them, nor my right hand hold them!' But presently—as ever in the vicissitudes of his existence—he turned his mind toward life everlasting. 'That is not a matter for grief,' he said. 'In Paradise I shall once more meet and embrace them all. In Paradise I shall be given ten fingers to each hand.'

Later on, after midnight, Pino led the conversation to Angelo's own circumstances, felt his way in them, and soon had them all at his seven fingers' ends.

In this way it happened that next night Angelo told him his whole story, as he would not have been able to tell it to any person in the world other than this crippled vagabond. At that the old man's face lit up in high, solemn harmony. 'That is not a matter for grief,' he said. 'It is a good thing to be a great sinner. Or should human beings allow Christ to have died on the Cross for the sake of our petty lies and our paltry whorings? We would have to fear that the Saviour might even come to think with disgust of His heroic achievement! For exactly this reason, as you will know, in the very hour of the Cross, care was taken that He had thieves by Him, one to each side, and could turn His eyes from the one to the other. At this moment He may look from you to me, and mightily recognise and repeat to Himself, "Aye, verily it was needed!"'

After a while Pino added, 'And I myself am the crucified thief Demas, to whom Paradise was promised.'

But early on Thursday morning Pizzuti quite suddenly vanished, like a rat into a gutter hole. He left the room on a necessary errand and did not return, and not till seven years later did Angelo again see this excellent man. And as the silence behind him grew deep and, as it were, conclusive, the outcast man realised that he no longer needed to hold on to a decision. It would not happen to him again to fall asleep.

For some time he walked among people, still absolutely lonely, like an unproved but ambitious young ascetic with a hair shirt next to his skin. So as not to meet his friends of the past he changed his lodgings, and found for himself a small closet high up under the roof in the opposite quarter of the town. During the first time he was surprised at the fact that his sleepless nights did not appear long, but that time simply seemed to have been abolished—night came, and then again morning, and to him it meant nothing.

But, just as unexpectedly, his body rose in rebellion against his mind and his will. The moment came in which he gave up his pride and prayed the great powers of the universe: 'Despise me, cast me away, but allow me to be like the others, allow me to sleep.'

He now bought himself opium, but it did not help him. He also purchased another strong sleeping draught, but it only conveyed to him a row of novel, quite confused sensations of distance, so that objects and times which were far away were felt by him as quite near, while such objects as he knew to be within reach—his own hands and feet and the stone steps of the stairs—were infinitely far off.

His brain by this time was working extremely slowly. One day in the street he saw Lucrezia, who had returned to the town and was living with her mother. But only late at night, when the church towers had rung out midnight, did he tell himself, *I saw a woman in the street today, it was Lucrezia.* And after another while, *I once promised to come to her. But I did not come.* For a long time he sat very still, handling this thought, and at last he smiled, like a very old man.

It was shortly after this day that he began to turn to other people and look to them for help. But when he begged their advice, he was in such deadly earnest that he made the persons he addressed smile, and they answered him in jest or altogether dismissed his questions.

One morning he bethought himself of Mariana, the old woman in whose tavern he had met Pizzuti. She had, he knew, given friends of his good advice—it was not impossible that she might be able to help him. But the lack of seriousness in his counsellors till now had frightened him out of asking straight-away, and he searched for a pretext for going to her house, until he remembered that he had left there his purple cloak with the brown embroidery. At that he went straight to her house.

Old Mariana looked at him for a while. 'Well, well, Angelo, pretty death's-head,' she said. 'We Christian people should bear one another no grudge, and I forgive you, today, that you did reject my fond love, and kept thinking of another woman, when I wanted you. I shall help you. Now listen well, and afterwards do exactly as I tell you. Walk from the broadest streets of the town into a narrower one, and from this narrow street into one still narrower, and go on like that. If from your narrowest alley you can find your way into a tighter passage, enter it, and follow it, and draw your breath lightly once or twice. And at that you will have fallen asleep.'

Angelo thanked Mariana for her advice, and pushed it down to the bottom of his mind. Only when it was quite dark did he make up his mind to test it.

His own room was in an out-of-the-way alley. He had to proceed into the broadest and best lighted of the boulevards. For a long time he had not been in this part of the town, and he was surprised to see how many people there were in the world. They walked faster than he, they were intent on their errands, and as far as he could judge an equal number were walking in each direction.

How, he asked himself, *has it become necessary for all people who live east of the boulevard to come west, as well as to all who live west to come east? It might make one feel that the world was badly managed. The whole city of Naples is now set up as a big loom, men and women are the shuttles to it, and the weaver is busy tonight. Yet this great pattern*, he reflected as he walked on, *is no concern of mine—others will have to look after it. I myself will keep my thoughts carefully collected on what I have got to do.*

At this he turned from the Via di Toledo into a smaller street, and from that into one still narrower. *It is not impos-sible*, he thought, hope strangely dawning in his heart, *that this time I have been well advised.*

After a while he found himself in a lane so narrow that,

looking up, he saw above him only a handbreadth of evening sky a little lighter than the eaves. The paving was here very rough, and there were no lamps; he had to place his hand on the wall of a house to walk on. The contact with solid matter did him good; he felt grateful toward this wall. It suddenly vanished under his palm. There was a doorway here, and the door was open. It gave into an exceedingly narrow passage. *I am in luck tonight*, he thought, *I am lucky to have come upon such an exceedingly narrow passage.* He proceeded until he came to a small door. Underneath this door a faint light shone.

Now for a while he stood perfectly still. In there sleep awaited him, and with the certitude of sleep memory came back to him. He felt, in the dark, his hard, drawn face smoothening, his eyelids lowering a little like the eyelids of a happy, sleeping person. This moment was a return and a beginning. He stretched out his hand, took care to draw his breath lightly twice, and opened the door.

By a table in a little, faintly lit room a red-haired man was counting his money.

The sudden entrance of a stranger did not seem to surprise the host of the room, he looked up casually and then sank back into his former occupation. But his guest felt the moment to be formidable.

The man by the table was ugly, and had nothing kind about him. Yet in the fact that even while counting his money he left his door unlocked, to be entered by a stranger, there was a kind of friendliness which might hold great possibilities. *But what am I to say to him?* Angelo thought.

After a while he said, 'I cannot sleep.'

The red-haired man waited a moment, then he looked up. 'I never sleep,' he declared with extreme arrogance.

After this short interruption he resumed his work. He carefully arranged his coins in piles of two, scattered them with his big hands and re-collected them in piles of five—to scatter these once more, and build up, absorbed in the task, new piles of six, of ten and fifteen, and at last of three. In the end he stopped, and without taking his hands off the silver leaned back in the chair. He gazed straight before him and repeated, with deep scorn, 'I never sleep.

'Only dolts and drudges sleep,' he took up his theme after

a while. 'Fishermen, peasants and artisans must have their hours of snoring at any cost. Their heavy natures cry out for sleep even in the greatest hour of life. Drowsiness settles on their eyelids. Divine agony sweats blood at a stone's throw, but they cannot keep awake, and the whizzing of an angel's wings will not wake them up. Those living dead will never know what happened, or what was said, while they themselves lay huddled and gaping. I alone know. For I never sleep.'

Suddenly he turned in his chair toward his guest. 'He said so Himself,' he remarked, 'and had He not been so hard driven, with what high disdain would He not have spoken! Now it was a moan, like the sea breaking against the shore for the very last time before doomsday. 'He Himself told them so, the fools: "What, could ye not watch with me one hour?"'

For a minute he looked Angelo straight in the face.

'But no one,' he concluded slowly, in indescribable pride, 'no one in the world could ever seriously believe that I myself did sleep—on that Thursday night in the garden.'

Gabriel García Márquez

Márquez's women characters are usually strong-willed, as is the mother in this 1949 short story. Insomnia afflicts the house, the sons in a constant state of dream-like watching, the mother having devised a fantastic interior life.

In Márquez's One Hundred Years of Solitude, *the town of Macondo is afflicted with an epidemic of insomnia. In a reversal of Ireneo Funes' experience, the townspeople lose their memories because of their insomnia.*

Márquez was born in 1928 in Columbia.

Bitterness for Three Sleepwalkers

Now we had her there, abandoned in a corner of the house. Someone told us, before we brought her things—her clothes which smelled of newly cut wood, her weightless shoes for the mud—that she would be unable to get used to that slow life, with no sweet tastes, no attraction except that harsh, wattled solitude, always pressing on her back. Someone told us—and a lot of time had passed before we remembered it—that she had also had a childhood. Maybe we didn't believe it then. But now, seeing her sitting in the corner with her frightened eyes and a finger placed on her lips, maybe we accepted the fact that she'd had a childhood once, that once she'd had a touch that was sensitive to the anticipatory coolness of the rain, and that she always carried any unexpected shadow in profile to her body.

All this—and much more—we believed that afternoon when we realised that above her fearsome subworld she was completely human. We found it out suddenly, as if a glass had been broken inside, when she began to give off anguished shouts; she began to call each one of us by name, speaking amidst tears until we sat down beside her; we began to sing and clap hands as if our shouting could put the scattered pieces

of glass back together. Only then were we able to believe that
at one time she had had a childhood. It was as if her shouts
were like a revelation somehow; as if they had a lot of remembered tree and deep river about them. When she got up, she
leaned over a little and, still without covering her face with
her apron, still without blowing her nose, and still with tears,
she told us:

'I'll never smile again.'

We went out into the courtyard, the three of us, not talking;
maybe we thought we carried common thoughts. Maybe we
thought it would be best not to turn on the lights in the house.
She wanted to be alone—maybe—sitting in the dark corner,
weaving the final braid which seemed to be the only thing that
would survive her passage towards the beast.

Outside, in the courtyard, sunk in the deep vapour of the
insects, we sat down to think about her. We'd done it so many
times before. We might have said that we were doing what
we'd been doing every day of our lives.

Yet it was different that night: she'd said that she would
never smile again, and we, who knew her so well, were certain
that the nightmare had become the truth. Sitting in a triangle,
we imagined her there inside, abstract, incapacitated, unable
even to hear the innumerable clocks that measured the
marked and minute rhythm with which she was changing into
dust. 'If we only had the courage at least to wish for her death,'
we thought in a chorus. But we wanted her like that: ugly and
glacial, like a mean contribution to our hidden defects.

We'd been adults since before, since a long time back. She,
however, was the oldest in the house. That same night she
had been able to be there, sitting with us, feeling the measured
throbbing of the stars, surrounded by healthy sons. She would
have been the respectable lady of the house if she had been
the wife of a solid citizen or the concubine of a punctual man.
But she became accustomed to living in only one dimension,
like a straight line, perhaps because her vices or her virtues
could not be seen in profile. We'd known that for many years
now. We weren't even surprised one morning, after getting up,
when we found her face down in the courtyard, biting the earth
in a hard, ecstatic way. Then she smiled, looked at us again;
she had fallen out of the second-story window on to the hard

clay of the courtyard and had remained there, stiff and concrete, face down on the damp clay. But later we learned that the only thing she had kept intact was her fear of distances, a natural fright upon facing space. We lifted her up by the shoulders. She wasn't as hard as she had seemed to us at first. On the contrary, her organs were loose, detached from her will, like a lukewarm corpse that hadn't begun to stiffen.

Her eyes were open, her mouth was dirty with that earth that already must have had a taste of sepulchral sediment for her when we turned her face up to the sun, and it was as if we had placed her in front of a mirror. She looked at us all with a dull, sexless expression that gave us—holding her in my arms now—the measure of her absence. Someone told us she was dead; and afterwards she remained smiling with that cold and quiet smile that she wore at night when she moved about the house awake. She said she didn't know how she got to the courtyard. She said that she'd felt quite warm, that she'd been listening to a cricket, penetrating, sharp, which seemed—so she said—about to knock down the wall of her room, and that she had set herself to remembering Sunday's prayers, with her cheek tight against the cement floor.

We know, however, that she couldn't remember any prayer, for we discovered later that she'd lost the notion of time when she said she'd fallen asleep holding up the inside of the wall that the cricket was pushing on from outside and that she was fast asleep when someone, taking her by the shoulders, moved the wall aside and laid her down with her face to the sun.

That night we knew, sitting in the courtyard, that she would never smile again. Perhaps her inexpressive seriousness pained us in anticipation, her dark and wilful living in a corner. It pained us deeply, as we were pained the day we saw her sit down in the corner where she was now; and we heard her say that she wasn't going to wander through the house any more. At first we couldn't believe her. We'd seen her for months on end going through the rooms at all hours, her head hard and her shoulders drooping, never stopping, never growing tired. At night we would hear her thick body noise moving between two darknesses, and we would lie awake in bed many times hearing her stealthy walking, following her all through the house with our ears. Once she told us that she had seen the cricket inside the mirror glass, sunken, submerged in the solid transparency, and that it had crossed through the glass surface to reach her. We really didn't know what she was trying to tell us, but we could all see that her clothes were wet, sticking to her body, as if she had just come out of a cistern. Without trying to explain the phenomenon, we decided to do away with the insects in the house: destroy the objects that obsessed her.

We had the walls cleaned; we ordered them to chop down the plants in the courtyard and it was as if we had cleansed the silence of the night of bits of trash. But we no longer heard her walking, nor did we hear her talk about crickets any more, until the day when, after the last meal, she remained looking at us, she sat down on the cement floor, still looking at us, and said: 'I'm going to stay here, sitting down,' and we shuddered, because we could see that she had begun to look like something already almost completely like death.

That had been a long time ago and we had even grown used to seeing her there, sitting, her braid always half wound, as if she had become dissolved in her solitude and, even though she was there to be seen, had lost her natural faculty of being present. That's why we now knew that she would never smile again; because she had said so in the same convinced and certain way in which she had told us once that she would never walk again. It was as if we were certain that she would tell us later: 'I'll never see again', or maybe 'I'll never hear again', and we knew that she was sufficiently human to go along willing the elimination of her vital functions and that spontaneously she would go about ending herself, sense by sense, until one day we would find her leaning against the wall, as if she had fallen asleep for the first time in her life. Perhaps there was still a lot of time left for that, but the three of us, sitting in the courtyard, would have liked to hear her sharp and sudden broken-glass weeping that night, at least to give us the illusion that a baby . . . a girl baby had been born in the house. In order to believe that she had been born renewed.

PROUST AND COMPATRIOTS

COLETTE

As with the earlier piece by Colette, the following is drawn from her autobiographical writings.

Marcel Proust

When I was a very young woman, he was a very good-looking young man. Trust the portrait of him by Jacques-Émile Blanche. That narrow mouth, that mist around the eyes, that tired freshness, both the features and the expression really are those of the young Marcel Proust. Pierre de Guingand looked very much like him later on. The appearance of Marcel Proust's eyes on Jacques Blanche's canvas and the picture they had left in my memory are exceedingly alike: opened very wide, more anxious than astonished, and wearing a deceptively naïve expression.

I was a regular visitor at Mme Arman de Caillavet's Wednesdays, and knew Marcel Proust at a time when he still had the appearance of an adolescent, as well as the bearing and the courtesy, which ought to have surprised no one but did surprise some people, of a young man taking his First Communion. Anatole France, under cover of a condescendingly goodhearted manner, displayed a very lively interest in him, whereas 'that goodhearted Madam Arman' (Anatole France never used the 'de' when referring to his friend) was rather harsh in her treatment of the very young man with the gentle face.

One evening, Proust came to the avenue Hoch with a companion scarcely older than himself and, like himself, graceful and soft-voiced. They arrived together, took their leave together, and left the room together walking with an identical gait. As soon as they had gone, Mme Arman de Caillavet, wheeling like a storm cloud, exploded.

'Ah no! This has become impossible,' she cried. 'Did you see them? Behaving like two doting twins! Billing like a pair of parakeets who can't be parted! That young man is really going too far! He's deliberately flaunting himself . . . And even if he's determined to shock people, at least he needn't make himself ridiculous! What do you think, Monsieur France? I ask you, do you really . . . Monsieur France! I am addressing you! Why are you looking at me like that?'

Our unanimous silence finally warned her, and she turned around. Behind her, Marcel Proust, in the frame of the door he had just opened, was leaning against one jamb, losing the delicate colours from his lips and cheeks.

'I came . . . I wanted to collect . . .' he stammered.

'What? What? You wanted what?' Mme Arman bayed.

'A book that Schwob gave me . . . Did I leave it here? There in the armchair . . . I'm sorry to have disturbed you . . .'

He managed to summon up just sufficient strength to pick up the book and make his escape.

The ensuing silence was not pleasant for any of us. But it did not take our intrepid hostess long to dismiss the matter with a shrug of her solid, bared, and diamond-hung shoulders:

'Ah well! It couldn't be helped . . .'

When I saw him again in the Ritz Hotel, where he lived during the war, his illness and the passing years had already done their swift work on him. His agitation and his pallor seemed to be the result of some terrible inner force. Dressed in tails, standing in his timidly lighted hallway, at the heart of a darkened Paris, Marcel Proust greeted me with faltering gaiety. Over his evening dress he was wearing an unfastened cape. The expression of the white, crumpled shirt front, and the convulsions of his tie terrified me as much as the black marks under his eyes and around his mouth, the sooty, telltale traces that an absent-minded malady had smeared haphazardly across his face. The same solitude and the same courteous manner, both of which he retained throughout his life, still accompanied all his gestures and all his words, like morbid relics of his early youth. He offered one a drink or held out a delicacy with the eager hesitancy of a sixteen-year-old boy. Like many exceptionally delicate people, he ceased to be conscious of fatigue at an hour when his healthy companions were all beginning to admit how tired they were—I remember certain evenings spent in the company of Mme de Noailles, later on, when I found myself thinking of Marcel Proust as I looked at her, as she sat, half reclining, pale, glittering, her nose pinched, her little shoulders melting away beneath a shawl, casting until the dawn, in that voice of bronze, to those present and those absent alike, a just tribute of flowers and darts, of wreaths and judgments without appeal . . .

At two in the morning, when Proust's guests left him, it was he who wanted to go with them. There was an old cab, a brougham, standing dreaming in the Place Vendôme, and Marcel Proust wanted to pay the driver to take us all home, for there were only four or five of us. Then he insisted that he ought to accompany us to our respective homes. But I lived in the heart of Auteuil, and neither the driver nor the horse was of an age to travel so far through a dark, wartime night. I prevented Proust from blaming himself and lamenting over my lot by telling him that since my eyes were not of the best, it sometimes happened, when I was returning home late, that I slipped off my footwear under one of the blue street lamps in the Place de la Concorde, and then, having knotted my shoes and stockings into a bundle, I would entrust myself, between the Cours-la-Reine and the boulevard Sucher, to my bare and path-divining feet.

Our host stood listening to me, in front of the Fitz colonnade. The silence of the night, and the mist cutting off our view of the square, surrounded Proust, with a halo exactly suited to his decline and his prestige. With his top hat pushed back, a great lock of hair covering his brow, ceremonious and dishevelled, he looked like a young and drunken wedding guest. The stifled light emerging from the entrance hall, and a white, theatrical reflection striking up from the cracked shirt front, highlighted his chin and the curving lines of his eyebrows. He greatly enjoyed my little barefoot-beggar-girl story, and when he exclaimed: 'No, really, do you?' a smile I could not describe, a sort of youthful astonishment, remodelled all his features. As we finally took our leave of him, he stepped back, waved goodbye with one hand, and the darkness once more hollowed out the deep sockets of his eyes and filled with ashes the black oval of his mouth, gaping in its quest for air.

MARCEL PROUST

Proust's insomnia and asthma began at an early age. While his family sat talking in the garden the little Marcel would watch from his bedroom window when he should have been sleeping. At the age of nine he experienced his first asthma attack. Both these maladies prompted his withdrawal from the world: his insomnia keeping him up when others slept, and his asthma sending him to bed.

Proust's mother, Jeanne Weil, was Jewish, a beautiful and cultured woman, and a good deal younger than his father Dr Proust. George D. Painter, in the preface to Proust's collected letters to his mother, writes that after her death in 1905, Marcel cried for weeks and couldn't sleep, but once he recovered he was less constrained in his writing and relationships.

The few letters included here are typical of his daily correspondence to his mother, repeating the themes of his daily life: how he slept, what time he went to bed, his asthma, his treatments of trionol and his regular fumigations, what to pay the servants, problems with friends. The letters are intimate and demanding of her time and intelligence. Always, Proust ends with endearments. Sometimes he writes about the politics of the day, and with real interest, such as with the Dreyfuss affair, but mostly the letters exhibit an exquisite banality.

Proust was born in Anteuil in 1871. He died in Paris in 1922 of asthma. These letters were first published in France in 1953.

I've just had a Word
with the Chamber-Maid,
she's Going to Move my Bed . . .

Hotel de France et d'Angleterre,
Fontainebleau,
Wednesday morning, 9.15, [21 October 1896]

Ma chère petite maman,

It's pouring with rain. I didn't have asthma last night, and it was not until just now that I had to have a little fumigation, after a great deal of sneezing. Since then I haven't felt very easy, because my bed is most uncomfortable, in fact the wall is on my best side. Not to mention that because of the numerous canopies, curtains, etc. (impossible to remove because they're fixed to the wall) this is very inconvenient, as it forces me always to lie facing the wall, everything I need—my coffee, my *tisane*, my candle, pen, matches, etc. etc.—is on my right, which means I keep having to turn over on my bad side, etc. My chest was quite free yesterday all morning, afternoon, evening (except as always when I went to bed) and all the night. (It's now that I feel the most discomfort.) But I'm not having enormous nights' sleep as in Paris, or at least the last few weeks in Paris. And once I wake up, instead of feeling well in bed I can't breathe till I get up, which isn't a good sign, whatever you think. Yesterday the rain didn't begin till 4 p.m., so that I was able to go for a walk. I didn't like what I saw. The mere fringe of woodland I saw is still green. The town is characterless. I can't tell you what a horrifying hour I spent yesterday between 4 and 6 (an hour which I've put back to before our telephone conversation in the little narrative I sent you, which I beg you to *keep*, and to remember where you keep it, because it will be in my novel). Never I think has any of my anguishes of whatever kind reached such a degree. I can't try to tell you about it. So as to have someone to talk to I went to the station at eleven o'clock to wait for Léon Daudet, who was returning from Paris. He is absolutely determined to have his meals with me. This means he will have to stay *en pension* like Jean. The hotel is certainly quite out of the ordinary. But not a soul in it will speak to me. No doubt it's because the servants have never been with anyone but some Doudeauville or other, where they heard nothing but 'I'm very well, thank you.' So I can't say to them 'I'm very ill' and explain my needs, nor have those pleasantly intimate relations which I had with Mme Renvoyzé or the people at the Hôtel Fermont. You've seen what they charge here. I think it will come to even more because of the fires I am obliged to get them to make, and my lamp, for as it's so late in the season there's no lounge with lights in the evening, and one has nowhere but one's room. I've nothing to read, and I'm wondering whether Reynaldo has forgotten about my books. If it wasn't such a business to change one's room, I'd certainly change mine so as to have a bed facing in the other direction. *Je t'embrasse tendrement.* Had another letter from Reynaldo this morning which I'm keeping because it will amuse you.

Ton petit
MARCEL.

P.S. I've just had a word with the chamber-maid, she's going to move my bed so that the head will be against the wall (because the canopies can't be taken off), but the bed itself in the middle of the room, I think it will be more comfortable for me. The rain is twice as heavy. What weather! I'm amazed that you don't say anything about the charges at the hotel. If they're exorbitant shouldn't I do better to come back? And from Paris I could go to Versailles every day to work.

2nd P.S. Léon Daudet would like us to go to Marlotte and stay in a cheaper hotel, because he knows someone with asthma who is comfortable there. But I believe it's much further from Paris, fewer trains, etc.—what do you think? The only thing is, I don't think Jean Lazard would come there . . . Do ask Papa for something to stop my nervous laughing. I'm so afraid of annoying Léon Daudet.

3rd P.S. No, I haven't taken trional.

4th P.S. Dr Brissaud, who knows this part of the country so well, would have been able to tell us the comparative advantages of Nemours, Marlotte, etc. etc.

[Late November or early December, 1902.]

Ma petite Maman,

As I'm unable to speak to you, I'm writing to tell you that I simply can't understand your behaviour. You know, or you must guess, that I've spent every night since I came back in weeping, and not without good cause; and all day long you say things to me like: 'I couldn't sleep last night because the servants didn't go to bed till eleven o'clock.' I only wish it was nothing worse than that that keeps *me* from sleeping! Today, when I had a choking fit and needed the things for fumigation, I was so misguided as to ring for Marie who'd just told me she'd finished her lunch, and you immediately punished me for it, as soon as I'd taken my trional, by seeing to it that there was a noise of hammering and shouting all day. Thanks to you I was in such a state of nerves, that when poor Fénelon came with Lauris, just for a few words he said (very disagreeable ones, I must say) I went for him with my fists (Fénelon, not Lauris) and without knowing what I was doing I took the new hat he'd just bought, stamped on it, tore it to pieces and ripped out the lining. As you might think that I'm exaggerating I enclose a piece of the lining so that you can see it's true. But please don't throw it away, as I shall be asking you to let me have it back in case it's still of any use to him. Of course, if you saw him you mustn't breathe a word of this. All the same, I'm very glad I worked it off on a friend. Because there's no doubt that if at that moment you or Papa had said anything disagreeable to me—well, I wouldn't have done anything, of course, but I don't know what I would have said. It was in consequence of this incident that I felt so hot, that I couldn't get dressed as I intended, and I made the servants ask you whether I was to have dinner here or not. Then you think you can please the servants and punish me at the same time by putting a ban on me and saying they're not to come when I ring, not to wait on me at table, etc. You are very much mistaken. You don't know how embarrassed your man-servant was this evening not to be able to wait on me. He put everything down by me and apologised for it by saying: 'Madame has ordered me to do this. I can't help it.' As for the piece of furniture you've taken away from me to pay me out, I can't do without it. If you need it, please give me another, or else I shall buy myself one. I'd sooner do without chairs. As far as the servants are concerned, you know I'm a psychologist, and have an instinct for these things, and I assure you you're completely and utterly mistaken. But that's no business of mine, and I shall always be glad to further your views in the matter when you give me notice of what you want. But I can't be expected to guess that when Marie has finished her lunch I'm running the risk of getting her dismissed by wanting her to light a fire in a room where Fénelon and Lauris couldn't stay even with their overcoats on, or asking her to bring me my things for fumigating. But it hurts me—although in my present distress all these petty quarrels leave me completely indifferent—not to find in these hours of real despair the moral encouragement that I should have thought I might have relied on having from you. The truth is that the moment I'm well, as the way of life that makes me well exasperates you, you demolish everything until I'm ill again. It isn't the first time this has happened. I took cold this evening; if it turns to asthma, which is certain to come on again before long in the present condition of affairs, I don't doubt you'll be nice to me again, when I'm in the state I was in last year at a similar period. But it's sad not to be able to have affection and health both at once. If I had them both at the present moment, it wouldn't be more than I need to help me to fight against a distress which, especially since yesterday evening (but I haven't seen you since), has become too violent for me to continue to struggle with it. The consequence is that I wanted—but too late—to have my letter to M. Vallette back again. I can write to him and countermand it, however, We must talk about this again.

Mille tendres baisers,

MARCEL

This letter is written on black-edged notepaper. Dr Proust had died on 26 November 1903.

[About December 1903.]

Ma chére petite Maman,

I'm writing you this little note, while it's impossible for me to get to sleep, to tell you I'm thinking of you. I should like, and I'm so absolutely determined, to be able to get up at the same time as you, and drink my morning coffee by your side. To feel that our sleeping and waking hours are portioned out over one and the same expanse of time will be my delight. With this end in view I went to bed at 1.30, but had to get up again, and then I couldn't find my safety-pin—the one I used to fasten and tighten the waist of my drawers. So it was good-bye to my night's sleep. I tried to find another in your dressing-room, etc. etc., but the only thing I succeeded in catching in those perambulations was a violent cold (I'm only joking when I say 'violent')—and no sign of a safety-pin. I got into bed again, but rest was impossible. All the same I'm feeling very comfortable and I'm whiling away the night with my plan for a new existence, one that will be to your liking, and will bring us still closer to one another materially, because we shall live to the same timetable, in the same rooms, at the same temperature, in accordance with the same principles, and—if contentment is now, alas, forbidden us—with mutual approbation. Forgive me for leaving the desk in the 'smoking-room' in disorder, I've worked so hard up till the last moment. And as for this magnificent envelope, it's the only one I have to hand. Please see that Marie Antoine doesn't make a noise, and ask her to keep the kitchen-door shut, as otherwise it lets her voice through.

> *Mille tendres baisers,*
> MARCEL

I feel that I'm going to sleep very well now.

[1905?]

Ma chére petite Maman,

I hope you will be appropriately astonished at the hard-luck story that I am going to tell you (*'car que faire en un gîte á moins que l'on ne conte?'*). I took cascara after I left you, felt better, and went to make my coffee in your cup just as if I was paying you a call, delighted at the prospect of *amusing work* to do. As is my habit the moment I finished my cup, I went to sit at the big table. The transpiration caused by the coffee continued, but when I sat down it cooled off, and this time it stopped dead in a second and I felt unwell. As I was in the middle of doing *something interesting*, I stayed where I was. But my feeling of cold grew worse and worse, and I still felt unwell (very slightly, I confess). I told myself the drawing-room door must be open, and that I'd better give you a serious talking-to, although that never does any good. At last daylight came, and I was quite astonished to see that the dining-room curtains were half-open, and what's more amazing still, the window was open! Whether you hadn't closed it properly, or you'd closed one and left another open, open it was, and as there'd been a wind last night the swinging of the window had displaced the curtain. So as I'd gone to sit down there without knowing this, immediately after drinking my boiling coffee, I felt cold all night. In the morning, late as it was, and in spite of the consequent delay in going to bed, I went to the kitchen to get hot water and drank a little more coffee. Now the congestion that the cold air gave me has disappeared, with the help of the cascara, and I don't feel bad at all for the moment. My story is quite uninteresting, I know, but I'm too tired to say anything more interesting, as I've read and written, etc. a great deal, and can't think where I found the strength for it. Thank you in advance for the letters. The one for Berstein is express post, very urgent. Or it could go by hand.

> *Mille tendres baisers,*
>
> MARCEL

As a matter of fact the one for Bernstein isn't so very urgent. But I should like Mme Lemaire's to be left at her house first thing this morning.

I'm feeling *extremely well* at the moment, in every way. Only now I've had this coffee so late, what time will it be when I can go to bed?

> *The passage below is drawn from the first pages of Proust's* Remembrance of Things Past, *translated by C. K. Scott Moncrieff. What time is best suited to recollection, to the memory of things past? The night time of insomnia.*

For a long time I used to go to bed early. Sometimes, when I had put out my candle, my eyes would close so quickly that I had not even time to say to myself: 'I'm falling asleep.' And half an hour later the thought that it was time to go to sleep would awaken me; I would make as if to put away the book which I imagined was still in my hands, and to blow out the light; I had gone on thinking, while I was asleep, about what I had just been reading, but these thoughts had taken a rather peculiar turn; it seemed to me that I myself was the immediate subject of my book: a church, a quartet, the rivalry between François I and Charles V. This impression would persist for some moments after I awoke; it did not offend my reason, but lay like scales upon my eyes and prevented them from registering the fact that the candle was no longer burning. Then it would begin to seem unintelligible, as the thoughts of a former existence must be to a reincarnate spirit; the subject of my book would separate itself from me, leaving me free to apply myself to it or not; and at the same time my sight would return and I would be astonished to find myself in a state of darkness, pleasant and restful enough for my eyes, but even more, perhaps, for my mind, to which it appeared incomprehensible, without a cause, something dark indeed.

I would ask myself what time it could be; I could hear the whistling of trains, which, now nearer and now farther off, punctuating the distance like the note of a bird in a forest, showed me in perspective the deserted countryside through which a traveller is hurrying towards the nearby station; and the path he is taking will be engraved in his memory by the excitement induced by strange surroundings, by unaccustomed activities, by the conversation he has had and the farewells exchanged beneath an unfamiliar lamp that still echo in his ears amid the silence of the night, and by the happy prospect of being home again.

I would lay my cheeks gently against the comfortable cheeks of my pillow, as plump and fresh as the cheeks of childhood. I would strike a match to look at my watch. Nearly midnight. The hour when an invalid, who has been obliged to set out on a journey and to sleep in a strange hotel, awakened by a sudden spasm, sees with glad relief a streak of daylight showing under his door. Thank God, it is morning! The servants will be about in a minute: he can ring, and someone will come to look after him. The thought of being assuaged gives him strength to endure his pain. He is certain he heard footsteps: they come nearer, and then die away. The ray of light beneath his door is extinguished. It is midnight; someone has just turned down the gas; the last servant has gone to bed, and he must lie all night in agony with no one to bring him relief.

I would fall asleep again, and thereafter would reawaken for short snatches only, just long enough to hear the regular creaking of the wainscot, or to open my eyes to stare at the shifting kaleidoscope of the darkness, to savour, in a momentary glimmer of consciousness, the sleep which lay heavy upon the furniture, the room, the whole of which I formed but an insignificant part and whose insensibility I should very soon return to share. Or else while sleeping I had drifted back to an earlier stage in my life, now for ever outgrown, and had come under the thrall of one of my childish terrors, such as that old terror of my great-uncle's pulling my curls which was effectually dispelled on the day—the dawn of a new era to me—when they were finally cropped from my head. I had forgotten that event during my sleep, but I remembered it again immediately I had succeeded in waking myself up to escape my great-uncle's fingers, and as a measure of precaution I would bury the whole of my head in the pillow before returning to the world of dreams.

Sometimes, too, as Eve was created from a rib of Adam, a woman would be born during my sleep from some strain in the position of my thighs. Conceived from the pleasure I was on the point of consummating, she it was, I imagined, who offered me that pleasure. My body, conscious that its own warmth was permeating hers, would strive to become one with her, and I would awake. The rest of humanity seemed very remote in comparison with this woman whose company I had left but a moment ago; my cheek was still warm from her kiss, my body ached beneath the weight of hers. If, as would sometimes happen, she had the features of some woman whom I had known in waking hours, I would abandon myself altogether to the sole quest of her, like people who set out on a journey to see with their eyes some city of their desire, and imagine that one can taste in reality what has charmed one's fancy. And then, gradually, the memory of her would dissolve and vanish, until I had forgotten the girl of my dream.

When a man is asleep, he has in a circle round him the chain of the hours, the sequence of the years, the order of the heavenly bodies. Instinctively he consults them when he awakes, and in an instant reads off his own position on the earth's surface and the time that has elapsed during his slumbers; but this ordered procession is apt to grow confused, and to break its ranks. Suppose that, towards morning, after a night of insomnia, sleep descends upon him while he is reading, in quite a different position from that in which he normally goes to sleep, he has only to lift his arm to arrest the sun and turn it back in its course, and, at the moment of waking, he will have no idea of the time, but will conclude that he has just gone to bed. Or suppose that he dozes off in some even more abnormal and divergent position, sitting in an armchair, for instance, after dinner: then the world will go hurtling out of orbit, the magic chair will carry him at full speed through time and space, and when he opens his eyes again he will imagine that he went to sleep months earlier in another place. But for me it was enough if, in my own bed, my sleep was so heavy as completely to relax my consciousness; for then I lost all sense of the place in which I had gone to sleep, and when I awoke in the middle of the night, not knowing where I was, I could not even be sure at first who I was; I had only the most rudimentary sense of existence, such as may lurk and flicker in the depths of an animal's consciousness; I was more destitute than the cave-dweller; but then the memory—not yet of the place in which I was, but of various other places where I had lived and might now very possibly be—would come like a rope let down from heaven to draw me up out of the abyss of not-being, from which I could never have escaped by myself: in a flash I would traverse centuries of civilisation, and out of a blurred glimpse of oil-lamps, then of shirts with turned-down collars, would gradually piece together the original components of my ego.

Perhaps the immobility of the things that surround us is forced upon them by our conviction that they are themselves and not anything else, by the immobility of our conception of them. For it always happened that when I awoke like this, and my mind struggled in an unsuccessful attempt to discover where I was, everything revolved around me through the darkness: things, places, years. My body, still too heavy with sleep to move, would endeavour to construe from the pattern of its tiredness the position of its various limbs, in order to deduce therefrom the direction of the wall, the location of the furniture, to piece together and give a name to the house in which it lay. Its memory, the composite memory of its ribs, its knees, its shoulder-blades, offered it a whole series of rooms in which it had at one time or another slept, while the unseen walls, shifting and adapting themselves to the shape of each successive room that it remembered, whirled round it in the dark. And even before my brain, lingering in cogitation over when things had happened and what they had looked like, had reassembled the circumstances sufficiently to identify the room, it, my body, would recall from each room in succession the style of the bed, the position of the doors, the angle at which the daylight came in at the windows, whether there was a passage outside, what I had had in my mind when I went to sleep and found there when I awoke. The stiffened side on which I lay would, for instance, in trying to fix its position, imagine itself to be lying face to the wall in a big bed with a canopy; and at once I would say to myself, 'Why, I must have fallen asleep before Mamma came to say good night,' for I was in the country at my grandfather's, who died years ago; and my body, the side upon which I was lying, faithful guardians of a past which my mind should never have forgotten, brought back before my eyes the glimmering flame of the night-light in its urn-shaped bowl of Bohemian glass that hung by chains from the ceiling, and the chimney-piece of Siena marble in my bedroom at Combray, in my grandparents' house, in those far distant days which at this moment I imagined to be in the present without being able to picture them exactly, and which would become plainer in a little while when I was properly awake.

Then the memory of a new position would spring up, and the wall would slide away in another direction; I was in my room in Mme de Saint-Loup's house in the country; good heavens, it must be ten o'clock, they will have finished dinner! I must have overslept myself in the little nap which I always take when I come in from my walk with Mme de Saint-Loup, before dressing for the evening. For many years have now elapsed since the Combray days when, coming in from the longest and latest walks, I would still be in time to see the reflection of the sunset glowing in the panes of my bedroom window. It is a very different kind of life that one leads at Tansonville, at Mme de Saint-Loup's, and a different kind of pleasure that I derive from taking walks only in the evenings, from visiting by moonlight the roads on which I used to play as a child in the sunshine; as for the bedroom in which I must have fallen asleep instead of dressing for dinner, I can see it from the distance as we return from our walk, with its lamp shining through the window, a solitary beacon in the night.

These shifting and confused gusts of memory never lasted for more than a few seconds; it often happened that, in my brief spell of uncertainty as to where I was, I did not distinguish the various suppositions of which it was composed any more than, when we watch a horse running, we isolate the successive positions of its body as they appear upon a bioscope. But I had seen first one and then another of the rooms in which I had slept during my life, and in the end I would revisit them all in the long course of my waking dream: rooms in winter, where on going to bed I would at once bury my head in a nest woven out of the most diverse materials—the corner of my pillow, the top of my blankets, a piece of a shawl, the edge of my bed, and a copy of a children's paper—which I had contrived to cement together, bird-fashion, by dint of continuous pressure; rooms where, in freezing weather, I would enjoy the satisfaction of being shut in from the outer world (like the sea-swallow which builds at the end of a dark tunnel and is kept warm by the surrounding earth), and where, the fire keeping in all night, I would sleep wrapped up, as it were, in a great cloak of snug and smoky air, shot with the glow of the logs intermittently breaking out again in flame, a sort of alcove without walls, a cave of warmth dug out of the heart of the room itself, a zone of heat whose boundaries were constantly shifting and altering in temperature as gusts of air traversed them to strike freshly upon my face, from the corners of the room or from parts near the window or far from the fireplace which had therefore remained cold;—or rooms in summer, where I would delight to feel myself a part of the warm night, where the moonlight striking upon the half-opened shutters would throw down to the foot of my bed its enchanted ladder, where I would fall asleep, as it might be in the open air, like a titmouse which the breeze gently rocks at the tip of a sunbeam;—or sometimes the Louis XVI room, so cheerful that I never felt too miserable in it, even on my first night, and in which the slender columns that lightly supported its ceiling drew so gracefully apart to reveal and frame the site of the bed;—sometimes, again, the little room with the high ceiling, hollowed in the form of a pyramid out of two separate storeys, and partly walled with mahogany, in which from the first moment, mentally poisoned by the unfamiliar scent of vetiver, I was convinced of the hostility of the violet curtains and of the insolent indifference of a clock that chattered on at the top of its voice as though I were not there; in which a strange and pitiless rectangular cheval-glass, standing across one corner of the room, carved out for itself a site I had not looked to find tenanted in the soft plenitude of my normal field of vision; in which my mind, striving for hours on end to break away from its moorings, to stretch upwards so as to take on the exact shape of the room and to reach to the topmost height of its gigantic funnel, had endured many a painful night as I lay stretched out in bed, my eyes staring upwards, my ears straining, my nostrils flaring, my heart beating; until habit had changed the colour of the curtains, silenced the clock, brought an expression of pity to the cruel, slanting face of the glass, disguised or even completely dispelled the scent of vetiver, and appreciably reduced the apparent loftiness of the ceiling. Habit! that skilful but slow-moving arranger who begins by letting our minds suffer for weeks on end in temporary quarters, but whom our minds are none the less only too happy to discover at last, for without it, reduced to their own devices, they would be powerless to make any room seem habitable.

Certainly I was now well awake; my body had veered round for the last time and the good angel of certainty had made all the surrounding objects stand still, had set me down under my bedclothes, in my bedroom, and had fixed, approximately in the right places in the uncertain light, my chest of drawers, my writing-table, my fireplace, the window overlooking the street, and both the doors. But for all that I now knew that I was not in any of the houses of which the ignorance of the waking moment had, in a flash, if not presented me with a distinct picture, at least persuaded me of the possible presence, my memory had been set in motion; as a rule I did not attempt to go to sleep again at once, but used to spend the greater part of the night recalling our life in the old days at Combray with my great-aunt, at Balbec, Paris, Doncières, Venice, and the rest; remembering again all the places and people I had known, what I had actually seen of them, and what others had told me.

GASTON BACHELARD

One of the amphitheatres of the Sorbonne is called 'l'amphi Gaston Bachelard', an honour the philosopher shared with Descartes and Richelieu. His work on the imagination was initially very influential in the 1950s and 1960s. Amongst his many works were a series of books on the presence of the four main elements in reverie and thought: water, fire, earth and air. The fragment below is from 'Oneiric Space', one of the essays collected and published posthumously in The Right to Dream.*

Bachelard was born in 1884 in rural France and died in 1962.

Oneiric Space

No sooner do we start to fall asleep than space relaxes and falls asleep, too—doing so a little ahead of us, losing its struts and fibres, losing its structural forces and its geometric coherence. The space in which we shall spend our nocturnal hours has no perspective, no distance. It is the immediate synthesis of things and ourselves. If we dream of an object, we enter into that object as into a shell. Our oneiric space always has this central coefficient. Sometimes in flying dreams we think we are very high up, but we are no more then than a little bit of flying matter. And the skies we soar through are wholly interior—skies of desire or hope or pride. We are too astonished at our extraordinary journal to make of it an occasion for spectacle. We ourselves remain the centre of our oneiric experience. If a star shines, it is with the sleeper's radiance: a tiny flash on the sleeping retina evokes an ephemeral constellation, conjuring up confused memories of a starry night.

Indeed, our sleeping space is very quickly the autonomy of our retina where minute chemical processes raise up whole worlds. The background to oneiric space is thus a veil, a veil which lights up by itself at intervals, just for a moment, these moments becoming fewer and more fleeting as night penetrates more deeply into our being. A veil of Maia cast not upon the world but upon ourselves by the bounty of night, a veil of Maia no larger than an eyelid. And how dense are the paradoxes conjured up by the thought that this eyelid, this terminal veil, belongs as much to night as to ourselves! It is as if the sleeper partakes of a will to occultation, the will of night. This is the starting point for an understanding of oneiric space, a space made up of essential envelopes, a space governed by the geometry and dynamics of envelopment.

Our eyes, then, themselves possess a will to sleep, a heavy, irrational, Schopenhauerian will. If our eyes do not share in this universal will to sleep, if they remember the brightness of the sun and the delicate colouring of flowers, then oneiric space has not found its centre. It retains too much depth of perspective; it is the broken, turbulent space of insomnia. It preserves the geometry of day—except that that geometry has of course loosened its stays and become false, comical and absurd in consequence. And its dreams and nightmares are as far removed from the truths of light as they are from the deep sincerity of night. To sleep properly we must obey the will to envelopment, the will of the chrysalis; with the smoothness of a well-coiled spiral we must follow the movement of envelopment right to its centre—an essentially curved, circular process eschewing all angles and edges. The symbols of night are governed by the ovoid. All such elongated or rounded shapes are fruits in which germs may ripen and mature.

Had we more space at our disposal, we would describe at this point how after the relaxation of the eyes comes the relaxation of the hands, for they, too, come to reject objects. When we bear in mind that the whole specific dynamism of the human being is *digital*, it follows inescapably that oneiric space unfolds as and when our knotted fists unclench themselves.

But enough has been said in this rapid outline to give an idea of the first of these two nocturnal directions. A space that abandons its horizons, draws in on itself, becomes rounded and enveloped is a space that trusts in the power of its core of being. It normally brings dreams of security and repose.

The images and symbols punctuating this process of concentration should be interpreted precisely in terms of their progressive centralisation. If we isolate them, if we fail to consider them as moments in the process of centralising sleep, we overlook an element in their interpretation.

Let us turn now to the stroke of our psychic midnight and follow the reflux of night's second direction leading us on to dawn.

Maurice Blanchot

In the first piece, from The Space of Literature, *Blanchot expresses suspicion towards the insomniac. The 'guilt' that he attributes to the insomniac is both temporal—bringing the day into the night—and spatial—a matter of displaced volumes. The insomniac tosses and turns because he/she hasn't found the place of sleep. Embedded in this fragment on sleep are some astute comments on insomnia, its vigilance and guilt.*

Discussion of time occurs throughout The Writing of the Disaster—*which goes a little way to explaining the immediate context for the second extract. 'I call disaster that which does not have the ultimate for a limit, but which bears the ultimate away in the disaster', says Blanchot. Disasters such as the Holocaust can be written about, but also write themselves upon us, so affecting are they. Helen Daniel's remarks in her column in the Melbourne* Age, *though not directed at Blanchot, may also help: '. . . cultural insomnia, the reluctance to recognise the ending of a day, an era, and thereby being afflicted with all manner of harassing night-thoughts, bound to enter the next era, tired, drained, stressed, still haunted by the past. Every age is subject to night-thoughts . . .'*

The Space of Literature *was first published in French in 1955 and* The Writing of the Disaster *in 1980. Born in 1907, Blanchot has influenced French thinking from the 1930s onwards.*

Sleep, Night

What happens at night? Generally we sleep. By means of sleep, day uses night to blot out the night. Sleep belongs to the world; it is a task. We sleep in accord with the general law which makes our daytime activity depend on our nightly repose. We call upon sleep and it comes. There is between sleep and us something like a pact, a treaty with no secret clauses, and according to this convention it is agreed that, far from being a dangerous, bewitching force, sleep will become domesticated and serve as the instrument of our power to act. We surrender to sleep, but in the way that the master entrusts himself to the slave who serves him. Sleeping is the clear action which promises us to the day. To sleep: admire this remarkable act of vigilance. Only deep sleep lets us escape what there is in the deep of sleep. Where is night? There is no longer any night.

Sleeping is an event which belongs to history, just as rest on the seventh day belongs to creation. Night, when men transform it into pure sleep, is not a nocturnal affirmation. I sleep. The sovereignty of the 'I' dominates this absence which it grants itself and which is its doing. I sleep: it is I who sleep and none other—and men of action, the great men of history, are proud of their perfect sleep from which they arise intact. This is why the sleep which in the normal pursuits of our life sometimes takes us by surprise is by no means a scandal. Our capacity to withdraw from everyday bustle, from daily concerns, from everything, from ourselves and even from the void is the sign of our mastery, an entirely human proof of our *sangfroid*. You must sleep: this is the watchword which consciousness assigns itself, and this commandment to renounce the day is one of day's first rules.

Sleep transforms night into possibility. Vigilance is sleep when night falls. Whoever does not sleep cannot stay awake. Vigilance consists of not always keeping watch, for it seeks *awakening* as its essence. Nocturnal wandering, the tendency to stray when the world is attenuated and grows distant, and even the honest professions which are necessarily practised at night attract suspicions. To sleep with open eyes is an anomaly symbolically indicating something which the general consciousness does not approve of. People who sleep badly always appear more or less guilty. What do they do? They make night present.

Bergson said that sleep is disinterestedness. Perhaps sleep is inattention to the world, but this negation of the world conserves us for the world and affirms the world. Sleep is an act of fidelity and of union. I entrust myself to the great natural rhythms, to the laws, of the stability of order. My sleep is the realisation of this trust, the affirmation of this faith. It is an attachment, in the affective sense of this term: I attach myself, not like Ulysses to the mast with bonds from which later I would like to free myself, but through an agreement expressed by the sensual accord of my head with the pillow, of my body with the peace and happiness of the bed. I retire from the world's immensity and its disquietude, but in order to give myself to the world, which is maintained, thanks to my 'attachment', in the sure truth of a limited and firmly circumscribed place. Sleep is my absolute interest in assuring myself of the world. From this limit which sleep provides, I take hold of the world by its finite side; I grasp it firmly enough so that it stays, puts me in place, puts me to rest. To sleep badly is precisely to be unable to find one's position. The bad sleeper tosses and turns in search of that genuine place which he knows is unique. He knows that only in that spot will the world give up its errant immensity. The sleepwalker is suspect, for he is the man who does not find repose in sleep. Asleep, he is nevertheless without a place and, it may be said, without faith. He lacks fundamental sincerity, or, more precisely, his sincerity lacks a foundation. It lacks that position he seeks, which is also repose, where he would affirm himself in the stable fixity of his absence, which would be his support. Bergson saw behind sleep the totality of conscious life minus the effort of concentration. On the contrary, sleep is intimacy with the centre. I am, not dispersed, but entirely gathered together where I am, in this spot which is my position and where the world, because of the firmness of my attachment, localises itself. Where I sleep, I fix myself and I fix the world. My person is there, prevented from erring, no longer unstable, scattered and distracted, but concentrated in the narrowness of this place where the world recollects itself, which I affirm and which affirms me. Here the place is present in me and I absent in it through an essentially ecstatic union. My person is not simply situated where I sleep; it is this very site, and my sleeping is the fact that now my abode is my being.

It is true that in sleep I seem to close in upon myself, in an attitude which recalls the ignorant bliss of early childhood. This may be; and yet it is not to myself alone that I entrust myself. I do not find support in myself, but in the world which has become in me the narrowness and the limit of my repose. Sleep is not normally a moment of weakness; it is not that I despondently abandon my resolute point of view. Sleep signifies that at a certain moment, in order to act it is necessary to cease acting—that at a certain moment, lest I lose my way in aimless roving, I must stop and manfully transform the instability of myriad possibilities into a single stopping point upon which I establish and reestablish myself.

Vigilant existence does not dissipate in the sleeping body near which things remain; it withdraws from the remove which is its temptation. It returns from there to the primordial affirmation which is the authority of the body when the body is not separated but fully in agreement with the truth of place. To be surprised at finding everything still there in the morning is to forget that nothing is surer than sleep and that the meaning of sleep lies precisely in its being vigilant existence concentrating upon certitude, linking up all errant possibilities to the fixity of a principle and satiating itself with this certitude, so that the morning's newness can welcome it and a new day can begin.

Who Watches?

- Lucidity, ray of the star, response to the day that questions, and sleep when night comes. 'But who will hide from the star that never sets?' Wakefulness is without beginning or end. To wake is neutral. 'I' do not wake: someone does, the night does, always and incessantly, hollowing the night out into the other night where there can be no question of sleeping. There is no waking save at night. Night is foreign to the vigilance which is exercised, carried out, and which conveys lucid reason toward what it must maintain in reflection—in the preservation, that is, of its own identity. Wakefulness is estrangement: it does not waken, as if emerging from a sleep that would precede it, yet it reawakens: constant and instant return to the immobility of the wake. Something wakes: something keeps watch without lying in wait or spying. The disaster watches. When there is such watching—when sleep consciousness, opening into unconsciousness, lets the light of the dream play—then what watches (the wake, or the impossibility of sleep at the heart of sleep) does not illuminate with an increase of visibility, of reflecting brilliance. Who watches? The question is obviated by the neutrality of the watch: no one watches. Watching is not the power to keep watch—in the first person; it is not a power, but the touch of the powerless infinite, exposure to the other of the night, where thought renounces the vigour of vigilance, gives up worldly clear-sightedness, perspicacious mastery, in order to deliver itself to the limitless deferral of insomnia, the wake that does not waken, nocturnal intensity.

- It might be said that within the disaster there occurs a falling short, if it were not also characteristic of the disaster to be a trance: the motionless fall and flight of the outside. Deficiency does not let the exception rest on high, but causes a ceaseless fall (without form or content) outside the attainable and the possible. The exceptional escapes, deficiency dissimulates. Consciousness can be catastrophic without ceasing to be consciousness: it does not reverse itself, turning into its opposite, but welcomes into itself this overturning. Only such re-turning, that wrests from the present, detours consciousness–unconsciousness.

- In the night, insomnia is dis-cussion: not the work of arguments bumping against other arguments, but the extreme shuddering of no thoughts, percussive stillness . . .

HUSH LITTLE BABY . . .

BARBARA BRANDT

In this poem, the tenderness between mother and daughter expressed through the child's insomnia is reminiscent of Colette's lovers in 'Night Without Sleep', where insomnia provides a time for loving.

Barbara Brandt is a West Australian poet. A number of her poems have been collected in Shore-lines. *The following poem was first published in the* Australian *in 1994.*

For Shannon

'What am I going to do when I leave home? I can do everything, but sometimes I can't go to sleep on my own.'

November 1993

The first time I held you like this,
you were less than a minute old.
The midwife showed me how to support your head
—and pressed your new, wet body to mine—
the joy was as sweet as quickening.

Tonight as I hold you I remember this
and know this child-woman in my arms—
soft, warm insomniac—will soon no longer
need my midnight touch.

I am holding my daughter.
For this the line of my shoulder
was made, the curve at the base of my neck.
And this joy is as sweet as quickening.
For now, this touch is all I need,
once, for a little while, you were mine.

Mary Wollstonecraft

Partly autobiographical and so both political and romantic, The Wrongs of Woman *was published in 1798 a few years after Wollstonecraft's* Vindication of the Rights of Men *and* A Vindication of the Rights of Women. *Below, Wollstonecraft's heroine Maria has been confined on her husband's orders, and separated from her baby girl in an attempt by him to secure her inheritance. Maria's guardian Jemima has just told her the story of her own difficult origins, and Maria hopes to gain her sympathy.*

Born in 1759, Wollstonecraft died in 1798 shortly after giving birth to her second daughter Mary, the author of Frankenstein.

The Wrongs of Woman

Active as love was in the heart of Maria, the story she had just heard made her thoughts take a wider range. The opening buds of hope closed, as if they had put forth too early, and the happiest day of her life was overcast by the most melancholy reflections. Thinking of Jemima's peculiar fate and her own, she was led to consider the oppressed state of women, and to lament that she had given birth to a daughter. Sleep fled from her eyelids, while she dwelt on the wretchedness of unprotected infancy, till sympathy with Jemima changed to agony, when it seemed probable that her own babe might even now be in the very state she so forcibly described.

Maria thought, and thought again. Jemima's humanity had rather been benumbed than killed, by the keen frost she had to brave at her entrance into life; an appeal then to her feelings, on this tender point, surely would not be fruitless; and Maria began to anticipate the delight it would afford her to gain intelligence of her child. This project was now the only subject of reflection; and she watched impatiently for the dawn of day, with that determinate purpose which generally insures success.

At the usual hour, Jemima brought her breakfast, and a tender note from Darnford. She ran her eye hastily over it, and her heart calmly hoarded up the rapture a fresh assurance of affection, affection such as she wished to inspire, gave her, without diverting her mind a moment from its design. While Jemima waited to take away the breakfast, Maria alluded to the reflections, that had haunted her during the night to the exclusion of sleep. She spoke with energy of Jemima's unmerited sufferings, and of the fate of a number of deserted females, placed within the sweep of a whirlwind, from which it was next to impossible to escape. Perceiving the effect her conversation produced on the countenance of her guard, she grasped the arm of Jemima with that irresistible warmth which defies repulse, exclaiming—'With your heart, and such dreadful experience, can you lend your aid to deprive my babe of a mother's tenderness, a mother's care? In the name of God, assist me to snatch her from destruction! Let me but give her an education—let me but prepare her body and mind to encounter the ills which await her sex, and I will teach her to consider you as her second mother, and herself as the prop of your age. Yes, Jemima, look at me—observe me closely, and read my very soul; you merit a better fate,' she held out her hand with a firm gesture of assurance; 'and I will procure it for you as a testimony of my esteem, as well as of my gratitude.'

Jemima had not power to resist this persuasive torrent; and, owning that the house in which she was confined, was situated on the banks of the Thames, only a few miles from London, and not on the sea-coast, as Darnford had supposed, she promised to invent some excuse for her absence, and go herself to trace the situation, and enquire concerning the health, of this abandoned daughter. Her manner implied an intention to do something more, but she seemed unwilling to impart her design; and Maria, glad to have obtained the main point, thought it best to leave her to the workings of her own mind; convinced that she had the power of interesting her still more in favour of herself and child, by a simple recital of facts.

In the evening, Jemima informed the impatient mother, that

on the morrow she should hasten to town before the family hour of rising, and received all the information necessary, as a clue to her search. The 'Good night!' Maria uttered was peculiarly solemn and affectionate. Glad expectation sparkled in her eye; and, for the first time since her detention, she pronounced the name of her child with pleasurable fondness; and, with all the garrulity of a nurse, described her first smile when she recognised her mother. Recollecting herself, a still kinder 'Adieu!' with a 'God bless you!'—that seemed to include a maternal benediction, dismissed Jemima.

The dreary solitude of the ensuing day, lengthened by impatiently dwelling on the same idea, was intolerably wearisome. She listened for the sound of a particular clock, which some directions of the wind allowed her to hear distinctly. She marked the shadow gaining on the wall; and, twilight thickening into darkness, her breath seemed oppressed while she anxiously counted nine.—The last sound was a stroke of despair on her heart; for she expected every moment, without seeing Jemima, to have her light extinguished by the savage female who supplied her place. She was even obliged to prepare for bed, restless as she was, not to disoblige her new attendant. She had been cautioned not to speak too freely to her; but the caution was needless, her countenance would still more emphatically have made her shrink back. Such was the ferocity of manner, conspicuous in every word and gesture of this hag, that Maria was afraid to enquire, why Jemima, who had faithfully promised to see her before her door was shut for the night, came not?—and, when the key turned in the lock, to consign her to a night of suspense, she felt a degree of anguish which the circumstances scarcely justified.

Continually on the watch, the shutting of a door, or the sound of a footstep, made her start and tremble with apprehension, something like what she felt, when, at her entrance, dragged along the gallery, she began to doubt whether she were not surrounded by demons?

Fatigued by an endless rotation of thought and wild alarms, she looked like a spectre, when Jemima entered in the morning; especially as her eyes darted out of her head, to read in Jemima's countenance, almost as pallid, the intelligence she dared not trust her tongue to demand. Jemima put down the

tea-things, and appeared very busy in arranging the table.
Maria took up a cup with trembling hand, then forcibly recovering her fortitude, and restraining the convulsive movement
which agitated the muscles of her mouth, she said, 'Spare
yourself the pain of preparing me for your information, I
adjure you!—My child is dead!' Jemima solemnly answered,
'Yes,' with a look expressive of compassion and angry emotions.
'Leave me,' added Maria, making a fresh effort to govern her
feelings, and hiding her face in her handkerchief, to conceal
her anguish—'It is enough—I know that my babe is no more—I
will hear the particulars when I am'—*calmer*, she could not
utter; and Jemima, without importuning her by idle attempts
to console her, left the room.

EMILY HOLMES COLEMAN

Following the birth of her son in 1924, Emily Holmes Coleman suffered puerperal fever which led to a mental breakdown and a period in an asylum, out of which came the story of Marthe Gail in The Shutter of Snow. *An ebullient and radical woman, Coleman transformed her terrible months in the asylum into prose. She was a close friend of Djuna Barnes, a part of whose novel* Nightwood *is included in this volume.*

Give Me My Baby

That night she cried aloud in her sleep and the nurse was afraid. You will wake them all up, there will be a scene. The nurse moved her bed out of her room and down the hall to the desk. Marthe looked from her bed down the ward where they all lay hunched under their shoulders. One of them sat bold upright and slept.

She reached for her sheepskin slipper and rocked it in her hands. He is sleeping in it and I will rock him. Papa les petits bateaux qu vont sur l'eau, ont-ils des jambes?

You will have to stop singing, it keeps them awake, But you idiot this is my baby and he has to go to sleep. There was rustling and eyes popped from bed to bed.

I cant sleep Miss Wright. I dont know what Im going to do with you she said, I'll have to have you taken downstairs to East Hall if you make any more noise.

Someone called the nurse at the far end and she went down the hall past the rooms. Marthe slipped from the covers and went over to Miss Lanier's bed and sat on it. Miss Lanier's long eyes shook. You mustnt stay here she shivered. Go away go away said a voice across the aisle, modulated in the throat. Marthe went down to where Bowels was sleeping quietly and blew in her ear. You can have some more crackers to-morrow if you want them.

The woman turned suddenly and screamed into the ceiling. All the beds began to tremble and all the voices began intermingling, stooping and rising. After the scream there was only the movement of the voices, like the waters of a lake when a wind had passed.

Miss Wright came fast from the other end and Marthe was back in her bed. All the voices indicated Marthe, all the hands pointed terror fingers shaking at her bed. All the heads were shaken grimly and some of them rubbed their hands across their woollen nightgowns and some began to braid their hair.

Miss Wright rang a bell and stood looking at Marthe. Presently the keys came from the other side and it was Miss Sheehan in white and black-browed, sweet to the touch and gentle.

I cant keep Mrs Gail here, she is keeping everybody awake.

Whats the matter Mrs Gail youve been so quiet lately? Miss Sheehan stood looking too. I cant sleep and she wont even let me sing.

Perhaps youd better come down in East Hall, just for the night. O no no no no I will be very quiet. Dr Brainerd's off said Miss Sheehan to Miss Wright, and I couldnt get an order. If she makes any more noise send her down to me. Now Mrs Gail said Miss Sheehan, Irish and smooth and down in her shoes she likes noise.

She turned her face to the wall and closed her eyes. Soon there were circles on the wall, pointed like the ones Annabel had made for her valentines. Mrs Fearing was coming upstairs they said, and they would make valentines. Come come come come, valentines for the doctor's wife. Annabel was sleeping there in that room right across there to the right. They had given her a room and she was sleeping in it. Miss Wright may I go in to see Annabel? Will you go to sleep? cried the nurse.

She was in a blanket in a chair by the desk. That if you wont move. She sat up there and watched the ward go back into slumber. Some of them saw her and began to fret again, chafing their hands. There was the heaviness of sleep in the night and the nurse nodded at the desk and went into circles. The blanket was too heavy and had been warmed at the radiator. It would make a large ponderous dance to be danced in mud and under dripping eaves.

There were eaves in this room and she could make them drip. She would practise the dance. All the drag of the blanket went into her lagging feet and into her ears went the music. The beds stirred again and drew back against the wall.

Its no use Mrs Gail, get your slippers and come with me.

She began to cry O no I will be good, O please dont take me down down that stairway. Just for tonight she said. O no no no I cannot ever go back there, O I will be so quiet.

They went down the stairs together. If you will behave theyll let you come back up said Miss Wright, so dont make a row. The heavy blanket trailed up behind her, up into the quiet places.

Now Mrs Gail. Miss Sheehan shook her head with pursed lips. You that was being so good. She unlocked the door into East Hall and Marthe was delivered.

Into the red light and the black warmth of the hallway went Marthe, back to the strange sounds of the dead bodies under the sheets. She blinked her eyes and saw Miss Godwin. My sweet Godwin let me sit up and talk to you. Whatve you been up to, I heard you was going home soon. Voices down the hall. Pauline praying for the Kaiser. Sarah Kemp marching. Other voices, new voices one young and high yelping a puppy.

Up and past them came Mrs Kemp heavily trodding and with strong intent. How do you do Mrs Kemp do you remember me? You poor woman aint you out of here yet cant you do anything for me? said Mrs Kemp. Same old line said Godwin. Old bitch said Mrs Kemp. Thats me said Godwin.

Marthe went down to her bed and got in obediently to go to sleep. It was a bed in the ward in the midst of the voices. O my brother my sister my God my God.

She did not sleep and the noises grew in volume and increased in weight until her ears shouted to each other, and round and round in the circles of Annabel went the lullaby she had sung in the sheepskin slipper. She sang it stridently. There was an instant of absolute silence, even the skeleton, then with triple confusion came forth loud words from every mouth that heard. Gradually the curses fell away until only the skeleton was left droning my brother my sister my God my God.

Louise Erdrich

This fragment is taken from The Blue Jay's Dance—A Birth Year. *It's rare to find writing about the insomnia that is so common to pregnancy, and interesting to find Erdrich's writerly self doubling her sleeplessness (or is it the other way around?). Erdrich is the author of a number of novels and poetry collections including* Love Medicine, The Beet Queen, Baptism of Desire *and* Tales of Burning Love.

She grew up in North Dakota and is of German–American and Chippewa descent.

Hour of the Wolf

Part of a writer's task is to put her failings at the service of her pen. Just so with insomnia, this habit of waking at the most inconvenient, still hour of what is technically morning—three or four A.M.—the hour of the wolf. My eyes flip open. All the lights are on in my head, thoughts alert and humming. In past times, I could think of the fictional question or problem I was facing, and my brain would snap right off as though confronted by a paralysing koan. No more. Pregnancy increases my tendency to wakefulness and makes any sleeping medication dangerous, since it passes into the baby affecting god-knows-what developmental moment. As a matter of practicality, knowing I'll be burnt-out and drowsy the next day if I lie stewing and planning in the dark, I get up. I make myself a cup of herbal tea and start writing poetry. The house is bleak and cold, the windows painted with ostrich ferns of frost. I stir the tea, quietly, then swaddle myself in afghans on the living room couch and write until my words lull me back to sleep. Often, satisfactorily weary at four-thirty or five, I pass Michael on the stairs as he rises to stoke the wood fire, make coffee, begin his day.

I write poems during the late nights up until the week of birth, and fiction by day. I suppose one could say, pulling in the obvious metaphors, that my work is hormone driven, inscribed in mother's milk, pregnant with itself. I do begin to think that I am in touch with something larger than me, one of the few things. I feel that I am transcribing verbatim from a flow of language running through the room, an ink current into which I dip the pen. It is a dark stream, swift running, a twisting flow that never doubles back. The amazement is that I need only to enter the room at those strange hours to be drawn back into the language. The frustration is that I cannot be there all the time.

HOUR OF THE WOLF

Elizabeth Jolley

Jolley has published numerous short story collections and novels, and many of her works are available in translation. This extract is taken from The Georges' Wife. *Born in 1923, Jolley left England for Western Australia with her family in 1959.*

The Hour of the Wolf

Sometimes I wake too early at that time described as the hour of the wolf. I think then of all the books and papers, the pictures and the cassettes, the dishes, the linen and the clothes and the furniture in the house. I think of the shabby paint and the deep cracks in the walls and the ceilings. And then there are the places where the roof leaks. I go round in the dark, putting pails and bowls to catch the dripping rain water. This house has, between the corrugated-iron gables, a flat roof similar to the flat roof years ago where I shovelled off the snow, when I was young and not at all fearful of the height of the ladder, perched on the top landing, with all the flights of stairs curving down, below me, down to the front hall. A flat roof, we all agreed at that time, gives the most trouble.

A flat roof is the worst kind of roof—Miss George always made the announcement on wet mornings in that other house. She was sure the wind had brought all the soaked leaves from the surrounding streets into the space between the gables.

Suffering is like art we create it within ourselves. Noël said this and said it was written by Strindberg. Felicity, as usual, answered Noël with a second quotation; 'Look,' she said, '*at the ruin of the individual when he isolates himself . . .*' 'Strindberg again,' Noël said.

It does not seem possible to avoid either of these truths. I am confronted daily in my consulting rooms with manifestations of both.

The raw inhospitable remains of the night are captured by the surprise of the morning. This soft patience waits outside the closed blinds where birds, unconcerned, squabble endlessly, perhaps going over the roosting disagreements of the previous evening.

Perhaps it can be said that the only thing in favour of blinds is the elevation when they are released in the mornings. This elevation is always forgotten during that hour when life is at its lowest ebb, that hour years ago when I was nursing; and in the stillness perhaps between three and four in the morning, a life, hovering, would slip away forever and Sister Bean, for thirty years the Night Superintendent, would add to her bedside prayers, while still on her knees, a reprimand saying that nurses should remember that they were only nurses and should not think of themselves as being capable of controlling the Divine Intervention.

This revelation, when the blinds are released in the mornings, is in the daylight which is so steadily and reassuringly increasing as if suggesting that, with the rising of the sun every morning, everything will be as usual. And that all I have to do is to go out into the new day in an ordinary way, as usual.

Franz Kafka

Kafka was born in 1863 in Prague. He died in 1924 leaving the instruction that all his unpublished writings be destroyed. His friend Max Brod disregarded his wishes, with The Trial *being published a year later and other works subsequently. The passages below are from his diary of 1911.*

Because I Write

Oct.2

I believe this sleeplessness comes only because I write. For no matter how little and how badly I write, I am still made sensitive by these minor shocks, feel, especially toward evening and even more in the morning, the approaching, the imminent possibility of great moments which would tear me open, which could make me capable of anything, and in the general uproar that is within me and which I have no time to command, find no rest. In the end this uproar is only a suppressed, restrained harmony, which left free, would fill me completely, which could even widen me and yet still fill me. But now such a moment arouses only feeble hopes and does me harm, for my being does not have sufficient strength or the capacity to hold the present mixture, during the day the visible world helps me, during the night it cuts me to pieces unhindered. I always think in this connection of Paris, where at the time of the siege and later, until the Commune, the population of the northern and eastern suburbs, up to that time strangers to the Parisians, for a period of months moved through the connecting streets into the centre of Paris, dawdling like the hands of a clock . . .

October 3

The same sort of night, but fell asleep with even more difficulty. While falling asleep a vertically moving pain in my head over the bridge of the nose, as though from a wrinkle too sharply pressed into my forehead. To make myself as heavy as possible, which I consider good for falling asleep, I had crossed my arms and laid my hands on my shoulders, so that I lay there like a soldier with his pack. Again it was the power of my dreams, shining forth into wakefulness even before I fall asleep, which did not let me sleep. In the evening and the morning my consciousness of the creative abilities in me is more than I can encompass. I feel shaken to the core of my being and can get out of myself whatever I desire.

CHARLES SIMIC

Sleeplessness is Like Metaphysics

There is something of Nabokov's chess insomnia in the two (of many) insomnia poems below, from Simic's collection Hotel Insomnia.

Charles Simic was born in 1938 in Yugoslavia, and lives in America.

Hotel Insomnia

I liked my little hole,
Its window facing a brick wall.
Next door there was a piano.
A few evenings a month
A crippled old man came to play
'My Blue Heaven'.

Mostly, though, it was quiet.
Each room with its spider in heavy overcoat
Catching his fly with a web
Of cigarette smoke and revery.
So dark,
I could not see my face in the shaving mirror.

At 5 a.m. the sound of bare feet upstairs.
The 'Gypsy' fortuneteller,
Whose storefront is on the corner,
Going to pee after a night of love.
Once, too, the sound of a child sobbing.
So near it was, I thought
For a moment, I was sobbing myself.

The Congress of the Insomniacs

Mother of God, everyone is invited:
Stargazing Peruvian shepherds,
Old men on sidewalks of New York.
You, too, doll with eyes open
Listening to the rain next to a sleeping child.

A big hotel ballroom with mirrors on each side.
Think about it as you lie in the dark.
Angels on its ornate ceilings,
Naked nymphs in what must be paradise.

There's a stage, a lectern,
An usher with a flashlight.
Someone will address this gathering yet
From his bed of nails.
Sleeplessness is like metaphysics.
Be there.

RAYMOND CARVER

Carver has written a number of stories and poems where the main character cannot sleep, including 'Menudo', 'I Could See the Smallest Things', 'Whoever Was Using this Bed' and 'The Student's Wife'. Carver had a short and arduous writing life (1939–1988), some of which is described in his collection Fires.

Winter Insomnia

The mind can't sleep, can only lie awake and
gorge, listening to the snow gather as
for some final assault.

It wishes Chekov were here to minister
something—three drops of valerian, a glass
of rose water—anything, it wouldn't matter.

The mind would like to get out of here
onto the snow. It would like to run
with a pack of shaggy animals, all teeth,

under the moon, across the snow, leaving
no prints or spoor, nothing behind.
The mind is sick tonight.

ANTON CHEKHOV

To Lidia Avilova, possibly a lover, Chekhov wrote:
'. . . You complain that my characters are
gloomy . . . It is noteworthy that gloomy people and
melancholiacs always write merry things, while the
cheerful depress people with their writings. And I am
a cheerful man; at least, as the saying goes, I've
enjoyed myself during the first thirty years of
life . . .'.

Chekhov was born in Russia in 1860. He trained
and worked in medicine, writing hundreds of short
stories, as well as plays and criticism. He died of
consumption in 1904.

A Case History

A professor received a telegram from the Lyalikov factory
asking him to come immediately. All he could decipher in that
rambling, muddled telegram was that the daughter of a Mrs
Lyalikov, who apparently owned the factory, was ill.

The professor did not go himself, but sent his house-surgeon
Korolyov instead. The house-surgeon had to go two stops by
train from Moscow, then travel the remaining three miles by
road. A coachman wearing a hat with a peacock's feather, who
shouted his replies to every question like a soldier—'No—sir'
or 'Yes—sir'—was sent to pick him up at the station in a
three-horse carriage. It was a Saturday evening and the sun
was setting. Workers thronged the road from the factory to the
station and they bowed to the horses as they went by. He was
enchanted by the evening, by the estates and villas to each
side of him, by the birch trees and an all-pervading atmosphere
of tranquillity, when it seemed that the fields, the forest and
the sun were preparing to join with the factory workers in
their rest on that Saturday evening—and perhaps to offer up
prayers as well.

He was born in Moscow, where he had grown up, was a stranger to country life and had never taken any interest in factories or even visited one. But he had read about them, had been invited to the houses of factory owners where he had had a chance to talk to them. Whenever he saw a factory, whether from far off or close by, he always thought that, while everything appeared so calm and peaceful from the outside, inside those walls there were surely nothing but blindly egotistic bosses who were completely and utterly ignorant; boring, unhealthy work for those who slaved away there; and filth, vodka and insects. And now, when those workers respectfully and timidly made way for the carriage, he could see sure signs of filth, drunkenness, nervousness and bewilderment in their faces, in the state of their peaked caps and in the way they walked.

They drove through the factory gates. On both sides he caught glimpses of the workers' cottages, women's faces, washing and blankets laid out on the front steps. 'Look out!' the coachman shouted as he gave full rein to the horses. They reached a wide open square, devoid of grass. Here there were five enormous factory blocks with chimneys, spaced out a little distance from each other, store-houses and wooden huts: everything was covered with a rather strange grey deposit that could have been dust. Miserable little gardens and the managers' houses with their green or red roofs were scattered here and there, like oases in a desert. The coachman suddenly pulled in the reins and the carriage came to a halt outside a house freshly painted grey. There was a small garden with a lilac tree covered in dust, and the yellow porch smelled strongly of new paint.

'This way please, Mr Doctor,' some female voices said in the entrance hall and at the same time he could hear sighing and whispering. 'Please come in, we're worn out with waiting . . . it's something shocking . . . this way, please.'

Mrs Lyalikov, a plump, elderly lady, was wearing a black silk dress with sleeves in the latest fashion; but her face showed she was a simple, uneducated woman. She glanced anxiously at the doctor and could not bring herself to offer him her hand—she dare not. A thin, middle-aged woman with close-cropped hair, pince-nez, and a brightly coloured floral pattern blouse was standing next to her. The servants called her Miss Christina and Korolyov guessed she was the governess. She was the most educated person in that household, and it was more than likely that she had been entrusted with receiving the doctor, since right away, without wasting any time, she launched into a minute account of the causes of the illness, giving every tiresome little detail, without saying who was ill and what the trouble was.

The doctor and governess sat talking, while the mistress of the house stood expectantly by the door without moving an inch. Korolyov gathered from the conversation that a twenty-year-old girl called Liza was ill. She was Mrs Lyalikov's only daughter and heiress to the estate; she had been ill for a long time and several doctors had treated her. The whole of the previous night she had suffered such violent palpitations that no one in the house could sleep and everyone feared for her life.

'She was always a sickly child, from the time she was a little girl,' Miss Christina said a sing-song voice, wiping her lips with her hand from time to time. 'The doctors say it's nerves, but when she was small they drove the scrofula back inside her, so perhaps that's the reason.'

They went to have a look at the patient. She was a large, tall girl, quite grown up, but ugly like her mother, with the same small eyes and a similar wide, oversized lower jaw. Her hair was uncombed and the blankets were drawn right up to her chin. Straight away she struck Korolyov as a miserable, unhappy creature who was being kept warm and well wrapped up because they felt sorry for her and he could not believe that here was the heiress to five huge factory blocks.

'I've come to give you some treatment,' Korolyov began. 'How do you do.' He introduced himself and shook her large, cold, ugly hand. She sat up and told him her story—she was obviously long-used to doctors and did not care about her shoulders and bosom being uncovered.

'I've been having palpitations,' she said. 'I was scared out of my life all night long . . . it was so bad I nearly died. Please give me something!'

'Yes, I will, I will! Now calm down.'

Korolyov examined her and shrugged his shoulders. 'Your

heart's perfectly sound, there's nothing wrong. Your nerves aren't too good, but that's normal. I don't think there'll be any more palpitations, try and get some sleep now . . . '

Just then a lamp was brought in. The lamp made the girl screw her eyes up and suddenly she clutched her head and burst out sobbing. His first impression of a wretched, ugly creature suddenly vanished and Korolyov no longer saw small eyes or an oversized jaw, but a gentle, suffering expression that seemed so rational, so touching. Now she appeared to embody all that was feminine, graceful and natural and he no longer wanted to supply her with sedatives or medical advice, but a few simple, kind words instead. The mother clasped her head and pressed it to her. How much despair and grief was written on that old woman's face! As a true mother she had nurtured her daughter, brought her up, spared no expense and devoted her entire life to her, so that she could learn French, dancing and music, and had engaged a dozen tutors, the best doctors, a governess; and now she could not understand the reason for all those tears, all that suffering, and consequently she was at her wits' end. Her expression was one of guilt, anxiety, despair, as if she had neglected something that was very important, had let things slip, had forgotten to invite someone—but who, that was a mystery.

'Lizanka, what is it now?' she said, pressing her daughter to her. 'My own little darling, tell me what's wrong! Show some pity, please tell me . . .'

Both wept bitterly. Korolyov sat on the edge of the bed and took Liza's hand. 'Now that's enough. Is it worth crying about?' he said in a kindly voice. 'Surely there's nothing in this world that's worth all these tears. Now, we're going to stop crying, there's no need to . . .' But he thought to himself: 'Time she was married . . .'

'The factory doctors gave her some bromide,' the governess said, 'but it's only made her worse. In my opinion, if it's the heart, there's some drops . . . I forget the name . . . lily of the valley, I think . . .'

And again came a flood of details. She kept interrupting the doctor, didn't let him get a word in and the effort she was making showed in her face—it was as if she had assumed, as the most educated woman in that house, that it was her responsibility to keep talking to the doctor—and only about medicine, of course.

Korolyov began to feel bored. 'I can't see anything very much wrong,' he said to the mother as he left the bedroom. 'If the factory doctor has been treating your daughter, there's no reason why he should stop. Up to now the treatment has been correct and I don't see the need to change doctor. The illness is really *so* normal, it's nothing serious . . .'

He did not hurry his words as he put his gloves on, but Mrs Lyalikov stood motionless and looked at him with tear-stained eyes.

'The ten o'clock train leaves in half an hour and I don't want to miss it,' he said.

'But can't you stay the night?' she asked and tears flowed down her cheeks again. 'I feel ashamed worrying you like this, but please do us the kindness . . . for God's sake,' she whispered as she glanced round at the door. '*Please* stay the night. She's all I have, my only daughter. She gave me such a fright last night, I still haven't got over it . . . *Please* don't go, for God's sake . . .'

He wanted to tell her that he had a great deal of work to do in Moscow, that his family was waiting for him. He felt depressed at the idea of spending a whole evening and night in a strange house when there was no need for it. But he looked at her face, sighed and silently started taking his gloves off.

All the lamps in the hall and drawing-room had been lit for him. He sat at the grand piano and turned over some pages of music. Then he looked at the portraits on the walls. There were oil paintings in gilt frames: Crimean landscapes, a storm at sea with small craft, a Catholic monk holding a wine glass—they were all dull, over-elaborate, amateurish. Among the portraits there wasn't one handsome, interesting face and all of them had wide cheek-bones and surprised-looking eyes. Lyalikov (Liza's father) had a small forehead, a smug look and a uniform that fitted his large clumsy body like a sack, and he sported the Red Cross with insignia on his chest. The house showed few signs of culture—any touches of luxury were purely accidental—and revealed poverty of ideas; and it looked uncomfortable, just like that uniform. The floors had a nasty gloss (there was something annoying about the chandeliers as well), and for some reason it all reminded you of the story of the merchant who wore a medal round his neck when he had a bath . . .

Whispers came from the hall and he could hear someone softly snoring. Suddenly there were sharp, abrupt metallic sounds from outside—sounds Korolyov had never heard before and which puzzled him now. They aroused a peculiar, unpleasant feeling and as he turned to the music-book again he thought: 'I don't think I could live here, not for anything!'

'Doctor, please come and have something to eat!' the governess called in a hushed voice.

He went off to have supper. The table was large, laden with many kinds of savouries and wines, but only two sat down to eat—himself and Miss Christina. She drank madeira, ate quickly, peered at him through her pince-nez and said, 'The workers are very happy. Every winter in the factory we have amateur dramatics, the workers play the parts themselves; there are lectures with magic-lantern slides, a marvellous canteen and a lot more. They are absolutely devoted to us and when they heard Liza was getting worse they said prayers. They may be illiterate, but they still have feelings.'

'It seems there are no men at all in the house,' Korolyov said.

'None. Mr Lyalikov died eighteen months ago and there's only the three of us. We spend the summers here, but stay on the Polyanka in Moscow during the winter. I've been with them eleven years. I'm one of the family.'

They had sturgeon, fried chicken and stewed fruit; the wines were French and very expensive.

'Please, doctor, don't stand on ceremony,' Miss Christina said, wiping her mouth on her sleeves as she ate. Clearly she was very satisfied with life in that house. 'Please, do eat.'

After supper the doctor was taken to a room where a bed had been made up for him. But he did not feel like sleeping as it was stuffy and the room smelled of paint. He put on his overcoat and went out.

It was cool outside; dawn was already breaking and all five factory blocks with their tall chimneys, the huts and store-houses stood out quite clearly in the moist air. No one was working, as it was a holiday, and all the windows were dark, except in one of the blocks where a stove was burning, turning the windows crimson; now and again flames leapt from the chimney, as well as smoke. Far beyond the factory yard, frogs were croaking and a nightingale was singing.

As he looked at the factory blocks and the wooden huts where the workers slept, he began to think as he had always done when he looked at factories. Even though there were shows for the workers, lantern-slides, factory doctors and various improvements in the standard of living, they were still those same workers he had met earlier that day on the way from the station and they didn't differ at all from those he had known a long time before when he was young, when there were no shows or improvements in factory conditions. As a doctor who had correctly diagnosed chronic incurable diseases whose cause had been unknown, he viewed factories as a puzzle of the same kind, just as vague and just as difficult to explain. He didn't actually think that these improvements were unnecessary but thought they were the same thing as treating an incurable disease.

'Of course, none of it makes sense,' he thought as he glanced at the crimson windows. 'Fifteen hundred or two thousand workers are slaving away, without a break, in unhealthy conditions, producing inferior cotton print, are half-starved and only now and then find relief from this nightmare in the pub. A hundred people supervise their work and the lives of these hundred supervisors are wasted entering fines in the record-book, swearing and being unfair to the workers; only two or three of them—the so-called bosses—enjoy the profits, although they don't do any work themselves and have nothing but contempt for the cheap fabric. But what exactly *are* these profits, how do they use them? Mrs Lyalikov and her daughter are unhappy and it makes me sorry to see them in such a state. Only Miss Christina, that stupid old maid with her pince-nez, gets any pleasure out of life. As I see it, there's five factories turning out cheap cotton print for sale on the Eastern markets just to keep Miss Christina supplied with madeira and sturgeon.'

Suddenly he hard a peculiar noise, just like the one before supper. Someone was banging away on a metal plate not far

from one of the blocks, immediately muffling the sound afterwards, so that it came over in brief, indistinct staccato bursts.
After about half a minute's silence the abrupt, unpleasant
noise started again, this time near one of the other blocks,
pitched lower, with a deep booming note. He counted eleven
strokes—obviously it was the night watchman beating out the
time.

Then he heard a metallic sound near the third block, then
from the others, and then from around the huts and beyond
the gates. It was as if that monster, the devil himself, who
had the bosses and the workers in his grasp, and who was
fooling all of them, was making these noises in the silence of
the night.

Korolyov walked out to the open fields.

Someone at the gate challenged, 'Who's there?'

'It's just like a prison,' he thought, and didn't reply.

Now he could hear the nightingales and frogs more clearly
and he was aware of the May night all around. The sound of
a train carried from the station. Somewhere sleepy cocks
crowed, and otherwise it was quiet, the world slept peacefully.
Out in the fields, not far from the factories, stood a pile of
timber and building materials. Korolyov sat on some planks
and continued his train of thought: 'Only the governess is
happy in this place—and the factory is working for *her* pleasure. But it seems she doesn't carry much weight round here.
The important one, for whom everyone is working, is the devil.'
And he thought about the devil, in whom he didn't believe,
and looked back at two windows where lights were burning.
It seemed these were really the crimson eyes of the devil who
was looking at him, of that mysterious force responsible for
the way the strong treated the weak, for a serious blunder
that was impossible to set right. It was nature's law that the
strong should oppress the weak, but this could be made easily
comprehensible only in newspaper articles or text-books, in
that chaos which everyday life seems to be made, in that
hotch-potch of trivia of which the intricate relationships between human beings are composed. It was no law, however,
but a logical *non sequitur*, when both the strong and weak fall
victim to their own relationships with one another and both
are compelled to surrender to some mysterious power standing

beyond ordinary life, alien to man. These were Korolyov's thoughts as he sat on the planks and gradually he was overcome by the feeling that this unknown, mysterious power was actually quite close and watching him. Meanwhile the sky in the east grew pale and time passed quickly. The five factory blocks and their chimneys, silhouetted against the grey dawn, with not a soul to be seen—as if everything had died—had a strange look, quite different from day-time. He completely forgot that there were steam engines, electricity, telephones inside those blocks, but for some strange reason he could only think about pile-dwellings, about the iron age and he sensed that some crude mindless power was lurking close by.

Again he heard that metallic tapping.

There were twelve beats. Then it stopped for about half a minute and started again at the other end of the factory yard—but this time the sound was deeper.

'Very nasty!' Korolyov thought.

Then came a staccato tapping from a third place—the sounds were sharp and abrupt and one could almost hear annoyance in them.

The watchman took four minutes to beat out twelve o'clock. Then all was quiet and he had that same feeling again, as if everything was dead.

Korolyov sat there a few minutes longer, then returned to the house, but it was a long time before he went to bed. He could hear whispering from the rooms to either side, and slippers and bare feet shuffling over the floor.

'Surely she's not having another attack?' Korolyov thought.

He left his room and went to see the sick girl. The rooms were already filled with bright daylight and the weak rays of the sun that had filtered through the morning mist played on the wall in the hall. The door to Liza's bedroom was open and she was sitting in an armchair near her bed with a house-coat wrapped around her like a shawl and her hair was uncombed. The blinds were drawn.

'How do you feel?' Korolyov asked.

'All right, thank you.'

He felt her pulse and smoothed back her hair which had fallen down over her forehead.

'So you're not sleeping,' he said. 'It's lovely outside, spring has come. The nightingales are singing and here you are sitting in the dark, brooding.'

She listened and looked straight into his face. Her eyes were sad and clever, and clearly she longed to tell him something.

'Does this happen often?' he asked.

'Yes. I feel bad nearly every night.'

At that moment the watchman beat two o'clock. At those sharp metallic tapping sounds she trembled.

'Does that noise bother you?'

'I'm not sure. Everything here bothers me,' she replied and became thoughtful. 'Everything. I can tell from your voice that you're concerned and the moment I saw you I sensed I could confide in someone like you—about everything.'

'Please do tell me then.'

'I'd like to tell you what *I* think. It seems that I'm not ill, and I'm worried and terrified for that reason, and because things can't possibly change. Even the healthiest man can't help worrying—for example, if there's a burglar lurking beneath his window.' She looked down at her knees with a timid smile and then continued, 'I'm always having medical treatment and of course I'm thankful and I wouldn't say it's all a waste of time. I don't want to talk to doctors, though, but to someone close to me, a friend who would understand me and could convince me whether I'm right or wrong.'

'Don't you have any friends?' Korolyov asked.

'I'm all on my own. There's my mother, and I love her, but I'm still alone. That's how my life has turned out . . . Lonely people read a great deal, but they don't say much and they don't listen. Life is a mystery for them. People like these are mystics and often see the devil when he's not there at all. Lermontov's Tamara was lonely and she saw the devil.'

'Do you read a lot?'

'Yes, a lot. As you can see, my time is my own from morning till night. I read during the day but at night-time my head is empty and instead of thoughts there are dark shadows.'

'Do you see things at night?' Korolyov asked.

'No, but I sense . . .'

She smiled again at the doctor and gave him such a sad, knowing look. He felt that she trusted him, that she wanted to have a heart-to-heart talk and that she thought about things as he did. But she did not speak and perhaps she was waiting for him.

He knew what he should say to her. There was no doubt in his mind that she should give up those five factory blocks and the million roubles—assuming she had that much—as soon as possible, and that devil who watched her at night. Quite obviously she thought the same and was only waiting for someone she trusted to confirm it.

But he did not know how to put it into words. How could he? One is reluctant to ask convicted persons the reason for their conviction, and in the same way it's awkward asking very wealthy people why they are so rich, why they put their wealth to such bad use, why they don't give it away, even when they can see that it's the reason for their unhappiness. Any discussions on the subject usually turn out to be inhibited, embarrassed and overlong.

'How can I tell her?' Korolyov wondered. 'And *should* I?'

And he told her what he wanted to—not straight out but in a rather roundabout way.

'You're unhappy being a factory owner and rich heiress, you don't believe in your own rights, and now you can't sleep. Of course this is better than being contented, sleeping soundly and thinking all's well with the world. Your insomnia is something *honourable*: whatever you may think, it's a good sign. In actual fact the conversation we're having now would be unthinkable for our parents. They never discussed things at night, but slept soundly. But our generation sleeps badly, we become weary and feel we can find the answers to everything, whether we're right or wrong. The problem whether they are right or wrong will already have been solved for our children or grandchildren. They will see things more clearly than us. Life will be good in fifty years' time and it's a pity we shan't live till then. It would have been interesting to see.'

'What will our children and grandchildren do?' Lisa asked.

'I don't know . . . probably abandon everything and go away somewhere.'

'Where?'

'Where? . . . Anywhere they like,' Korolyov said, laughing. 'There's no shortage of places for a good, clever man.'

He looked at his watch.

'The sun's up already,' he said. 'It's time you got some sleep. Undress and have a good rest now.'

As he shook her hand he added, 'I'm very glad I met you. You're a wonderful, interesting person. Good night!'

He went to his room and climbed into bed.

Next morning, when the carriage was brought round, everyone went on to the front steps to say goodbye. Liza was dressed in her Sunday best, in a white dress, with a flower in her hair; she looked pale, lifeless. She glanced at him sadly and knowingly, as she had the day before, smiled, and her tone of voice suggested she wished to tell him (and him alone) something quite special and important. The larks were singing and the church bells rang out. The factory windows shone cheerfully and, as he drove across the yard and then along the road to the station, Korolyov had forgotten all about factory workers, pile-dwellings, the devil, and was thinking of the time—perhaps not far away—when life would be just as radiant and joyful as that calm Sunday morning. And he thought how pleasant it was riding in a fine troika that spring morning and warming himself in the sun.

ALEXANDER PUSHKIN

Pushkin's 1830 poem is typical of a great many insomnia poems, being both a little gloomy and resigned, and persists with the question that all insomniacs ask: why can't I sleep? (Pushkin will not answer of course.)

Born in 1799, Pushkin died in 1837 during a duel.

Lines Written at Night During Insomnia

I can't sleep; no light burns;
All round, darkness, irksome sleep.
Only the monotonous
Ticking of the clock,
The old wives' chatter of fate,
Trembling of the sleeping night,
Mouse-like scurrying of life . . .
Why do you disturb me?
What do you mean, tedious whispers?
Is it the day I have wasted
Reproaching me or murmuring?
What do you want from me?
Are you calling me or prophesying?
I want to understand you,
I seek a meaning in you . . .

Mary Shelley

In 1816 Mary Shelley, her husband Percy, the poet, and Lord Byron summered together in Geneva. As Shelly explains in her introduction to Frankenstein, *it was there that she conceived the story.*

Mary Wollstonecraft Godwin Shelley was born in London in 1797 to Mary Wollstonecraft. She died in 1851.

Frankenstein

Many and long were the conversations between Lord Byron and Shelley, to which I was a devout but nearly silent listener. During one of these, various philosophical doctrines were discussed, and among others the nature of the principle of life, and whether there was any probability of its ever being discovered and communicated. They talked of the experiments of Dr Darwin, (I speak not of what the Doctor really did, or said that he did, but, as more to my purpose, of what was then spoken of as having been done by him,) who preserved a piece of vermicelli in a glass case, till by some extraordinary means it began to move with voluntary motion. Not thus, after all, would life be given. Perhaps a corpse would be re-animated; galvanism had given token of such things: perhaps the component parts of a creature might be manufactured, brought together, and endued with vital warmth.

Night waned upon this talk, and even the witching hour had gone by, before we retired to rest. When I placed my head on my pillow, I did not sleep, not could I be said to think. My imagination, unbidden, possessed and guided me, gifting the successive images that arose in my mind with a vividness far beyond the usual bounds of reverie, I saw—with shut eyes, but acute mental vision,—I saw the pale student of unhallowed arts kneeling beside the thing he had put together. I saw the hideous phantasm of a man stretched out, and then, on the working of some powerful engine, show signs of life, and stir with an uneasy, half vital motion. Frightful must it be; for supremely frightful would be the effect of any human endeavour to mock the stupendous mechanism of the Creator of the world. His success would terrify the artist; he would rush away from his odious handy-work, horror-stricken. He would hope that, left to itself, the slight spark of life which he had communicated would fade; that this thing, which had received such imperfect animation, would subside into dead matter; and he might sleep in the belief that the silence of the grave would quench for ever the transient existence of the hideous corpse which he had looked upon as the cradle of life. He sleeps; but he is awakened; he opens his eyes; behold the horrid thing stands at his bedside, opening his curtains, and looking on him with yellow, watery, but speculative eyes.

I opened mine in terror. The idea so possessed my mind, that a thrill of fear ran through me, and I wished to exchange the ghastly image of my fancy for the realities around. I see them still; the very room, the dark *parquet*, the closed shutters, with the moonlight struggling through, and the sense I had that the glassy lake and white high Alps were beyond. I could not so easily get rid of my hideous phantom; still it haunted me. I must try to think of something else. I recurred to my ghost story,—my tiresome unlucky ghost story! O! if I could only contrive one which would frighten my readers as I myself had been frightened that night!

Swift as light and as cheering was the idea that broke in upon me. 'I have found it! What terrified me will terrify others; and I need only describe the spectre which had haunted my midnight pillow.' On the morrow I announced that I had *thought of a story*. I began that day with the words, *It was on a dreary night of November*, making only a transcript of the grim terrors of my waking dream . . .

M.W.S.

London, October 15, 1831

Phillip K. Dick

Empty Apartments *is the book that inspired the film* Bladerunner. *Earth has been depopulated following a 'World War Terminus' which released so much radioactivity that entire human populations, and insect, plant and animal species were wiped out. Immigration to Mars is encouraged, but a few people stay on. In the extract below, the android-hunter, Rick Decard, and his wife Iran, are talking one grey morning on waking up.*

Dick is an American science-fiction writer, born in Chicago in 1928.

Empty Apartments

'. . . and then the awful commercial came on, the one I hate; you know, for Mountibank Lead Codpieces. And so for a minute I shut off the sound. And I heard the building, this building; I heard the—' She gestured.

'Empty apartments,' Rick said. Sometimes he heard them at night when he was supposed to be asleep. And yet, for this day and age a one-half occupied building rated high in the scheme of population density; out in what had been before the war the suburbs one could find buildings entirely empty . . . or so he had heard. He had let the information remain second-hand; like most people he did not care to experience it directly.

PATRICK WHITE

This short extract is taken from White's novel Voss,
*a story based on the explorer Leichhardt's adventures
in central Australia. In 1945 Johann Ulrich Voss sets
out with a band of men, horses, sheep, goats and
cattle; Palfreyman, an ornithologist, is one of his
company.*

Born in 1912, White won the Nobel Prize for Literature in 1970, dying in 1990.

Sleepwalking

Heavy moons hung above Jildra at that season. There was a golden moon, of placid, swollen belly. There were the ugly, bronze, male moons, threateningly lopsided. One night of wind and dust, there was a pale moonstone, or, as rags of cloud polished its face, delicate glass instruments, on which the needle barely fluttered, indicating the direction that some starry destiny must take. The dreams of men were influenced by the various moons, with the result that they were burying their faces in the pregnant moon-women, of shaking their bronze fists at any threat to their virility. Their dreams eluded them, however, under the indicator of that magnetic moon. The white dust poured out from between their fingers, as they turned and turned on hairy blankets that provoked their nakedness. On the other hand, there were some who lay and listened to their own eyelids grate endlessly.

Such was the predicament of Palfreyman on one particularly white night. Unable to sleep, he had passed the time reviewing houses in which he had lived, minor indignities he had suffered, and one tremendous joy, a white eagle fluttering for a moment on the branch of a dead tree and almost blotting out the sky with the span of its wings.

The sound of the strong feathers, heard again above the squeak of mice and groans of sleep in Boyle's squalid shack, had almost freed the wakeful Palfreyman, when Voss rose.

There he was, striped by moonlight and darkness, the stale air moving round him, very softly. Voss himself did not move. Rather was he moved by a dream, Palfreyman sensed. Through some trick of moonlight or uncertainty of behaviour, the head became detached for a second and appeared to have been fixed upon a beam of the wooden wall. The mouth and the eyes were visible. Palfreyman shivered. Ah, Christ is an evil dream, he feared, and all my life I have been deceived. After the bones of the naked Christ had been drawn through the fetid room, by sheets of moonlight, and out the doorway, the fully conscious witness continued to lie on his blanket, face to face with his own shortcomings and his greatest error.

But there was an end to this unhappiness, he was surprised to find. The moonlight returned Voss to the room. As he was moved back, his bones were creaking, and his skin had erupted in a greenish verdigris.

Palfreyman nearly put out his hand, to recall them both to their normal relationship, but was restrained by an access of cold.

Next morning he remarked:

'Mr Voss, do you know you were sleep-walking last night?'

The German was engaged in putting on his socks, his backbone exposed to his accuser.

'I have never been known to, before. Never,' he replied, but most irritably, as if refusing a crime with which he had been unjustly charged.

Boyle, who had just then come through the partition, scratching an armpit, felt compelled to say:

'We welcome you, Voss, through the gate of human weaknesses.'

NIGHT WATCHES

CHARMIAN CLIFT

Clift was born in the seaside town of Kiama in 1923. She loved to travel and lived on the Greek island of Kalymnos for some years before returning to Australia. 'Things that go Boomp' is one of the many essays that she wrote for the women's pages of the Sydney Morning Herald *and the Melbourne* Herald *(with syndications in other newspapers) from the 1960s until her suicide in 1969. She was regarded as very cosmopolitan by Anglo-Australians in the 1960s, and so the places and experiences suggested by the essay would have held a special interest for local readers. Clift's novels include* Mermaid Singing *and* Peel Me a Lotus.

Things that go Boomp in the Night

Lately, having galloped up all unwitting and unprepared to one of those crossroads that are forever complicating the straight and simple way of things with the necessity for pause and choice and decision, I have been awake often at night.

I don't know whether I have something positively nefarious in my nature—and am reminded suddenly that one of my ancestors was reputedly hanged at Tyburn Tree for his midnight exploits as a gentleman of the roads (I say reputedly because all my family were terrible liars and inventors and embroiderers, and could well have made it up)—but I have always loved nocturnal prowling in a house where everybody else is sleeping.

Perhaps, in a busy and eventful life, these night-watches are the only times when one can ever be truly alone, and there is a sort of elation in this, a sense of quickened heartbeats, of heightened perceptions, of self-surprise. Of complicity even.

Lodged in my head is a line from a poem read somewhere once in some anthology and never tracked down since. I read it then and remember it now with a sharp sting of recognition.

'How strange we grow when we're alone and how unlike our other selves who talk and laugh and put the candles out and say goodnight . . .'

And it is not only that we ourselves grow strange. Our familiar surroundings grow strange too. A house at night, at the full ebb of the tide of human activity that has crashed and surged through it all day, is eloquent with its own life. It breathes and sighs and creaks with relaxation. You can hear it easing itself out of the seams, as it were, and settling a fraction more comfortably on its foundations. The loose window you had so firmly and definitely closed has opened itself enticingly to the night insects, the cupboard door to the ants: there are scuttlings and scurryings and rustlings it would be better, perhaps, not to investigate. If you flick a light switch suddenly the revealed room has a look both bland and furtive, as though it had composed itself just in time not to be caught out.

I don't find these manifestations of a house's individuality at all frightening. Much more inimical are the mechanical noises, especially in an old house where machines have been imposed on it long after the personality of the place has declared itself and developed its own eccentricities.

Padding quietly down the darkened hall towards the stealthy indulgence of coffee and cigarettes one is paralysed into immobility as the low purr of the refrigerator changes to a sort of shuddering snort and all the milk bottles chatter dementedly. Downstairs the hot water system makes an intermittent gulping sound, wrathful somehow, biding its time, and—after fifteen minutes of pretending not to hear it—that soft sinister intrusive whirring from the living room is identified as the record player that somebody, carelessly, forgot to switch off.

Streets away there is the wild high agonised squeal of tyres and brakes. With dry mouth and prickling scalp one waits for the hideous crash of metal and glass . . . and waits . . . and waits . . . and the room heater thrums on, indifferent and unwearied, and the clock fills up the silence neatly and with precision: so loud: one had never noticed before.

Yet under the mechanical sounds are the reassuring human ones, close and familiar, breathings and turnings and sleep-

mutterings, and the coffee is scalding and bitter and good—
better than it ever tastes at any other time, like the
cigarette—and one can let one's thoughts go nosing down
strange new corridors of possibility, never suspected in all the
busy day, or drift back in exploration of old stores of experience
without urgency or haste or distraction.

I was thinking, on one of my prowls the other night, of other
cups of coffee, other cigarettes, other wakeful hours in other
places.

Ships' decks and shepherds' huts and pebbled beaches and
herb-hung kitchens and terraces dazzling with moonlight.
Then the coffee was thick and black, brewed Turkish style on
a few coals still glowing in the charcoal brazier, and the
cigarettes were that sharp acrid Macedonian tobacco to which
one so quickly becomes addicted, and the night-light was the
moon or the stars or a kerosene lamp turned low.

The night sounds were of bells mostly, thin drifts of them
from high sheepfolds, or the clamour of cockerels gone a bit
mental and hurling imprecations, dogs howling, the demonia-
cal screaming of love-maddened cats swarming on roof-tiles
and garden walls, and sometimes, in the spring, the pure sweet
notes of a little night owl, Athena's symbol of wisdom, dropped
separately into the darkness from a mountain top.

I am glad of all those wakeful nights. I might never have
got to know the Pleiades so well otherwise, or plotted the
nightly course of the gri-gri boats. Over against the mainland
their acetylene lamps made as lovely a constellation on the
black silky water as the Pleiades overhead, and I used to wish
that I might go with the boats sometime (only I was too
constrained by being a woman and a foreigner ever to ask)
and spear octopi in the moving cones of water lit before every
prow like brilliant green glass, and eat olives and cheese and
drink retsina and listen to tall fisher tales. Or tales of love
and revenge and supernatural happenings, which are the
proper things to discuss in such a setting at such an hour.

I used to think about the gri-gri boats years later, at a very
troubled time when we were staying in a Tudor farmhouse in
the Cotswolds. It was spring then, too, and aching cold in the
prowling hours with the fires sighing and whispering, and
there were more noises in the walls and the wainscotting than

I could ever identify, and Mau-Mau the Siamese cat with the crumpled ears used to prowl with me, arching and purring: she knew what I was about.

And instead of the gri-gri boats there would be the cackle and scrunch of boots on the frost-spiked grass outside, and the low buzz and burr of voices, and that would be Jack and Harry back from the lambing. And sometimes they would come in and let me look after the damp new lamb in front of the fire, and I would give them mugs of tea and cider, and we would sit and talk, as I knew we would, of lambing seasons past, and country lore, and tales of love and revenge and supernatural happenings.

So much of life goes on in the night. Here, in a city, I think of boats hooting and the melancholy sound of train whistles at sidings, of people hurtling through the night at impossible speeds, of destinations and departures, people running away from things, hurrying towards things. I think of border police and customs barriers, conspirators, lovers, city markets, hospitals, air terminals. I think of people watching, people waiting, people hiding and people searching, people dying and people being born.

And people, like me, who have talked and laughed and put the candles out and said good-night, and are prowling around in dark houses all over the place, being as strange as they please.

GWEN HARWOOD

The setting for a number of Gwen Harwood's Bone Scan *poems is hospital. There insomnia is experienced during sickness. It figures almost as a time away from the illness, a time to think and watch— private time.*

Born in 1920 in Australia, Harwood published collections of poetry from 1963 onwards. She died in 1995.

The Night Watch

I am lying like a creature
from outer space, equipped
for sound and colour vision,
in a capsule of discomfort.
Tubes issue from my body,
one taking, one receiving.

Here and there a window
in the hospital, the space ship,
glows and returns to blankness.
The night crew keep their stations.
Who can make sense of pain
with stars and clouds obscured

in a near-but-never darkness:
the backsides of old buildings
and the Savings Bank sign turning,
symbol of some bizarre
religion of this planet—
Invest and find salvation.

Save and be saved. No use
to me, I can save nothing.
Only watch, in my sleepless
journey towards a grounding
I dare not think about,
the neon sign revolving.

I know a bank . . . where
the wild thyme grows . . . indeed
time has grown wild and warped
near the black hole of oblivion:
mind beaten, body showing
its true colours to strangers.

O that tongue of cadmium red
in one of Miro's paintings!
Salveo, I am well.
Salvus, well, sound, unharmed,
entire, whole, safe, uninjured.
And salvia, scarlet sage—

what sage would lie here playing
intellectual variations
for a night, a thousand hours,
on a single neon sign.
Here there's no price on heroes.
Better to ring for sleep.

So the mercy of a needle
brings me to a rough landing:
the rubbish men are loading
unspeakable detritus,
crashing with cheerful shouts
through a freezing mortal morning.

And the bank, no doubt for reasons
of economy, has turned
its symbol off. The crescent
moon and the morning star
over the Lands Department
fade into greater light.

Marguerite Duras

Drinking and insomnia mark many of Marguerite Duras' works. Her sleeplessness suggests ambivalent desire and feelings of dread and longing, all bound up with the loss of love. In the extract below, Maria has travelled to a town outside Madrid with her husband Pierre, child Judith, and friend Claire. They unexpectedly spend a night in the town because of a violent storm, bedding down in the corridors of an overcrowded hotel. Rodrigo Paestra has killed his young wife and her lover that morning and is hiding on the rooftops.

Duras has written for film and stage, but is best known for her restless fiction. She was born in 1914 at Gia-Dinh near Saigon.

10.30 on a Summer Night *dates from 1962.*

10.30 on a Summer Night

So much time went by that no trace of twilight was left in the sky.

'Don't expect any electricity tonight,' the manager of the hotel had said. 'Usually around here the storms are so violent that there's no electricity all night.'

There was no electricity. There were going to be more storms, more sudden showers throughout the night. The sky was still low and small, still whipped by a very strong wind, toward the west. The sky could be seen, perfectly arched up to the horizon. And the limits of the storm could be seen too, trying to take over more of the clearer part of the sky.

From the balcony where she was standing, Maria could see the whole expanse of the storm. They remained in the dining room.

'I'll be back,' Maria had said.

Behind her, in the corridor, all the children were now sleeping. Among them was Judith. When Maria turned around she saw her asleep, her body outlined in the soft light of the oil lamps hooked up on the walls.

'As soon as she's asleep, I'll come back,' Maria had told them.

Judith was asleep.

The hotel was full. The rooms, the corridors, and later on the hall, would be still more crowded. There were more people in the hotel than in a whole district of the town. The town, beyond which stretched deserted roads, all the way to Madrid, toward which the storm was moving since five o'clock, bursting here and there, its clouds breaking and then mending again. To the point of exhaustion. Until when? It was going to last all night.

There was no longer a single café open.

'We'll wait for you, Maria,' Pierre had said.

The town was small, it covered about five acres, all of it was crowded into an irregular, but full, neatly outlined shape. Beyond it, whichever way you turned, open country stretched out, bare, rolling (this was hardly noticeable that night, and yet, in the east, there seemed to be a sudden drop). A stream previously dried out, would overflow in the morning.

If you looked at the time it was ten o'clock. In the evening. It was summer.

Policemen were walking under the hotel balconies. They must have been tired from searching. They dragged their feet in the muddy streets. The crime had been committed a long time ago, hours ago, and they were talking about the weather.

'Rodrigo Paestra is on the rooftops.'

Maria remembered. The rooftops were there, they were empty. They were shining dimly under the balcony where she was standing. Empty.

They were waiting for her in the dining room in the midst of cleared tables, oblivious of her, looking at each other, motionless. The hotel was full. There was no other place for them to look at each other except there.

Whistling started again at the other end of the town, well beyond the square, in the direction of Madrid. Nothing happened. Policemen gathered at the street corner, on the left, stopped, moved off again. It was just a break in the waiting period. The policemen walked by under the balcony, and turned into another street.

It wasn't much later than ten. It was later than when she should have gone back to the dining room, entered, moved in between them, sat down, and told them once more the surprising news.

'I've been told that Rodrigo Paestra is hiding on the rooftops.'

She left the balcony, entered the hall and lay down next to her sleeping child, her own, the body which, among all the other children in the hall, belonged to her. She kissed her hair lightly.

'My life,' she said.

The child didn't wake up. She barely moved, sighed, and fell back into a calm sleep.

And the town was like her, already locked in sleep. Some still talked about Rodrigo Paestra whose wife was found naked next to Perez, both asleep after hours of love. And then dead. The nineteen-year-old body was in the town hall.

If Maria were to get up, if she were to go to the dining room, she could ask for a drink. She thought of the first sip of manzanilla in her mouth and the peace in her body that would follow. She didn't move. Beyond the hall, through the yellow and vacillating screen of the oil lamps, you could imagine the rooftops, covered with the moving sky, its darkness deepening. The sky was there, against the frame of the open balcony.

Maria got up, hesitant about going back to the dining room where they would still be immersed in the wonder of their overpowering desire, still alone in the midst of cleared tables and exhausted waiters who were waiting for them to leave, and whom they didn't see.

She walked back to the balcony, smoked a cigarette. The rain hadn't returned yet. It was slow. The sky was still brooding, it would still be a while. In the back of her, there were couples coming into the hall. They were speaking softly because of the children. They lay down. They kept quiet at first, hoping for sleep that did not come, and then they talked again. From everywhere, particularly from the crowded rooms,

came the muted sound of voices, regularly interrupted by the
fateful passing of the police.

After each passing, the conjugal hum started again, in the
rooms, in the circular corridors, the everyday sound, slow and
tired. Behind the doors, in the twin beds, in the embraces born
in the cool of the storm, there was talk of the summer, of this
summer storm, and of Rodrigo Paestra's crime.

At last the shower. In a few seconds it filled the streets.
The earth was too dry and couldn't drink up so much rain.
The trees on the square were twisted by the wind. Maria could
see their tops appear and disappear behind the angle of the
roofs and, when lightning lit up the town and the open country,
in its livid illumination, she could at the same time see Rodrigo
Paestra's motionless and drowned shape clutching a dark stone
chimney.

The shower lasted a few minutes. Calm returned as the
strength of the wind weakened. A vague glimmering, so long
hoped for, descended from the appeased sky. And in this
glimmering, which increased as you hoped it would, but which
you knew would quickly fade with the beginnings of another
phase of the storm, Maria could see the indefinite shape of
Rodrigo Paestra, Rodrigo Paestra's dazzling, shrieking and
indefinite shape.

Again the police started their search. They returned as the
storm subsided. They marched through the mud again. Maria
leaned over the railing of the balcony and saw them. One of
them laughed. At regular intervals, the whole town rang with
the sound of whistling. Just more pauses in the waiting period,
which was going to last until morning.

In addition to the balcony where Maria was standing, there
were others on the north side of the hotel. They were empty,
except one, just one, on Maria's right, one flight above. They
must have been there for a very short time. Maria hadn't seen
them arrive. She moved back slightly into the corridor where
people were now asleep.

This must have been the first time they had kissed. Maria
put out her cigarette. She could see them fully outlined against
the moving sky. While Pierre kissed her, his hands touched
Claire's breasts. They were probably talking. But very softly.
They must have been speaking the first words of love.

Irrepressible, bursting words which came to their lips between two kisses.

The lightning made the town look livid. It was unforeseeable, striking irregularly. But every time it made their kisses livid too, as well as their single, nearly blinding shape. Was it on her eyes, behind the screen formed by the dark sky, that he had first kissed her? How could one know? Your eyes were the colour of your fear in the afternoon, the colour of rain at that very moment, Claire, your eyes, I could hardly see them, how could I have noticed it before, your eyes must be gray.

Opposite these kisses, a few yards away, Rodrigo Paestra wrapped in his brown blanket was waiting for the infernal night to end. At dawn, it would be all over.

A new phase of the storm was coming up that was going to separate them and prevent Maria from seeing them.

As he did it, so did she, bringing her hands to her lonely breasts, then her hands fell and, useless, grasped the balcony. While she had moved too far out onto the balcony while they were merging into a single, nearly blinding shape, she now moved back a little from the balcony, towards the corridor where the new wind was already sweeping into the lamp chimneys. No, she couldn't help seeing them. She could still see them. And their shadows were on that roof. Now their bodies broke apart. The wind raised her skirt, and, in a flash, they laughed. The same wind that had raised her skirt, again crossed the whole town, bumping up against the edges of the rooftops.

Two more minutes, and the storm would come, sweeping over the whole town, emptying the streets, the balconies. He must have stepped back in order to hold her better, to be reunited with her for the first time, their happiness intensified by the suffering he created by holding her far from him. They didn't know, they were still unaware that the storm would separate them for the night.

More waiting. And the impatience of the waiting grew so intense it reached its climax, and at last calm set in. One of Pierre's hands was moving all over another woman's body. His other hand held her close against him. It was done now, forever.

It was ten-thirty. And summer.

And then it was a little later. Night had come at last, completely. There was no room that night, in that town, for love. Maria lowered her eyes before this reality: their thirst for love would remain unfulfilled, the town was bulging, in this summer night made for their love. The flashes of lightning kept lighting up the shape of their desire. They were still there, folded in each other's arms, and motionless, his hand now resting on her hip, hers forever, while she, she, her hands unable to move as they clung to his shoulders, her mouth against his mouth, she was devouring him.

The same flashes, at the same time, lit up the roof opposite them and on its top, around a chimney, the shrouded shape of Rodrigo Paestra, the murderer.

The wind increased, swept into the hallway and moved over the sleeping children. A lamp had gone out. But nothing would wake them. The town was dark and asleep. In the rooms there was silence. Judith was good.

They had disappeared from the balcony as suddenly as they had come. He must have led her away without letting go of her—how could he—into the shadow of the sleeping corridor. The balcony was deserted. Maria looked at her watch once again. It was almost eleven. Because of the wind that was still growing stronger, one of the children—it wasn't that one—uttered a cry, isolated, turned over and fell back to sleep.

The rain. And again its ineffable smell, its lifeless smell of muddy streets. Just as it did on the fields, the rain was falling on the dead shape of Rodrigo Paestra, dead of sorrow, dead of love.

Where could they have found a place to be together that night, in that hotel? Where would he take off her light skirt, that very night? How beautiful she is. How beautiful you are, God how beautiful. With the rain, their shapes had vanished from the balcony.

Summer was everywhere, in the rain, in the streets, in the courtyards, in the bathrooms, in the kitchens, summer, everywhere, summer was everywhere for their love. Maria stretched, went back in, lay down in the hallway, stretched again. Was it done now? Perhaps there was no one in another dark, stifling corridor—could anyone know all of them?—the corridor extending from their balcony, for example, right above this one, in this miraculously forgotten corridor, along the wall, on the floor, was it done?

Tomorrow would be there in a few hours. You had to wait. The shower was longer than the previous one. It kept coming down with force. And also on the skylight, echoing horribly throughout the hotel.

'We waited for you, Maria,' Pierre said.

They appeared with the end of the shower. She saw their two shadows move towards her while she was lying next to Judith, two huge shadows. Claire's skirt had risen above her knees, bulging around her hips. The wind in the corridor. Too fast. They hadn't had much time between leaving the balcony and arriving there, next to Maria. They were smiling. So that hope had been foolish. Love hadn't been fulfilled that night in the hotel. More waiting. The rest of the night.

'You said you would be back, Maria,' Pierre said again.

'Well, I was tired.'

She had seen him looking for her on the floor of the corridor carefully, almost walk past her, and stop in front of her; she was the last one, just where the corridor ended, engulfed in the darkness of the dining room. Claire was following him.

'Well,' Maria repeated—she was pointing at Judith—'she would have been afraid.'

Pierre smiled. He stopped looking at Maria and discovered an open window leading onto a balcony at the end of the corridor.

'What weather,' he said.

He brushed away his discovery of the window at the very moment he made it. Was it fear?

'And it will last all night,' he said. 'It will end by daybreak.'

She could have told just from his voice, trembling, shaky, affected by desire for that woman.

Then Claire also smiled at Judith. At the small, lopsided shape, wrapped in a brown blanket. Her hair was still wet from the rain on the balcony. Her eyes in the yellow light of the oil lamp. Your eyes, blue stones. I'll eat your eyes, he was telling her, your eyes. The youthfulness of her breasts showed clearly under her white sweater. Her blue gaze was haggard, paralysed by frustration, by the very fulfilment of frustration. Her gaze left Judith and moved back to Pierre.

'Did you go back to a café, Maria?'

'No. I stayed here.'

'A good thing we didn't leave for Madrid,' Pierre said. 'You see.'

He turned again toward the open window.

'A good thing, yes.'

In the street alongside the hotel, a whistle rang out. Was it over? There was no second whistle. The three of them waited. No. Once more, just a pause in the waiting period. Steps made heavy by the mud in the streets moved toward the northern part of town. They didn't talk about it.

'She isn't warm tonight,' Claire said.

Maria stroked Judith's forehead.

'Not really. Less than usual. It's comfortable.'

Maria could have told just from Claire's breasts that they were in love. They were going to lie down there, next to her, separated while torn and tortured by desire. And both were smiling, equally guilty, terrified and happy.

'We waited for you,' Pierre repeated.

Even Claire raised her eyes. Then she lowered them and only a vague, indelible smile remained on her face. Maria would have known just from seeing her eyes lowered on that smile. What glory. On what glory were those eyes closing? They must have looked, looked all over the hotel for a spot. It had been impossible. They had had to give up. Pierre had said Maria is waiting for us. What a future ahead of them, the days to come.

Pierre's hands were dangling beside him. For eight years they had caressed her body. Now Claire was stepping into the misfortune that flowed straight from those hands.

'I'm going to sleep,' she announced.

She took a blanket that had been put on a table. She wrapped herself in it, still laughing, and, with a sigh, stretched out below the oil lamp. Pierre did not move.

'I'm sleeping,' Claire said.

Pierre also took a blanket, then lay down next to Maria, on the other side of the corridor.

Did Rodrigo Paestra still exist, there, twenty yards from them? Yes. The police had again walked by in the street. Claire sighed again.

'Ah, I'm already asleep,' she said. 'Good night, Maria.'

'Good night, Claire.'

Pierre lit a cigarette. The sound of regular breathing rose in the freshness of the corridor, in its odour of rain and of Claire.

'It's very pleasant,' Pierre said softly.

Some time went by. Maria should have told Pierre again: 'You know, it's crazy, but Rodrigo Paestra is really there, on the roof. Opposite. And with daybreak, he'll be caught.'

Maria said nothing.

'You're tired, Maria?' Pierre asked even more softly.

'Less than usual. The storm I suppose. It feels better.'

'Yes,' Claire said, 'we're less tired than the other nights.'

She wasn't sleeping. A gust of wind put out the last light. Lightning again at the end of the corridor. Maria turned slightly, but you couldn't see the roof from where they were.

'It will never stop,' Pierre said. 'Do you want me to put the light back on, Maria?'

'It's not worth it. I like it like that.'

'I like it too,' Claire went on again.

She stopped talking. Maria knew it: Pierre was hoping she would fall asleep. He was no longer smoking and lay motionless against the wall. But Claire was talking again.

'Tomorrow,' she said, 'we'll have to reserve rooms in Madrid by noon.'

'We should, yes.'

She yawned. Pierre and Maria were waiting for her to fall asleep. It was raining hard. Can you die if you want to from having to bear the brunt of a storm? Maria seemed to remember that it was Rodrigo Paestra's dead shape that she had seen on the roof.

Maria knew that Pierre wasn't sleeping, that he was aware of her, Maria, his wife, and that the desire he felt for Claire, was becoming corrupted by the memory of his wife; that he was becoming gloomy for fear she had guessed something; that he was disturbed at the thought of Maria's new loneliness, tonight, compared to what had been before.

'Are you sleeping?'

'No.'

They had spoken very softly once more. They were waiting. Yes, this, time, Claire was asleep.

'What time is it?' Maria asked.

With the end of the rain, there came the policeman whom Rodrigo Paestra must have also heard. Pierre looked at his watch in the light of the cigarette he had just started.

'Eleven twenty. Do you want a cigarette?'

Maria did.

'It's already lighter,' Pierre said. 'Maybe it's clearing up now. Here, Maria.'

He handed it to her. They sat up a little, just long enough for him to light it, then they lay down again. At the end of the corridor, Maria saw the dark blue screen of the balcony.

'Nights like this are so long,' Pierre said.

'Yes. Try to sleep.'

'And you?'

'I would like a manzanilla. But it's impossible.'

Pierre waited before answering. A last cloudburst, very light, fell on Rodrigo Paestra. You could hear singing and laughing in the street. The police, once again. But in the corridor all was quiet.

'Won't you try to drink a little less, Maria? Just once?'

'No,' Maria said. 'No more.'

The earthy smell came up from the street, endless, the smell of tears along with its complement, the smell of wet, fully ripened wheat. Was she going to tell him: 'It's crazy, Pierre, but Rodrigo Paestra is there. There. Right there. And with daybreak he will be caught.'

She said nothing. It was he who spoke.

'You remember? Verona?'

'Yes.'

If he reached out, Pierre would touch Maria's hair. He had spoken of Verona. Of love all night, the two of them, in a bathroom in Verona. A storm too, and it was summer, and the hotel was full. 'Come, Maria.' He was wondering. 'When, when will I have enough of you?'

'Give me another cigarette,' Maria said.

He gave it to her. This time she didn't sit up.

'If I spoke to you about Verona, it's because I couldn't help it.'

The smell of mud and wheat came in whiffs into the corridor. The hotel was bathed in this odour, as well as the town. Rodrigo Paestra and his dead, and the inexhaustible but perfectly vain memory of a night of love in Verona.

Claire was sleeping soundly. Then she turned suddenly and moaned because of the recent stir of Pierre's hands, that night, on her body. Pierre also heard Claire's moan. It was over. Claire grew quiet. And Maria next to Pierre only heard the sound of children breathing, and the police kept marching by more and more regularly as morning came closer.

'You're not asleep?'

'No,' said Maria. 'What time is it?'

'A quarter to twelve'—he was waiting. 'Here, have another cigarette.'

'All right. At what time is dawn in Spain?'

'Very early at this time of year.'

'I wanted to tell you, Pierre.'

She took the cigarette that he was holding out to her. Her hand trembled a little. He waited until he was lying down again before asking her.

'What do you want to tell me, Maria?'

Pierre waited a long time for an answer which didn't come. He didn't insist. Both of them were smoking, lying on their backs because of the tiles that bruised their hips. You had to suffer this bruise as best you could. She couldn't remove the free end of Judith's blanket that was covering her without being exposed to Pierre's look. She could only try to close her eyes between each puff of her cigarette, open them again, without moving at all, keeping quiet.

'Lucky we found this hotel,' Pierre said.

'Lucky, yes.'

He was smoking faster than she. He had finished his cigarette. He put it out in the narrow space between him and Maria, in the middle of the corridor, between the sleeping bodies. The showers lasted only a short length of time now, the length of one of Claire's sighs.

'You know, Maria. I love you.'

Maria also was through with her cigarette, she put it out, just like Pierre, on an empty tile in the corridor.

'Yes, I know,' she said.

What was happening? What was in the air? Was this really the end of the storm? Whenever there were showers, it was like pails of water spilled on the skylight and the roofs. A sound of showering that would only last a few seconds. They should have fallen asleep before this phase of the storm. Have accepted the idea of this last night before this moment.

'You must sleep, Maria.'

'Yes. But the noise,' she said.

She could do it, she could turn over and find herself right against him. They would get up. They would go away together far from Claire's sleep whose memory would grow dimmer with the passing of night. He knew it.

'Maria, Maria. You are my love.'

'Yes.'

She hadn't moved. In the street, more whistling announced that dawn was close, always closer. There was no more lightning, except weak and far away. Claire moaned again because of the memory of Pierre's hands clasping her hips. But that too you became accustomed to like the soft scraping noise of the children breathing. And the smell of rain engulfed the uniqueness of Claire's desire, mixing it with the sea of desire which, that night, raged through the town.

Maria sat up quietly, hardly turned toward him, stopped moving and looked at him.

'It's crazy, but I saw Rodrigo Paestra. He is there on the roof.'

Pierre was asleep. He had just fallen asleep, as suddenly as a child. Maria remembered that it had always been like that.

He was sleeping. Her need to be sure was funny. Hadn't she been sure?

She sat up a little more. He didn't move. She got up completely, brushed against his body, freed, lonely, abandoned in its sleep.

When Maria reached the balcony, she looked at the time she carried with her on her wrist, her time. It was half past midnight. In about three hours, at this time of year, it would be dawn. Rodrigo Paestra, the same statue of death she had seen earlier, was waiting for this dawn, and to be killed.

Oscar Wilde

In this extract, the narrator speaks for a condemned man. In the days leading up to the hanging he watches the condemned man walk the trial yard, and is surprised that the man can look with wistfulness and cheer at the 'little tent of blue sky above', just as on the eve of his death he wonders that the man can sleep. Unable to sleep himself, the narrator watches over his fellow prisoner, imagining his hell to come. The last lines of this extract remark poignantly on a writer's ability to empathise with others' deaths.

Wilde himself spent two years in jail. He was born in Ireland in 1854 and died in Paris in 1900.

The Ballad of Reading Gaol

That night the empty corridors
   Were full of forms of Fear,
And up and down the iron town
   Stole feet we could not hear,
And through the bars that hide the stars
   White faces seemed to peer.

He lay as one who lies and dreams
   In a pleasant meadow-land,
The watchers watched him as he slept,
   And could not understand
How one could sleep so sweet a sleep
   With a hangman close at hand.

But there is no sleep when men must weep
   Who never yet have wept:
So we—the fool, the fraud, the knave—
   That endless vigil kept,
And through each brain on hands of pain
   Another's terror crept.

Alas! it is a fearful thing
    To feel another's guilt!
For, right, within, the Sword of Sin
    Pierced to its poisoned hilt,
And as molten lead were the tears we shed
    For the blood we had not spilt.

The warders with their shoes of felt
    Crept by each padlocked door,
And peeped and saw, with eyes of awe,
    Grey figures on the floor,
And wondered why men knelt to pray
    Who never prayed before.

All through the night we knelt and prayed,
    Mad mourners of a corse!
The troubled plumes of midnight shook
    The plumes upon a hearse:
And bitter wine upon a sponge
    Was the savour of Remorse.

The grey cock crew, the red cock crew,
    But never came the day:
And crooked shapes of Terror crouched,
    In the corners where we lay:

We waited for the stroke of eight:
    Each tongue was thick with thirst:
For the stroke of eight is the stroke of Fate
    That makes a man accursed,
And Fate will use a running noose
    For the best man and the worst.

We had no other thing to do,
    Save to wait for the sign to come:
So, like things of stone in a valley lone,
    Quiet we sat and dumb:
But each man's heart beat thick and quick,
    Like a madman on a drum!

With sudden shock the prison-clock
    Smote on the shivering air,
And from all the gaol rose up a wail
    Of impotent despair,
Like the sound that frightened marshes hear
    From some leper in his lair.

And as one sees most fearful things
    In the crystal of a dream,
We saw the greasy hempen rope
    Hooked to the blackened beam,
And heard the prayer the hangman's snare
    Strangled into a scream.

And all the woe that moved him so
    That he gave that bitter cry,
And the wild regrets, and the bloody sweats,
    None knew so well as I:
For he who lives more lives than one
    More deaths than one must die.

IAN BECK

This story is taken from Jumping the Chasm, *first published in 1990. Bed, sleep, wakefulness, dreams, the past and of course the new morning, are all experienced with considerable ambivalence.*
Ian Beck was born in Sydney in 1948.

The Nightwatchman

On the centre pod of the starship an old man in Marine fatigues was looking at a supernova—an orange cloud with threads of black in it that rolled like exploding gasoline—and tapping a cigarette on the back of his hand. That's why you shouldn't smoke in bed, he said. I keep a glass of water handy in case that happens. Like Van Gogh in that painting. Sure, the man said. Van Gogh was standing before them, steaming in swirls of grey paint. But of course, that could have been a river, the man said. Then he was moving across a red plain at the level of a car's bumper bar, skimming over tiny cairns of stones and hoping the taller ones would not scrape his face. A tower the colour and texture of dried coral, and twisted like a unicorn's horn, rose on the horizon. Mars is like that, his guide said, and showed him a newspaper with a photograph of the scene, under the headline: Almost Like Home. A globe drifted above it, as aimless as a dandelion seed, and turned on its axis to show a pattern of continents and cloud cover. The light on its surface was golden and changed by stages into the glow of a tulip-shaped light fixture, its cup angled up and filled with yellow light, like a flower waiting for a humming-bird to spear it. The room beyond had the overly-opulent look of a casino. There were tapestries on the walls and a bed the width of a side-street. She was taller than he remembered. Her spectacles had left pinch-marks on the bridge of her nose, and there was a tiny linen flower between the cups of her brassiere. We never really did get together at your place, did we? she said. Always my place. You said you liked the fire.

They were in bed, naked against the sheets that clung to him
with the warm, exciting feel of a shower curtain against his
body. He buried his face in her hair and listened to the braying
hee-haw of a siren as an ambulance or fire-engine pulled up
in the street outside. Oh Valerie, he said, I love you so much.
I love you more than I've ever loved anyone. Sssh, she said.
Sssh, darling. Just move . . . Yes—like that. More like that.
That's the way. Not so fast though—not so rough. We've got
plenty of time. That's good. Like that. I'll always love you,
Valerie. That's right . . . keep going. He felt her rise under
him and her hands grip his buttocks. You're very physical, she
said. You know that? You're . . . really . . . quite physical. She
was slippery and warm—a lovely slippery river. A trickle of
sweat ran between her breasts, like a pearl sliding down a
string, and moved in an icy track down his stomach. She
shuddered and he rolled his face away from the downpour of
hair on the pillow and kissed her lips and forehead. It's all
right, she said. It's all right—you can come now. Oh darling,
he said, hold me—hold me. It's all right, she said. Just move
when I do . . . that's it. A bit faster. Faster, now. Across the
river the pine trees stood upright in the breeze. They did not
move. He was standing in the warm shadows of a forest where
the breeze did not reach, and the ground gave off the meaty
smell of a factory where hides are boiled. The branches of the
trees had squirmed around each other, the way shirts entwine
their arms when they come out of a washing machine, and
when he touched them their leaves rattled. He moved up a
path so steep he had to use both hands to get a purchase, and
stood on the crest of a hill covered with trees the heights of
young children. There was a valley beyond, with a housing
development on its far slope. The light was as gloomy as the
light under snow clouds. All the houses were brightly lit, but
there were no cars or people in the streets. The scene made
him uneasy. It seemed that all the life in the valley had been
taken in payment for some enormous debt—and yet things still
moved: a forest edged into the backyards of the houses and
black shapes soared above it, folding in on themselves and
expanding like jellyfish pumping against a current—and once,
moving down the slope towards the main street, he saw a grey
flash in the distance as a wolverine dog bounded through a

patch of mist. The street was deserted and walking along it he felt a strange unfolding dread, as though he was being dragged by inches to the edge of a precipice. He began knocking on doors and picture-windows and calling on whoever was inside to join him. Something was coming for them—something that stalked souls in a place where distances did not count— and they must all band together to fight it. But the houses were empty and his cries had the lack of resonance of statements in a dream. He ran into a shop with televisions and broken radios on its shelves. Christ was standing behind the counter. He was looking into a glass of blue wine and smiling with private knowledge. They shook hands. Like many short men, he had a ferocious handshake. My son, he said, you are—I regret to say—*misinformed*. Oh Jesus, he said, get me out of this place. It was coming for him now—silent, invisible; a presence so ageless and elemental that not even a collapsing universe could destroy it. It's just a dream, Christ said. That's not objective at all. Oh get me out, he said. Get me out! It was darkening the door and windows—a void that nothing could challenge, and life was the film that lay on it, as insubstantial as fingerprints on an anvil. You could try throwing a pen at it, Christ said. He was screaming now—screaming and rising, like a balloon filling with blasts of heated air from the jet under its canopy, and moving into the underside of a cloud the colour and texture of cured sheepskin.

A panel of light stretched across a ceiling and down a wall covered with Impressionist prints. There was something odd about its position in the room and for a moment he felt the same disorientation he had felt as a child, waking in the night and wondering what side of the bed he was sleeping on.

He kicked away the sheets and swung his legs from the bed. Although every window in the apartment was open, the air was motionless and packed with tropical heat.

His flat was on the top floor of a block that overlooked a retirement village—a complex of boxes on the side of a hill, with tiered gardens around a central administration block. At night, or whenever a dark storm approached, the grounds were lit by globes the size of meteorological balloons. They brought the glow of dawn on a cloudy day to the sheet that hung across the bedroom window, and projected panels of light onto the ceiling.

He moved to the window and pushed the sliding glass panel as far along its track as it would go. The air outside was stagnant and the brickwork along the sill warmed the palms of his hands.

The dream was still with him, but all he could remember of it was a street full of brightly-lit houses and a residue of dread, like the tea leaves in the cup his grandmother had once poured, and then carefully drained, to read the future.

He wiped the sweat from his eyebrows and flicked it into the void. If his flat had been another two storeys higher he would have felt uneasy looking down from that window. Christ, it was crazy. When he was a kid he had gone to building sites with his father and ridden to the top floors of apartment blocks in the giant buckets they used to carry concrete. Now he had to get three-quarters drunk to make it past the twentieth storey of an office tower. Where had that phobia come from— and why had it focused on heights?

There was no traffic in the street and the houses lining it seemed out of place and threatened, like the residential homes that survive as pay offices on factory sites. Beyond them, on the far side of a darkened suburb where hundred-year oaks canopied the street, skyscrapers blazed against a cloudy sky.

The silence was eerie. He was used to the hiss of air-brakes as container trucks turned onto the highway two blocks away, and drunken farewells cut short by the thud of car doors, but at that hour of the morning there was nothing—not even the click of a dog's nails on the pavement as it foraged around the garbage bins. He felt like the nightwatchman for an entire planet, on duty in a place where the air outside was poisoned.

It was close to dawn, but the lights were still on in the village's administration block and the glassed-in foyer where the residents ate their meals. Every three months they held a fete on the grounds. At the last one an old woman with skin the colour of tobacco and a growth on her face had told his youngest son not to touch anything until he had paid for it. He could see two of them in the foyer—sexless people in dressing gowns as garish as the robes professional wrestlers wore into the ring—talking to a nurse who looked too young for a nurse's duties.

An ambulance was parked outside. Its rear doors were open and the rotating light on its roof flicked over the grounds in slow pulses. In the shadow of the building its windscreen had the dusty-black look of the visor on a combat pilot's helmet.

Two men in uniform were wheeling a body on a stretcher through the foyer. The group parted to let them through, without glancing down or interrupting their conversation. The body was covered in a bag so heavily padded that from a distance it looked like the chrysalis of some enormous insect.

They slid it into the back of the ambulance and moved to the cabin with a funny springing stride, as though they were used to the gravity of a heavier planet, and turned off the flashing light. The night was so still he could hear snatches of their conversation and the squeak of the ambulance's suspension as it cleared a dip in the driveway and turned into the street. It moved off as slowly as a taxi cruising for a fare, and did not sound its siren.

He sat on the edge of the bed and breathed in the sickly, over-ripe smell of the apartment—the smell of malt in the sunlit corner of a brewery—and looked at his shadow on the wall. The backlighting had enlarged his head and shoulders to monolithic proportions and given his silhouette a brooding quality. In the half-light he looked like a giant in a Goya etching, pondering humanity's terror and despair while its representatives swarmed around his feet.

There was a packet of cigarettes and a lighter in the trough of shadows beside the bed, and he reached into it with his fingers spread wide, like a spider slowing to a landing on its thread, and probed around a half-full glass of water. The pack's cellophane wrapping was as moist as freshly-peeled skin and stuck to his fingertips.

He lit a cigarette and lifted an ashtray onto his thighs, tensing himself for the poultice of cold stone, but the unglazed terracotta had absorbed most of the warmth from the sill. The room was so hot he could feel the sweat trickling through his hair and the puckered flesh of fingers wrinkled by moisture. No-one could sleep in this heat, he thought. It was like being sown into the belly of an animal and left to die in a desert.

He lay back on the bed and blew a stream of smoke at the ceiling, and watched it burst in a perfectly symmetrical pattern, like the petals of a flower unfolding in a fast-action movie. It held its shape for a few seconds—an embossed ceiling picture with an ornate, translucent design—and then wilted and broke into separate strands that twisted around each other, as though the ghosts of serpents were fighting on the air.

There was a slight tremor in the heated bubble around him—a movement as faint as the expulsion of air from a lift's door—and the sound of something light—a sheet of newspaper or an advertising handbill—scraping the concrete outside. The smoke under the ceiling shivered for a moment before setting back into languid coils.

Maybe everything was a dream, he thought—like smoke, or something he had written. Maybe reality was something that existed only on the film of the senses, without depth or perspective, so that the furthest star was no more distant than the sparks that flashed behind your eyelids when you closed them.

But of course, it was not like that. All that was nonsense. There were parts in it as solid as the promontories waves broke against—things hard enough to cripple and kill—and beyond those outcrops, in the heart of a dark country that could only be reached in dreams, there was something much worse.

He ashed the cigarette, stubbing out the embers with the extinguished tip until the ashtray no longer glowed in the palm of his hand, and wiped the sweat from his forehead. Smoke hung a few inches from his face and stung his eyes as it fell, and he brushed it away and spread his arms and legs wide, ready to catch whatever disturbances the air could offer. The night was stale, and seemed to add new layers of heat to his body every moment. In a while, he thought, he would take a cold shower and go back to bed without drying himself, and wait until the sound of early-morning traffic in the street brought the illusion of air being torn into draughts.

It seemed he was breathing lukewarm water—forcing it into his lungs in soft lumps that swelled his throat, and expelling it through his skin. Each breath was an exercise, and his head throbbed from the strain of keeping his lungs working.

There was a rustling sound outside the apartment, as though the trees in the grounds of the retirement village were being hosed by a light spray, and the sound of paper sliding across stonework, but this time with enough force to pin itself against something and flutter there with the frantic snapping motions of the plastic strips of an electric fan.

A breeze was rising. He could hear it gaining strength and feel the sudden change of pressure on his eardrums. It moved along the side of the apartments like the slipstream beside a train and sent eddies of air into the room, gathering the smoke on the ceiling and dragging it out in a single continuous thread.

He felt it chill the soles of his feet and move up his thighs, and groaned as it reached the heated hollows of his groin. The feeling was luxurious—luxurious. It was as though someone was sprinkling cologne on his body. It was as though Valerie was with him again.

He drew the sheet up to his waist and took a deep breath of the renewed air. Christ, it was wonderful. He could feel the tension easing in his neck and shoulders and a beautiful physical exhaustion spreading through him, pinning him into place the way a small child is tucked into tight sheets by its mother. In a few minutes he would have to rearrange his body for sleep, before his limbs became too heavy to move.

The light on the ceiling had expanded and the edges of the shadows seemed sharper. It canopied the bed and gave him the feeling he was standing on the threshold of a brightly-lit room. If he could move through that doorway he would find himself in the kitchen of the country house his parents had once owned.

Those were the earliest times he could remember. His bed had been bigger then. He and his brother had made roads for their cars in its lumpy eiderdown. On the floor of the bedroom the linoleum had peeled away in places, and running in from the bath the corroded patches had felt like scabs on the soles of your feet. A hallway of painted boards had led to the kitchen and a giant wood-burning stove that reminded him of the bunkhouse scenes in cowboy movies and brought an exciting element of realism when you strapped on your six-guns and asked for a cup of Java.

The draught was chilling his exposed arms, but the cold and his body seemed a long way off and beyond the control of his will. Lying in that coolness was like camping near a waterfall, or sleeping on the verandah of the old house. On heat-wave nights he and his brother had slept on canvas folding beds in a corner of the verandah screened from insects. He remembered the way the netting had looked when the morning dew was on it, and the oily glow that developed on its surface, like the light on a dragonfly's wings, whenever a breeze swelled it inside its frame. The mesh had shimmered and obliterated the view of the yard in a silvery light, and then straightened and become transparent again.

It had been a good place for kids. There was a backyard with a clothes line long enough to accommodate the washing from a country hospital, and apple trees that had probably once been part of an orchard. The apples were small and glossy and snapped loud enough to be heard right across the yard when someone bit into them. If you had an apple after dinner you did not have to brush your teeth. The stems of their toothbrushes had plastic carvings of cartoon characters on them, and the toothpaste had come out in red and white stripes. It tasted like peppermint musk and had a picture of a chipmunk on the tube. The chipmunk moved through a pine forest and sang with a chorus of children. The tops of the pines swayed in time with the song and pinpoints of light spun on the chipmunk's teeth whenever he grinned. The crowd that followed was so densely packed the back rows had to march on the spot as the children in the leading ranks turned into the forest. He was marching with a friend from primary school, pumping his legs up and down so vigorously his knees reached his chest. Don't swing your elbows so much, his friend said— you hit me just then. The trees had faces halfway up their trunks and swayed their branches in the undulating movements of the hula dancers in movies. Brush, brush, up and down, the chipmunk sang, and you won't make the dentist frown. A baton that was really a drawing cartwheeled over their heads, and a crow with a beak full of pointed teeth swooped down and caught it. I'm going home early tomorrow, his friend said. Dad's driving to Sydney. He took a sodden handkerchief from his pocket and grimaced at something in its folds. We're going to Aunt Kathy's, and then we're going to buy a new car. They were marching beside a lake of stagnant water that looked as though it would ignite if a match was thrown on it. Charlie the Chipmunk was still singing, but his voice had developed a booming quality and seemed to be coming from the floor of the forest. The faces on the trees were not so pleasant now, and most of the sunlight had gone. For a while paper streamers had corkscrewed and coiled, and blizzards of confetti—as bright and insubstantial as the points of light that sweep around a ballroom under a mirrored globe— had dappled the trees, but now the light had a leaden quality, and the streamers seemed stuck to the air. He flicked something at a tree trunk—a pebble or glass marble—and heard it strike with the hiss of acid. The ranks around him had thinned to shuffling figures, as dispirited as a retreating army, and the ground was slippery underfoot. And then, like a burglar testing the lock on his door, something intruded on that part of his mind that was still close to consciousness—an animated dread that seemed to paralyse and imprison everything in its path. It moved on the fringes of his senses, flexing with the merciless precision of a snake working its jaws over its prey, and began rearranging the darkness to give itself shape. He watched it flutter and grow, and felt the same panic a man would feel looking down on his own autopsy, or sensing the jolt of the runners under his casket as it moved into a crematory oven. It was almost solid now, shadowing the walls and ceiling and working some inner core of darkness into a vaguely human shape—an outsized, corroded statue covered with patches of electric green, like bronze that had been buried in damp soil. Almost there, it said—almost with you now. Its voice was the sound of a wire brush scraping brickwork, or a blade on a grinding wheel. It had moved in from that suburb where the lights were always burning and the cloudcover hung like an inverted continent—and this time, he knew, there would be no escape. He could feel its breath on his neck, and smell the oily odour of meat in cold storage. The universe fell out of my arse, it said, and when your time comes I'll torture you to death, along with all the others. He was screaming now—the chirping, high-pitched scream of a cricket when a fish hook is being worked through its body. And then everything was gone—obliterated by a terror as pure and self-focusing as any physical pain. He was in a white place without sensations or emotions, where what remained of himself examined its existence with the same disinterest as a mathematician evaluating a new equation. Although he could not create or destroy, there was feeling of stasis—only the vague awareness that he was drifting, the way you would drift in a universe with more dimensions than you had known. The glare around him diminished, and he found himself standing on a factory floor. He could see the stencilled outlines where machinery had once stood, and pillars of light, as bright as the well in a movie projector, under the skylights. At the far end of the room a man with a short beard and greasy hair was standing beside a pool table and tapping the base of his cue on the concrete as he waited for his opponent to make a shot. My turn now, the man said. Have you been buying enough stamps? The balls on the table clicked and rattled and fell into a single pocket. I don't want another dream like that, he said. The man laughed—an unpleasant, disfiguring laugh. Nobody does, he said. The light around him was growing brighter—so bright he wished he had brought his sunglasses. You know who he is? the man said, gesturing with his pool cue at the brightly-lit figure beside him. He's the blade of grass that can cut a diamond. The light was so sharp now it seemed to be tugging at the back of his eyes. In a few seconds the whole room would collapse under its weight, like those glowing, transparent jellyfish that fell to pieces the moment you lifted them from the sand. Look, the man said, circling the table, I'll tell you this because I know you'll forget it in about two seconds. Life isn't a mystery—it's a secret; and when you've been initiated, you keep your mouth shut. You understand that? Yes, he said. A lot of grief for everyone if you don't, the man said, leaning forward for a shot. What was it? he said. The man frowned at a difficult set-up and slammed the cue ball into the pack with enough force to put every ball on the table in motion. It's the core of everything, he said. It's the complete absence of love. He felt himself slipping into that weird motion-within-motion you feel when a train on the far side of a platform moves away at a different speed to yours. What was it? he said. The man grinned. It's God, he said. What else? He turned towards the blaze of light that had once been a man and felt himself moving down, as though an earthquake had pushed up a fold of ground between them. A dirt road stretched through fields ploughed and ready for seeding, and as he walked along it he could hear his boots crunching pebbles and the buzz of flies feeding on the manure the iceman's horse had left. There were no laces in his boots and he had to lift his feet carefully to avoid stepping out of them. The road ahead was clear, and there was nothing following him. You can't run in those, his brother said—I'll give you my sneakers. They were moving along a tarred footpath, in light so bright it seemed to mist his eyes, as though he was seeing things through a membrane. I'm in Canada now, his brother said. Everyone's safe if they keep moving. From the air Canada was a series of ice floes, with polar bears yawning up at him in a misty blue light. The shadow of his helicopter swung out below him, rippling over the floes, and swept in close as he moved through a crevasse of ice. There were snowfields beyond, and a straight muddy road that seemed to tug his helicopter into alignment with it. He watched it pass overhead from the deck of a yacht, and accepted a drink from someone. Pennants fluttered in the yacht's rigging and far off, across a bay packed with boats, he could see circles of smoke as a line of cannons fired a salute. Then he was back in that sunlit kitchen, where the light shafted through a haze of flour, watching his mother poke a straw into a cake to see if its centre had cooked properly. Then it was morning, and for a moment it seemed his whole past lay ahead of him, at the foot of the bed.

EDGAR ALLAN POE

The new cities of the 19th century, bustling with crowds at all hours, offered the insomniac some relief from the comparative silence of earlier centuries. In Poe's story the man who loves the crowd is regarded as suspicious by the flanneur who follows him: it is one thing to ramble amongst the crowds as a man of means, like the flanneur does, another to rush amongst them all night long. The old man's insomnia is a kind of frantic loneliness. He craves the crowds, but following them wherever they go doesn't put him to sleep or allay his loneliness.

Many of Poe's early stories were parodies of the best-selling stories of the day. 'The Man of the Crowd' was first published in 1840: it parodies no one and remains strikingly original. Born in Boston in 1809, Poe died in 1849.

The Man of the Crowd

Ce grand malheur, de ne pouvoir être seul.
La Bruyére

It was well said of a certain German book that '*es lässt sich nicht lesen*'—it does not permit itself to be read. There are some secrets which do not permit themselves to be told. Men die nightly in their beds, wringing the hands of ghostly confessors, and looking them piteously in the eyes—die with despair of heart and convulsion of throat, on account of the hideousness of mysteries which will not *suffer themselves* to be revealed. Now and then, alas, the conscience of man takes up a burden so heavy in horror that it can be thrown down only into the grave. And thus the essence of all crime is undivulged.

Not long ago, about the closing in of an evening in autumn, I sat at the large bow window of the D—Coffee-House in

London. For some months I had been ill in health, but was now convalescent, and, with returning strength, found myself in one of those happy moods which are so precisely the converse of *ennui*—moods of the keenest appetency, when the film from the mental vision departs—the ἀχλὺς ἣ πρὶν ἐπῆεν—and the intellect, electrified, surpasses as greatly its every-day condition, as does the vivid yet candid reason of Leibnitz, the mad and flimsy rhetoric of Gorgias. Merely to breathe was enjoyment; and I derived positive pleasure even from many of the legitimate sources of pain. I felt a calm but inquisitive interest in everything. With a cigar in my mouth and a newspaper in my lap, I had been amusing myself for the greater part of the afternoon, now in poring over advertisements, now in observing the promiscuous company in the room, and now in peering through the smoky panes into the street.

This latter is one of the principal thoroughfares of the city, and had been very much crowded during the whole day. But, as the darkness came on, the throng momently increased; and, by the time the lamps were well lighted, two dense and continuous tides of population were rushing past the door. At this particular period of the evening I had never before been in a similar situation, and the tumultuous sea of human heads filled me, therefore, with a delicious novelty of emotion. I gave up, at length, all care of things within the hotel, and became absorbed in contemplation of the scene without.

At first my observations took an abstract and generalising turn. I looked at the passengers in masses, and thought of them in their aggregate relations. Soon, however, I descended to details, and regarded with minute interest the innumerable varieties of figure, dress, air, gait, visage, and expression of countenance.

By far the greater number of those who went by had a satisfied business-like demeanour, and seemed to be thinking only of making their way through the press. Their brows were knit, and their eyes rolled quickly; when pushed against by fellow-wayfarers they evinced no symptom of impatience, but adjusted their clothes and hurried on. Others, still a numerous class, were restless in their movements, had flushed faces, and talked and gesticulated to themselves, as if feeling in solitude on account of the very denseness of the company around. When impeded in their progress, these people suddenly ceased muttering, but redoubled their gesticulations, and awaited, with an absent and overdone smile upon the lips, the course of the persons impeding them. If jostled, they bowed profusely to the jostlers, and appeared overwhelmed with confusion.—There was nothing very distinctive about these two large classes beyond what I have noted. Their habiliments belonged to that order which is pointedly termed the decent. They were undoubtedly noblemen, merchants, attorneys, tradesmen, stock-jobbers—the Eupatrids and the commonplaces of society—men of leisure and men actively engaged in affairs of their own—conducting business upon their own responsibility. They did not greatly excite my attention.

The tribe of clerks was an obvious one; and here I discerned two remarkable divisions. There were the junior clerks of flash houses—young gentlemen with tight coats, bright boots, well-oiled hair, and supercilious lips. Setting aside a certain dapperness of carriage, which may be termed *deskism* for want of a better word, the manner of these persons seemed to me an exact facsimile of what had been the perfection of *bon ton* about twelve or eighteen months before. They wore the cast-off graces of the gentry;—and this, I believe, involves the best definition of the class.

The division of the upper clerks of staunch firms, or of the 'steady old fellows', it was not possible to mistake. These were known by their coats and pantaloons of black or brown, made to sit comfortably, with white cravats and waistcoats, broad solid-looking shoes, and thick hose or gaiters.—They had all slightly bald heads, from which the right ears, long used to pen-holding, had an odd habit of standing off on end. I observed that they always removed or settled their hats with both hands, and wore watches, with short gold chains of a substantial and ancient pattern. Theirs was the affectation of respectability;—if indeed there be an affectation so honourable.

There were many individuals of dashing appearance, whom I easily understood as belonging to the race of swell pickpockets, with which all great cities are infested. I watched these gentry with much inquisitiveness, and found it difficult to imagine how they should ever be mistaken for gentlemen by gentlemen themselves. Their voluminousness of wristband, with an air of excessive frankness, should betray them at once.

The gamblers, of whom I descried not a few, were still more easily recognisable. They wore every variety of dress, from that of the desperate thimble-rig bully, with velvet waistcoat, fancy neckerchief, gilt chains, and filigreed buttons, to that of the scrupulously inornate clergy man than which nothing could be less liable to suspicion. Still all were distinguished by a certain sodden swarthiness of complexion, a filmy dimness of eye, and pallor and compression of lip. There were two other traits, moreover, by which I could always detect them;—a guarded lowness of tone in conversation, and more than ordinary extension of the thumb in a direction at right angles with the fingers.—Very often, in company with these sharpers, I observed an order of men somewhat different in habits, but still birds of a kindred feather. They may be defined as the gentlemen who live by their wits. They seem to prey upon the public in two battalions—that of the dandies and that of the military men. Of the first grade the leading features are long locks and smiles; of the second, frogged coats and frowns.

Descending in the scale of what is termed gentility, I found darker and deeper themes for speculation. I saw Jew pedlars, with hawk eyes flashing from countenances whose every other feature wore only an expression of abject humility; sturdy professional street beggars scowling upon mendicants of a better stamp, whom despair alone had driven forth into the night for charity; feeble and ghastly invalids, upon whom death had placed a sure hand, and who sidled and tottered through the mob, looking every one beseechingly in the face, as if in search of some chance consolation, some lost hope; modest young girls returning from long and late labour to a cheerless home, and shrinking more tearfully than indignantly from the glances of ruffians, whose direct contact, even, could not be avoided; women of the town of all kinds and of all ages—the unequivocal beauty in the prime of her womanhood, putting one in mind of the statue in Lucian, with the surface of Parian marble, and the interior filled with filth—the loathsome and utterly lost leper in rags—the wrinkled, bejewelled and paint-begrimed beldame, making a last effort at youth—the mere child of immature form, yet, from long association, an adept

in the dreadful coquetries of her trade, and burning with a
rabid ambition to be ranked the equal of her elders in vice;
drunkards innumerable and indescribable—some in shreds
and patches, reeling, inarticulate, with bruised visage and
lack-lustre eyes—some in whole although filthy garments, with
a slightly unsteady swagger, thick sensual lips, and hearty-
looking rubicund faces—others clothed in materials which had
once been good, and which even now were scrupulously well
brushed—men who walked with a more than naturally firm
and springy step, but whose countenances were fearfully pale,
whose eyes were hideously wild and red, and who clutched
with quivering fingers, as they strode through the crowd, at
every object which came within their reach; beside these,
pie-men, porters, coal-heavers, sweeps; organ-grinders,
monkey-exhibitors and ballad-mongers, those who vended with
those who sang; ragged artisans and exhausted labourers of
every description, and all full of a noisy and inordinate vivacity
which jarred discordantly upon the ear, and gave an aching
sensation to the eye.

As the night deepened, so deepened to me the interest of
the scene; for not only did the general character of the crowd
materially alter (its gentler features retiring in the gradual
withdrawal of the more orderly portion of the people, and its
harsher ones coming out into bolder relief, as the late hour
brought forth every species of infamy from its den) but the
rays of the gas-lamps feeble at first in their struggle with the
dying day, had now at length gained ascendancy, and threw
over every thing a fitful and garish lustre. All was dark yet
splendid—as that ebony to which had been likened the style
of Tertullian.

The wild effects of the light enchained me to an examination
of individual faces; and although the rapidity with which the
world of light flitted before the window, prevented me from
casting more than a glance upon each visage, still it seemed
that, in my then peculiar mental state, I could frequently read,
even in that brief interval of a glance, the history of long years.

With my brow to the glass, I was thus occupied in scruti-
nising the mob, when suddenly there came into view a
countenance (that of a decrepid old man, some sixty-five or
seventy years of age,)—a countenance which at once arrested

and absorbed my whole attention, on account of the absolute idiosyncrasy of its expression. anything even remotely resembling that expression I had never seen before. I well remember that my first thought, upon beholding it, was that Retszch, had he viewed it, would have greatly preferred it to his own pictorial incarnations of the fiend. As I endeavoured, during the brief minute of my original survey, to form some analysis of the meaning conveyed, there arose confusedly and paradoxically within my mind, the idea of vast mental power, of caution, of penuriousness, of avarice, of coolness, of malice, of blood-thirstiness, of triumph, of merriment, of excessive terror, of intense—of extreme despair. I felt singularly aroused, startled, fascinated. 'How wild a history,' I said to myself, 'is written within that bosom!' Then came a craving desire to keep the man in view—to know more of him. Hurriedly putting on an overcoat, and seizing my hat and cane, I made my way into the street, and pushed through the crowd in the direction which I had seen him take; for he had already disappeared. With some little difficulty I at length came within sight of him, approached, and followed him closely, yet cautiously, so as not to attract his attention.

I had now a good opportunity of examining his person. He was short in stature, very thin, and apparently very feeble. His clothes, generally, were filthy and ragged; but as he came, now and then, within the strong glare of a lamp, I perceived that this linen, although dirty, was of beautiful texture; and my vision deceived me, or, through a rent in a closely-buttoned and evidently second-hand *roquelaire* which enveloped him, I caught a glimpse both of a diamond and of a dagger. These observations heightened my curiosity, and I resolved to follow the stranger whither-soever he should go.

It was now fully night-fall, and a thick humid fog hung over the city, soon ending in a settled and heavy rain. This change of weather had an odd effect upon the crowd, the whole of which was at once put into new commotion, and overshadowed by a world of umbrellas. The waver, the jostle, and the hum increased in a tenfold degree. For my own part I did not much regard the rain—the lurking of an old fever in my system rendering the moisture somewhat too dangerously pleasant. Tying a handkerchief about my mouth, I kept on. For half an hour the old man held his way with difficulty along the great thoroughfare; and I here walked close at his elbow through fear of losing sight of him. Never once turning his head to look back, he did not observe me. By and bye he passed into a cross street, which, although densely filled with people, was not quite so much thronged as the main one he had quitted. Here a change of his demeanour became evident. He walked more slowly and with less object than before—more hesitatingly. He crossed and re-crossed the way repeatedly without apparent aim; and the press was still so thick, that at every such movement, I was obliged to follow him closely. The street was a narrow and long one, and his course lay within it for nearly an hour, during which the passengers had gradually diminished to about that number which is ordinarily seen at noon on Broadway near the Park—so vast a difference is there between a London populace and that of the most frequented American city. A second turn brought us into a square, brilliantly lighted, and overflowing with life. The old manner of the stranger reappeared. His chin fell upon his breast, while his eyes rolled wildly from under his knit brows, in every direction, upon those who hemmed him in. He urged his way steadily and perseveringly. I was surprised, however, to find upon his having made the circuit of the square, that he turned and retraced his steps. Still more was I astonished to see him repeat the same walk several times—once nearly detecting me as he came round with a sudden movement.

In this exercise he spent another hour, at the end of which we met with far less interruption from passengers than at first. The rain fell fast; the air grew cool; and the people were retiring to their homes. With a gesture of impatience, the wanderer passed into a by-street comparatively deserted. Down this, some quarter of a mile long, he rushed with an activity I could not have dreamed of seeing in one so aged, and which put me to much trouble in pursuit. A few minutes brought us to a large and busy bazaar, with the localities of which the stranger appeared well acquainted, and where his original demeanour again became apparent, as he forced his way to and fro, without aim, among the host of buyers and sellers.

During the hour and a half, or thereabouts, which we passed in this place, it required much caution on my part to keep him within reach without attracting his observation. Luckily I wore a pair of caoutchouc over-shoes, and could move about in perfect silence. At no moment did he see that I watched him. He entered shop after shop, priced nothing, spoke no word, and looked at all objects with a wild and vacant stare. I was now utterly amazed at his behaviour, and firmly resolved that we should not part until I had satisfied myself in some measure respecting him.

A loud-toned clock struck eleven, and the company were fast deserting the bazaar. A shop-keeper, in putting up a shutter, jostled the old man, and at the instant I saw a strong shudder come over his frame. He hurried into the street, looked anxiously around him for an instant, and then ran with incredible swiftness through many crooked and people-less lanes, until we emerged once more upon the great thoroughfare whence we had started—the street of the D—Hotel. It no longer wore, however, the same aspect. It was still brilliant with gas; but the rain fell fiercely, and there were few persons to be seen. The stranger grew pale. He walked moodily some paces up the once populous avenue, then, with a heavy sigh, turned in the direction of the river, and, plunging through a great variety of devious ways, came out, at length, in view of one of the principal theatres. It was about being closed, and the audience were thronging from the doors. I saw the old man gasp as if for breath while he threw himself amid the crowd; but I thought that the intense agony of his countenance had, in some measure, abated. His head again fell upon his breast; he appeared as I had seen him at first. I observed that he now took the course in which had gone the greater number of the audience—but, upon the whole, I was at a loss to comprehend the waywardness of his actions.

As he proceeded, the company grew more scattered, and his old uneasiness and vacillation were resumed. For some time he followed closely a party of some ten or twelve roisterers; but from this number one by one dropped off, until three only remained together, in a narrow and gloomy lane little frequented. The stranger paused, and, for a moment, seemed lost in thought; then, with every mark of agitation, pursued rapidly a route which brought us to the verge of the city, amid regions very different from those we had hitherto traversed. It was the most noisome quarter of London, where everything wore the worst impress of the most deplorable poverty, and of the most desperate crime. By the dim light of an accidental lamp, tall, antique, worm-eaten, wooden tenements were seen tottering to their fall, in directions so many and capricious that scarce the semblance of a passage was discernible between them. The paving-stones lay at random, displaced from their beds by the rankly growing grass. Horrible filth festered in the dammed-up gutters. The whole atmosphere teemed with desolation. Yet, as we proceeded, the sounds of human life revived by sure degrees, and at length large bands of the most abandoned of a London populace were seen reeling to and fro. The spirits of the old man again flickered up, as a lamp which is near its death-hour. Once more he strode onward with elastic tread. Suddenly a corner was turned, a blaze of light burst upon our sight, and we stood before one of the huge suburban temples of Intemperance—one of the palaces of the fiend, Gin.

It was now nearly day-break; but a number of wretched inebriates still pressed in and out of the flaunting entrance. With a half shriek of joy the old man forced a passage within, resumed at once his original bearing, and stalked backward and forward, without apparent object, among the throng. He had not been thus long occupied, however, before a rush to the doors gave token that the host was closing them for the night. It was something even more intense than despair that I then observed upon the countenance of the singular being whom I had watched so pertinaciously. Yet he did not hesitate in his career, but, with a mad energy, retraced his steps at once, to the heart of the mighty London. Long and swiftly he fled, while I followed him in the wildest amazement, resolute not to abandon a scrutiny in which I now felt an interest all-absorbing. The sun arose while we proceeded, and, when we had once again reached that most thronged mart of the populous town, the street of the D—Hotel, it presented an appearance of human bustle and activity scarcely inferior to what I had seen on the evening before. And here, long, amid the momently increasing confusion, did I persist in my pursuit of the stranger. But, as usual, he walked to and fro, and during the day did not pass from out the turmoil of that street. And, as the shades of the second evening came on, I grew wearied unto death, and, stopping fully in front of the wanderer, gazed at him steadfastly in the face. He noticed me not, but resumed his solemn walk, while I, ceasing to follow, remained absorbed in contemplation. 'This old man,' I said at length, 'is the type and the genius of deep crime. He refuses to be alone. *He is the man of the crowd.* It will be in vain to follow; for I shall learn no more of him, nor of his deeds. The worst heart of the world is a grosser book than the "Hortulus Animae", and perhaps it is but one of the great mercies of God that "es lässt sich niche lesen".'

A Private Madness

Charlotte Perkins Gilman

The extract which follows is from Gilman's 1892 novella, an exploration of a woman's physical and psychic imprisonment. The young wife spends each day in a garret room that was once a nursery, the walls papered with a torn and intricately patterned yellow wallpaper. Her husband is a physician and has recommended that her 'nerves' be cured with quiet rest in the nursery bedroom. She would rather be outside, doing things and writing. Only when her husband is asleep has she privacy to think her own thoughts. She is also vigilant, her insomnia a private madness induced by the very conditions that seek to cure it.

Gilman was treated for 'nerves', and also found the 'cure' worse than the illness. She sent The Yellow Wallpaper *to her physician, and was very glad to hear that he subsequently changed his methods of treatment. Born in 1860 in America, Gilman was a feminist, and a writer of fiction and social commentary. She experienced some difficulty in publishing this story.*

The Yellow Wallpaper

There are things in that paper that nobody knows but me, or ever will.

Behind that outside pattern the dim shapes get clearer every day.

It is always the same shape, only very numerous.

And it is like a woman stooping down and creeping about behind that pattern. I don't like it a bit. I wonder—I begin to think—I wish John would take me away from here!

It is so hard to talk with John about my case, because he is so wise, and because he loves me so.

But I tried it last night.

It was moonlight. The moon shines in all around just as the sun does.

I hate to see it sometimes, it creeps so slowly, and always comes in by one window or another.

John was asleep and I hated to waken him, so I kept still and watched the moonlight on that undulating wallpaper till I felt creepy.

The faint figure behind seemed to shake the pattern, just as if she wanted to get out.

I got up softly and went to feel and see if the paper *did* move, and when I came back John was awake.

'What is it, little girl?' he said. 'Don't go walking about like that—you'll get cold.'

I thought it was a good time to talk, so I told him that I really was not gaining here, and that I wished he would take me away.

'Why darling!' said he, 'our lease will be up in three weeks, and I can't see how to leave before.

'The repairs are not done at home, and I cannot possibly leave town just now. Of course if you were in any danger, I could and would, but you really are better, dear, whether you can see it or not. I am a doctor, dear, and I know. You are gaining flesh and colour, your appetite is better, I feel really much easier about you.'

'I don't weigh a bit more,' said I, 'nor as much; and my appetite may be better in the evening when you are here, but it is worse in the morning when you are away!'

'Bless her little heart!' said he with a big hug, 'she shall be as sick as she pleases! But now let's improve the shining hours by going to sleep, and talk about it in the morning!'

'And you won't go away?' I asked gloomily.

'Why, how can I, dear? It is only three weeks more and then we will take a nice little trip of a few days while Jennie is getting the house ready. Really dear you are better!'

'Better in body perhaps—' I began, and stopped short, for he sat up straight and looked at me with such a stern, reproachful look that I could not say another word.

'My darling,' said he, 'I beg of you, for my sake and for our child's sake, as well as for your own, that you will never for one instant let that idea enter your mind! There is nothing so dangerous, so fascinating, to a temperament like yours. It is a false and foolish fancy. Can you not trust me as a physician when I tell you so?'

So of course I said no more on that score, and we went to sleep before long. He thought I was asleep first, but I wasn't and lay there for hours trying to decide whether that front pattern and the back pattern really did move together or separately.

On a pattern like this, by daylight, there is a lack of sequence, a defiance of law, that is a constant irritant to a normal mind.

The colour is hideous enough, and unreliable enough, and infuriating enough, but the pattern is torturing.

You think you have mastered it, but just as you get well underway in following, it turns a back-somersault and there you are. It slaps you in the face, knocks you down, and tramples upon you. It is like a bad dream.

The outside pattern is a florid arabesque, reminding one of a fungus. If you can imagine a toadstool in joints, an interminable string of toadstools, budding and sprouting in endless convolutions—why, that is something like it.

That is, sometimes!

There is one marked peculiarity about this paper, a thing nobody seems to notice but myself, and that is that it changes as the light changes. When the sun shoots in through the east window—I always watch for that first long, straight ray—it changes so quickly that I never can quite believe it.

That is why I watch it always.

By moonlight—the moon shines in all night when there is a moon—I wouldn't know it was the same paper.

At night in any kind of light, in twilight, candle light, lamplight, and worst of all by moonlight, it becomes bars! The outside patterns I mean, and the woman behind it is as plain as can be.

I didn't realise for a long time what the thing was that showed behind, that dim sub-pattern, but now I am quite sure it is a woman.

By daylight she is subdued, quiet. I fancy it is the pattern that keeps her so still. It is so puzzling. It keeps me quiet by the hour.

I lie down ever so much now. John says it is good for me, and to sleep all I can.

Indeed he started the habit by making me lie down for an hour after each meal.

It is a very bad habit I am convinced, for you see I don't sleep.

And that cultivates deceit, for I don't tell them I'm awake— O no!

The fact is I am getting a little afraid of John.

He seems very queer sometimes, and even Jennie has an inexplicable look.

It strikes me occasionally, just as a scientific hypothesis— that perhaps it is the paper!

I have watched John when he did not know I was looking, and come into the room suddenly on the most innocent excuses, and I've caught him several times *looking at the paper*! And Jennie too. I caught Jennie with her hand on it once.

She didn't know I was in the room, and when I asked her in a quiet, a very quiet voice, with the most restrained manner possible, what she was doing with the paper—she turned around as if she had been caught stealing, and looked quite angry—asked me why I should frighten her so!

Then she said that the paper stained everything it touched, that she had found yellow smooches on all my clothes and John's, and she wishes we would be more careful!

Did not that sound innocent? But I know she was studying that pattern, and I am determined that nobody shall find it out but myself!

Life is much more exciting now than it used to be. You see I have something more to expect, to look forward to, to watch. I really do eat better, and am more quiet than I was.

John is so pleased to see me improve! He laughed a little the other day, and said I seemed to be flourishing in spite of my wallpaper.

I turned it off with a laugh. I had no intention of telling him it was *because* of the wallpaper—he would made fun of me. He might even want to take me away.

I don't want to leave now until I have found it out. There is a week more, and I think that will be enough.

I'm feeling ever so much better! I don't sleep much at night, for it is so interesting to watch developments; but I sleep a good deal in the daytime.

In the daytime it is tiresome and perplexing.

There are always new shoots on the fungus, and new shades of yellow all over it. I cannot keep count of them, though I have tried conscientiously. It is the strangest yellow, that wallpaper! It makes me think of all the yellow things I ever saw—not beautiful ones like buttercups, but old foul, bad yellow things.

But there is something else about that paper—the smell! I noticed it the moment we came into the room, but with so much air and sun it was not bad. Now we have had a week of fog and rain, and whether the windows are open or not, the smell is here.

It creeps all over the house.

I find it hovering in the dining-room, skulking in the parlour, hiding in the hall, lying in wait for me on the stairs.

It gets into my hair.

Even when I go to ride, if I turn my head suddenly and surprise it—there is that smell!

Such a peculiar odour, too! I have spent hours in trying to analyse it, to find what it smelled like.

It is not bad—at first, and very gentle, but quite the subtlest, most enduring odour I ever met.

In this damp weather it is awful. I wake up in the night and find it hanging over me.

It used to disturb me at first. I thought seriously of burning the house—to reach the smell.

But now I am used to it. The only thing I can think of that it is like is the *colour* of the paper! A yellow smell.

There is a very funny mark on this wall, low down, near the mop board. A streak that runs round the room. It goes behind every piece of furniture, except the bed, a long, straight, even *smooch*, as if it had been rubbed over and over.

I wonder how it was done and who did it, and what they did it for. Round and round and round—round and round and round—it makes me dizzy! . . .

Vladimir Nabokov

Nabokov began The Defence *in 1929 at a small spa in the Pyreness Orientales where he was hunting butterflies. The Grandmaster Luzhin comes to see everything about him as a chess game and his own actions as strategic moves, looking increasingly to his own defence in wary, Escher-like reflections. Waking and sleeping merge, the daytime becoming a 'fine dream' after nights of insomnia during the game series leading up to the plays against his rival Turati. Never a strong man, Luzhin is undone by his chess insomnia.*

Born in St Petersburg in 1899, Nabokov died in Montreaux in 1977.

Chess Insomnia

The whole time, however, now feebly, now sharply, shadows of his real chess life would show through this dream and finally it broke through and it was simply night in the hotel, chess thoughts, chess insomnia and meditations on the drastic defence he had invented to counter Turati's opening. He was wide-awake and his mind worked clearly, purged of all dross and aware that everything apart from chess was only an enchanting dream, in which, like the golden haze of the moon, the image of a sweet, clear-eyed maiden with bare arms dissolved and melted. The rays of his consciousness, which were wont to disperse when they came into contact with the incompletely intelligible world surrounding him, thereby losing one half of their force, had grown stronger and more concentrated now that this world had dissolved into a mirage and there was no longer any need to worry about it. Real life, chess life, was orderly, clear-cut, and rich in adventure, and Luzhin noted with pride how easy it was for him to reign in this life, and the way everything obeyed his will and bowed to his schemes. Some of his games at the Berlin tournament had been even then termed immortal by connoisseurs. He had won one after sacrificing in succession his Queen, a Rook and a Knight; in another he had placed a Pawn in such a dynamic position that it had acquired an absolutely monstrous force and had continued to grow and swell, balefully for his opponent, like a furuncle in the tenderest part of the board; and finally in a third game, by means of an apparently absurd move that provoked a murmuring among the spectators, Luzhin constructed an elaborate trap for his opponent that the latter divined too late. In these games and in all the others that he played at this unforgettable tournament, he manifested a stunning clarity of thought, a merciless logic. But Turati also played brilliantly, Turati also scored point after point, somewhat hypnotising his opponents with the boldness of his imagination and trusting too much, perhaps, to the chess luck that till now had never deserted him. His meeting with Luzhin was to decide who would get first prize and there were those who said that the limpidity and lightness of Luzhin's thought would prevail over the Italian's tumultuous fantasy, and there were those who forecast that the fiery, swift-swooping Turati would defeat the far-sighted Russian player. And the day of their meeting arrived.

Luzhin awoke fully dressed, even wearing his overcoat; he looked at his watch, rose hastily and put on his hat, which had been lying in the middle of the room. At this point he recollected himself and looked round the room, trying to understand what exactly he had slept on. His bed was unrumpled and the velvet of the couch was completely smooth. The only thing he knew for sure was that from time immemorial he had been playing chess—and in the darkness of his memory, as in two mirrors reflecting a candle, there was only a vista of converging lights with Luzhin sitting at a chessboard, and again Luzhin at a chessboard, only smaller, and then smaller still, and so on an infinity of times. But he was late, he was late, and he had to hurry. He swiftly opened the door and stopped in bewilderment. According to his concept of things, the chess hall, and his table, and the waiting Turati should have been right here. Instead of this he saw an empty corridor and a staircase beyond it. Suddenly from that direction, from the stairs, appeared a swiftly running little man who caught sight of Luzhin and spread out his hands, 'Maestro,' he exclaimed, 'what is this? They are waiting for you, they are waiting for you, Maestro . . . I telephoned you three times and they said you didn't answer their knocks. Signor Turati has been at his post a long time.' 'They removed it,' said Luzhin sourly, pointing to the empty corridor with his cane. 'How was I to know that everything would be removed?' 'If you don't feel well . . .' began the little man, looking sadly at Luzhin's pale, glistening face. 'Well, take me there!' cried Luzhin in a shrill voice and banged his cane on the floor. 'With pleasure, with pleasure,' muttered the other distractedly. His gaze concentrated on the little overcoat with its raised collar running in front of him. Luzhin began to conquer the incomprehensible space. 'We'll go on foot,' said his guide, 'it's exactly a minute's walk.' With a feeling of relief Luzhin recognised the revolving doors of the café and then the staircase, and finally he saw what he had been looking for in the hotel corridor. Upon entering he immediately felt fullness of life, calm, clarity and confidence. 'There's a big victory coming,' he said loudly, and a crowd of dim people parted in order to let him through. '*Tard, tard, très tard*,' jabbered Turati, materialising suddenly and shaking his head. '*Avanti*,' said Luzhin and laughed. A table appeared between them and upon it was a board with pieces set out ready for battle. Luzhin took a cigarette from his waistcoat pocket and unconsciously lit up.

At this point a strange thing happened. Turati, although having white, did not launch his famous opening and the defence Luzhin had worked out proved an utter waste. Whether because Turati had anticipated possible complications or else had simply decided to play warily, knowing the calm strength which Luzhin had revealed at this tournament, he began in the most banal way. Luzhin momentarily regretted the work done in vain, but nevertheless he was glad: this gave him more freedom. Moreover, Turati was evidently afraid of him. On the other hand there was undoubtedly some trick concealed in the innocent, jejune opening proposed by Turati, and Luzhin settled down to play with particular care. At first it went softly, softly, like muted violins. The players occupied their positions cautiously, moving this and that up but doing it politely, without the slightest sign of a threat—and if there was any threat it was entirely conventional—more like a hint to one's opponent that over there he would do well to build a cover, and the opponent would smile, as if all this were an insignificant joke, and strengthen the proper place and himself move forward a fraction. Then, without the least warning, a chord sang out tenderly. This was one of Turati's forces occupying a diagonal line. But forthwith a trace of melody very softly manifested itself on Luzhin's side also. For a moment mysterious possibilities were quivering and then all was quiet again: Turati retreated, drew in. And once more for a while both opponents, as if having no intention of advancing, occupied themselves with sprucing up their own squares—nursing, shifting, smoothing things down at home—and then there was another sudden flare up, a swift combination of sounds: two small forces collided and both were immediately swept away: a momentary, masterly motion of the fingers and Luzhin removed and placed on the table beside him what was no longer an incorporeal force but a heavy, yellow Pawn; Turati's fingers flashed in the air and an inert, black Pawn with a gleam of light on its head was in turn lowered onto the table. And having got rid of these two chess quantities that had so suddenly turned into wood the players seemed to calm down and forget the momentary flare-up the vibration in this part of the board, however, had not yet quite died down, something was still endeavouring to take shape . . .'

. . . Luzhin's thought roamed through entrancing and terrible labyrinths, meeting there now and then the anxious thought of Turati, who sought the same thing as he. Both realised simultaneously that white was not destined to develop his scheme any further, that he was on the brink of losing rhythm. Turati hastened to propose an exchange and the number of forces on the board was again reduced. New possibilities appeared, but still no one could say which side had the advantage. Luzhin, preparing an attack for which it was first necessary to explore a maze of variations, where his every step aroused a perilous echo, began a long meditation: he needed, it seemed, to make one last prodigious effort and he would find the secret move leading to victory. Suddenly, something occurred outside his being, a scorching pain—and he let out a loud cry, shaking his hand stung by the flame of a match, which he had lit and forgotten to apply to his cigarette. The pain immediately passed, but in the fiery gap he had seen something unbearably awesome, the full horror of the abysmal depths of chess. He glanced at the chessboard and his brain wilted from hitherto unprecedented weariness. But the chessmen were pitiless, they held and absorbed him. There was horror in this, but in this also was the sole harmony, for what else exists in the world besides chess? Fog, the unknown, non-being . . . He noticed that Turati was no longer sitting; he stood stretching himself. 'Adjournment, Maestro,' said a voice from behind. 'Note down your next move.' 'No, no, not yet,' said Luzhin pleadingly, his eyes searching for the person who spoke. 'That's all for today,' the same voice went on, again from behind, a gyratory kind of voice. Luzhin wanted to stand up but was unable to. He saw that he had moved backwards somewhere together with his chair and that people had hurled themselves rapaciously upon the position on the chessboard, where the whole of his life had just been, and were wrangling and shouting as they nimbly moved the pieces this way and that. He again tried to stand up and again was unable to. 'Why, why?' he said plaintively, trying to distinguish the board between the narrow, black backs bent over it. They dwindled completely away and disappeared. On the board the pieces were mixed up now and stood about in disorderly groups. A phantom went by, stopped and began swiftly to stow the pieces away in a tiny coffin. 'It's all over,' said Luzhin and groaning from the effort, wrenched himself out of the chair. A few phantoms still stood about discussing something. It was cold and fairly dark. Phantoms were carrying off the boards and chairs. Tortuous and transparent chess images roamed about in the air, wherever you looked—and Luzhin, realising that he had got stuck, that he had lost his way in one of the combinations he had so recently pondered, made a desperate attempt to free himself, to break out somewhere—even if into non-existence. 'Let's go, let's go,' cried someone and disappeared with a bang. He remained alone. His vision became darker and darker and in relation to every vague object in the hall he stood in check. He had to escape; he moved, the whole of his fat body shaking, and was completely unable to imagine what people did in order to get out of a room—and yet there should be a simple method—abruptly a black shade with a white breast began to hover about him, offering him his coat and hat. 'Why is this necessary?' he muttered, getting into the sleeves and revolving together with the obliging ghost. 'This way,' said the host briskly and Luzhin stepped forward and out of the terrible hall. Catching sight of the stairs he began to creep upward, but then changed his mind and went down, since it was easier to descend than to climb up. He found himself in a smoky establishment where noisy phantoms were sitting. An attack was developing in every corner—and pushing aside tables, a bucket with a gold-necked glass Pawn sticking out of it and a drum that was being beaten by an arched, thick-maned chess Knight, he made his way to a gently revolving glass radiance and stopped, not knowing where to go next. People surrounded him and wanted to do something with him. 'Go away, go away,' a gruff voice kept repeating. 'But where?' said Luzhin, weeping. 'Go home,' whispered another voice insinuatingly and something pushed against Luzhin's shoulder. 'What did you say?' he asked again, suddenly ceasing to sob. 'Home, home,' repeated the voice, and the glass radiance, taking hold of Luzhin, threw him out into the cool dusk. Luzhin smiled. 'Home,' he said softly. 'So that's the key to the combination.'

And it was necessary to hurry. At any minute these chess growths might ring him in again. For the first time he was surrounded by twilight murk, thick, cotton-wool air. He asked a ghost slipping by how to get to the manor. The ghost did not understand and passed on. 'One moment,' said Luzhin, but it was already too late. Then, swinging his short arms, he quickened his step. A pale light sailed past and disintegrated with a mournful rustle. It was difficult, difficult to find one's way home in this yielding fog. Luzhin felt he should keep left, and then there would be a big wood, and once in the wood he would easily find the path. Another shadow slipped by. 'Where's the wood, the wood?' Luzhin asked insistently and since this word evoked no reply he cast around for a synonym: 'Forest? Wald?'

he muttered. 'Park?' he added indulgently. Then the shadow pointed to the left and disappeared from view. Upbraiding himself for his slowness, anticipating pursuit at any minute, Luzhin strode off in the direction indicated. And indeed—he was suddenly surrounded by trees, ferns crepitated underfoot, it was quiet and damp. He sank down heavily on the ground and squatted there for he was quite out of breath, and tears poured down his face. Presently he got up, removed a wet leaf from his knee and after wandering among tree trunks for a short time he found the familiar footpath. '*Marsch, marsch,*' Luzhin kept repeating, urging himself on as he walked over the sticky ground. He had already come halfway. Soon there would be the river, and the sawmill, and then the manor house would peep through the bare bushes. He would hide there and would live on the contents of large and small glass jars. The mysterious pursuit had been left far behind. You wouldn't catch him now. Oh no. If only it were easier to breathe, and one could get rid of this pain in the temples, this numbing pain . . . The path twisted through the wood and came out onto a transverse road, while farther on a river glinted in the darkness. He also saw a bridge and a dim pile of structures on the other side of it, and at first, for one moment, it seemed to him that over there against the dark sky was the familiar triangular roof of the manor with its black lightning conductor. But immediately he realised that this was some subtle ruse on the part of the chess gods, for the parapet of the bridge produced the rain-glistening, trembling shapes of great female figures and a queer reflection danced on the river. He walked along the bank, trying to find another bridge, the bridge where you sink up to your ankles in sawdust. He looked for a long time and finally, quite out of the way, he found a narrow, quiet little bridge and thought that here at least he could cross peacefully. But on the other bank everything was unfamiliar, lights flashed past and shadows slid by. He knew the manor was somewhere here, close by, but he was approaching it from an unfamiliar angle and how difficult everything was . . . His legs from hips to heels were tightly filled with lead, the way the base of a chessman is weighted. Gradually the lights disappeared, the phantoms grew sparser, and a wave of oppressive blackness washed over him. By the light of a last reflection he made out a front garden and a couple of round bushes, and it seemed to him he recognised the miller's house. He stretched out a hand to the fence but at this point triumphant pain began to overwhelm him, pressing down from above on his skull, and it was if he were becoming flatter and flatter, and then he soundlessly dissipated.

AUGUST STRINDBERG

'But why should I complain? Is it not insomnia and dissipation that have sharpened my senses and my nerves?' This remark, taken from Strindberg's essay 'Deranged Sense Impressions', is typical in that the author didn't always reject the effects of trauma. He wanted to be a 'modern', but was also too sensitive for it, asking himself in words that recall Rilke: '. . . am I deranged because I have been involuntarily forced to live too rapidly through this era of steam and electricity?' The extract below is taken from Inferno.

Born in 1849, Strindberg practised occultism, worked as a scientist, and wrote diaries, plays and prose. He was often poor, and his science and sometimes his writings were derided. He died in 1908.

What is our Goal?

Six months have ebbed away and I still take my walk on the ramparts. As I let my eyes stray over the lunatic asylum and try to catch sight of the blue streak in the distance that is the sea, I fancy that I am on the look-out for the new era that is coming, the new religion of which the world is dreaming.

Dark winter is buried, the fields are growing green, the trees are in blossom, the nightingale is singing in the Observatory Gardens, but the melancholy of winter still weighs upon our spirits because of the many ominous things that are happening, the many inexplicable things that make even the sceptical uneasy. Cases of sleeplessness are increasing, serious nervous disorders are multiplying, invisible presences are of common occurrence, real miracles are taking place. People are waiting for something to happen.

A young man came to visit me. He asked:

'What ought I to do to sleep peacefully at night?'

'What has happened?'

'Upon my word, I cannot tell you, but I have a horror of my bedroom, and I am moving elsewhere tomorrow.'

'You man, you are an atheist and a believer in naturalism. What has happened?'

'Devil take it! When I got home last night and opened my door someone took hold of my arm and shook me.'

'So there was someone in your room.'

'Why, no! I lit the candles and I could not see anyone.'

'Young man, there is one whom we cannot see by the light of a candle.'

'What manner of thing is he?'

'He is the Unseen, young man. Have you taken sulphonal, potassium bromide, morphia, or chloral?'

'I have tried them all.'

'And the Unseen won't decamp? Well, then, you want to sleep peacefully at night, and you have come to ask me how to do so. Listen to me, young man. I am no doctor, nor am I a prophet; I am an old sinner, doing penance. Do not expect any sermons or prophecies from a ruffian who needs all the time he can spare to preach sermons to himself. I too have suffered from sleepless nights and deep dejection. I too have fought face to face with the Unseen, and I have at last regained the power of sleep and got back my health. Do you know how? Guess!'

The young man guessed what I meant and lowered his eyes.

'So you have guessed. Depart in peace and sleep well.'

You see, I had to hold my tongue and let people guess what I meant, for the instant I presumed to play the friar, people turned their backs upon me.

SYLVIA PLATH

The chapter in The Bell Jar *that this extract is taken
from begins: 'It was a queer, sultry summer, the
summer they electrocuted the Rosenburgs . . .' Like
Wilde's narrator watching over the condemned man
on the eve of his execution, Esther Greenwood can't
help wondering 'what it would be like being burned
alive all along your nerves'.*

*Home for the summer, the teenage Esther isn't able
to deal with her impending womanhood—her desire
for a lover and her fear and interest in sex—and her
need to write. Esther's insomnia is severe—she doesn't
sleep for a month. She lies, a little like Kafka, with
a weight upon her.*

*Plath was born in 1932 in Massachusetts. She died
by her own hand in London in 1963.*

The Summer they Electrocuted the Rosenburgs

I told my mother I had a terrible headache, and went to bed.

An hour later the door inched open, and she crept into the
room. I heard the whisper of her clothes as she undressed. She
climbed into bed. Then her breathing grew slow and regular.

In the dim light of the streetlamp that filtered through the
drawn blinds, I could see the pin curls on her hair glittering
like a row of little bayonets.

I decided I would put off the novel until I had gone to
Europe and had a lover, and that I would never learn a word
of shorthand. If I never learned shorthand I would never have
to use it.

I thought I would spend the summer reading *Finnegan's
Wake* and writing my thesis.

Then I would be way ahead when college started at the end
of September, and able to enjoy my last year instead of swot-
ting away with no make-up and stringy hair, on a diet of coffee

and benzedrine, the way most of the seniors taking honours did, until they finished their thesis.

Then I thought I might put off college for a year and apprentice myself to a pottery maker.

Or work my way to Germany and be a waitress, until I was bilingual.

Then plan after plan started leaping through my head like a family of scatty rabbits.

I saw the years of my life spaced along a road in the form of telephone poles, threaded together by wires. I counted one, two, three . . . nineteen telephone poles, and then the wires dangled into space, and try as I would, I couldn't see a single pole beyond the nineteenth.

The room blued into view, and I wondered where the night had gone. My mother turned from a foggy log into a slumbering, middle-aged woman, her mouth slightly open and a snore ravelling from her throat. The piggish noise irritated me, and for a while it seemed to me that the only way to stop it would be to take the column of skin and sinew from which it rose and twist it to silence between my hands.

I feigned sleep until my mother left for school, but even my eyelids didn't shut out the light. They hung the raw, red screen of their tiny vessels in front of me like a wound. I crawled between the mattress and the padded bedstead and let the mattress fall across me like a tombstone. It felt dark and safe under there, but the mattress was not heavy enough.

It needed about a ton more weight to make me sleep.

Haruki Murakami

The young Japanese wife in 'Sleep' wakes up one night both literally and figuratively. Interestingly she sees herself as beyond insomnia; she is simply awake and way past sleep. Except for the pleasure she finds in reading books, reality becomes machine-like—until a break in her constant wakefulness occurs, and another's reality steps in one dark night.

This story is taken from the collection The Elephant Vanishes, *first published in English in 1993. Japanese writer Murakami is also the author of* Hard-Boiled Wonderland And the End of the World, A Wild Sheep Chase *and* A Place I've Never Been.

Sleep

This is my seventeenth straight day without sleep.

I'm not talking about insomnia. I know what insomnia is. I had something like it in college—'something like it' because I'm sure that what I had then was exactly the same as what people refer to as insomnia. I suppose a doctor could have told me. But I didn't see a doctor. I knew it wouldn't do any good. Not that I had any reason to think so. Call it woman's intuition—I just felt they couldn't help me. So I didn't see a doctor, and I didn't say anything to my parents or friends, because I knew that that was exactly what they would tell me to do.

Back then, my 'something like insomnia' went on for a month. I never really got to sleep that entire time. I'd go to bed at night and say to myself, 'All right now, time for some sleep.' That was all it took to wake me up. It was instantaneous—like a conditioned reflex. The harder I worked at sleeping, the wider awake I became. I tried alcohol, I tried sleeping pills, but they had absolutely no effect.

Finally, as the sky began to grow light in the morning, I'd feel that I might be drifting off. But this wasn't sleep. My fingertips were just barely brushing against the outermost edge of sleep. And all the while my mind was wide-awake. I would feel a hint of drowsiness, but my mind was there, in its own room, on the other side of a transparent wall, watching me. My physical self was drifting through the feeble morning light, and all the while it could feel my mind staring, breathing, close beside it. I was both a body on the verge of sleep and a mind determined to stay awake.

This incomplete drowsiness would continue on and off all day. My head was always foggy. I couldn't get an accurate fix on the things around me—their distance or mass or texture. The drowsiness would overtake me at regular, wavelike intervals: on the subway, in the classroom, at the dinner table. My mind would slip away from my body. The world would sway soundlessly. I would drop things. My pencil or my purse or my fork would clatter to the floor. All I wanted was to throw myself down and sleep. But I couldn't. The wakefulness was always there beside me. I could feel its chilling shadow. It was the shadow of myself. Weird, I would think as the drowsiness overtook me, I'm in my own shadow. I would walk and eat and talk to people inside my drowsiness. And the strangest thing was that no one noticed. I lost fifteen pounds that month, and no one noticed. No one in my family, not one of my friends or classmates realised that I was going through life asleep.

. . .

And then one day it ended, without warning, without any external cause. I started to lose consciousness at the breakfast table. I stood up without saying anything. I may have knocked something off the table. I think someone spoke to me. But I can't be sure. I staggered to my room, crawled into bed in my clothes, and fell fast asleep. I stayed that way for twenty-seven hours. My mother became alarmed and tried to shake me out of it. She actually slapped my cheeks. But I went on sleeping for twenty-seven hours without a break. And when I finally did awaken, I was my old self again. Probably.

I have no idea why I became an insomniac then nor why the condition suddenly cured itself. It was like a thick, black cloud brought from somewhere by the wind, a cloud crammed full of ominous things I have no knowledge of. No one knows where such a thing comes from or where it goes. I can only be sure that it did descend on me for a time, and then departed.

In any case, what I have now is nothing like that insomnia, nothing at all. I just can't sleep. Not for one second. Aside from that simple fact, I'm perfectly normal. I don't feel sleepy, and my mind is as clear as ever. Clearer, if anything. Physically, too, I'm normal: my appetite is fine; I'm not fatigued. In terms of everyday reality, there's nothing wrong with me. I just can't sleep.

Neither my husband nor my son has noticed that I'm not sleeping. And I haven't mentioned it to them. I don't want to be told to see a doctor. I know it wouldn't do any good. I just know. Like before. This is something I have to deal with myself.

So they don't suspect a thing. On the surface, our life flows on unchanged. Peaceful. Routine. After I see my husband and son off in the morning, I take my car and go marketing. My husband is a dentist. His office is a ten-minute drive from our condo. He and a dental-school friend own it as partners. That way they can afford to hire a technician and a receptionist. One partner can take the other's overflow. Both of them are good, so for an office that has been in operation for only five years, and that opened without any special connections, the place is doing very well. Almost too well. 'I didn't want to work so hard,' said my husband. 'But I can't complain.'

And I always say, 'Really, you can't.' It's true. We had to get an enormous bank loan to open the place. A dental office requires a huge investment in equipment. And the competition is fierce. Patients don't start pouring in the minute you open your doors. Lots of dental clinics have failed for lack of patients.

Back then, we were young and poor and we had a brand-new baby. No one could guarantee that we would survive in such a tough world. But we have survived, one way or another. Five years. No, we really can't complain. We've still got almost two-thirds of our debt left to pay, though.

'I know why you've got so many patients,' I always say to him. 'It's because you're such a good-looking guy.'

This is our little joke. He's not good-looking at all. Actually, he's kind of strange-looking. Even now I sometimes wonder why I married such a strange-looking man. I had other boyfriends who were far more handsome.

What makes his face so strange? I can't really say. It's not a handsome face, but it's not ugly, either. Nor is it the kind that people would say has 'character'. Honestly, 'strange' is about all that fits. Or maybe it would be more accurate to say that it has no distinguishing features. Still, there must be some element that *makes* his face have no distinguishing features, and if I could grasp whatever that is, I might be able to understand the strangeness of the whole. I once tried to draw his picture, but I couldn't do it. I couldn't remember what he looked like. I sat there holding the pencil over the paper and couldn't make a mark. I was flabbergasted. How can you live with a man so long and not be able to bring his face to mind? I knew how to recognise him, of course. I would even get mental images of him now and then. But when it came to drawing his picture, I realised that I didn't remember anything about his face. What could I do? It was like running into an invisible wall. The one thing I could remember was that his face looked strange.

The memory of that often makes me nervous.

Still, he's one of those men everybody likes. That's a big plus in his business, obviously, but I think he would have been a success at just about anything. People feel secure talking to him. I had never met anyone like that before. All my women friends like him. And I'm fond of him, of course. I think I even love him. But, strictly speaking, I don't actually *like* him.

Anyhow, he smiles in this natural, innocent way, just like a child. Not many grownup men can do that. And I guess you'd expect a dentist to have nice teeth, which he does.

'It's not my fault I'm so good-looking,' he always answers when we enjoy our little joke. We're the only ones who understand what it means. It's a recognition of reality—the fact that we have managed in one way or another to survive—and it's an important ritual for us.

He drives his Sentra out of the condo parking garage every morning at eight-fifteen. Our son is in the seat next to him. The elementary school is on the way to the office. 'Be careful,' I say. 'Don't worry,' he answers. Always the same little dialogue. I can't help myself. I have to say it. 'Be careful.' And my husband has to answer, 'Don't worry.' He starts the engine, puts a Haydn or a Mozart tape into the car stereo, and hums along with the music. My two 'men' always wave to me on the way out. Their hands move in exactly the same way. It's almost uncanny. They lean their heads at exactly the same angle and turn their palms toward me, moving them slightly from side to side in exactly the same way, as if they'd been trained by a choreographer.

I have my own car, a used Honda Civic. A girlfriend sold it to me two years ago for next to nothing. One bumper is smashed in, and the body style is old-fashioned, with rust spots showing up. The odometer has over a hundred and fifty thousand kilometres on it. Sometimes—once or twice a month—the car is almost impossible to start. The engine simply won't catch. Still, it's not bad enough to have the thing fixed. If you baby it and let it rest for ten minutes or so, the engine will start up with a nice, solid *vroom*. Oh, well, everything—everybody—gets out of whack once or twice a month. That's life. My husband calls my car 'your donkey'. I don't care. It's mine.

I drive my Civic to the supermarket. After marketing I clean the house and do the laundry. Then I fix lunch. I make a point of performing my morning chores with brisk, efficient movements. If possible, I like to finish my dinner preparations in the morning, too. Then the afternoon is all mine.

My husband comes home for lunch. He doesn't like to eat out. He says the restaurants are too crowded, the food is no good, and the smell of tobacco smoke gets into his clothes. He prefers eating at home, even with the extra travel time involved. Still, I don't make anything fancy for lunch. I warm up leftovers in the microwave or boil a pot of noodles. So the actual time involved is minimal. And, of course, it's more fun to eat with my husband than all alone with no one to talk to.

Before, when the clinic was just getting started, there would often be no patient in the first afternoon slot, so the two of us would go to bed after lunch. Those were the loveliest times with him. Everything was hushed, and the soft afternoon sunshine would filter into the room. We were a lot younger then, and happier.

We're still happy, of course. I really do think so. No domestic troubles cast shadows on our home. I love him and trust him. And I'm sure he feels the same about me. But little by little, as the months and years go by, your life changes. That's just how it is. There's nothing you can do about it. Now all the afternoon slots are taken. When we finish eating, my husband brushes his teeth, hurries out to his car, and goes back to the office. He's got all those sick teeth waiting for him. But that's all right. We both know you can't have everything your own way.

After my husband goes back to the office, I take a bathing suit and towel and drive to the neighbourhood athletic club. I swim for half an hour. I swim hard. I'm not that crazy about the swimming itself: I just want to keep the flab off. I've always liked my own figure. Actually, I've never liked my face. It's not bad, but I've never felt I liked it. My body is another matter. I like to stand naked in front of the mirror. I like to study the soft outlines I see there, the balanced vitality. I'm not sure what it is, but I get the feeling that something inside there is very important to me. Whatever it is, I don't want to lose it.

I'm thirty. When you reach thirty, you realise it's not the end of the world. I'm not especially happy about getting older, but it does make some things easier. It's a question of attitude. One thing I know for sure, though: if a thirty-year-old woman loves her body and is serious about keeping it looking the way it should, she has to put in a certain amount of effort. I learned that from my mother. She used to be a slim, lovely woman, but not anymore. I don't want the same thing to happen to me.

After I've had my swim, I use the rest of my afternoon in various ways. Sometimes I'll wander over to the station plaza and window-shop. Sometimes I'll go home, curl up on the sofa and read a book or listen to an FM station or just rest. Eventually my son comes home from school. I help him change into his playclothes, and give him a snack. When he's through eating, he goes out to play with his friends. He's too young to go to an afternoon cram school, and we aren't making him take piano lessons or anything. 'Let him play,' says my husband. 'Let him grow up naturally.' When my son leaves the house, I have the same little dialogue with him as I do with my husband. 'Be careful,' I say, and he answers, 'Don't worry.'

As evening approaches, I begin preparing dinner. My son is always back by six. He watches cartoons on TV. If no emergency patients show up, my husband is home before seven. He doesn't drink a drop and he's not fond of pointless socialising. He almost always comes straight home from work.

The three of us talk during dinner, mostly about what we've done that day. My son always has the most to say. Everything that happens in his life is fresh and full of mystery. He talks, and we offer our comments. After dinner, he does what he likes—watches television or reads or plays some kind of game with my husband. When he has homework, he shuts himself up in his room and does it. He goes to bed at eight-thirty. I tuck him in and stroke his hair and say good night to him and turn off the light.

Then it's husband and wife together. He sits on the sofa, reading the newspaper and talking to me now and then about his patients or something in the paper. Then he listens to Haydn or Mozart. I don't mind listening to music, but I can never seem to tell the difference between those two composers. They sound the same to me. When I say that to my husband, he tells me it doesn't matter. 'It's all beautiful. That's what counts.'

'Just like you,' I say.

'Just like me,' he answers with a big smile. He seems genuinely pleased.

. . .

I remember with perfect clarity that first night I lost the ability to sleep. I was having a repulsive dream—a dark, slimy dream. I don't remember what it was about, but I do remember how it felt: ominous and terrifying. I woke at the climactic moment—came fully awake with a start, as if something had dragged me back at the last moment from a fatal turning point. Had I remained immersed in the dream for another second, I would have been lost forever. My breath came in painful gasps for a time after I awoke. My arms and legs felt paralysed. I lay there immobilised, listening to my own laboured breathing, as if I were stretched out full length on the floor of a huge cavern.

'It was a dream,' I told myself, and I waited for my breathing to calm down. Lying stiff on my back, I felt my heart working violently, my lungs hurrying the blood to it with big, slow, bellowslike contractions. I began to wonder what time it could be. I wanted to look at the clock by my pillow, but I couldn't turn my head far enough. Just then I seemed to catch a glimpse of something at the foot of the bed, something like a vague, black shadow. I caught my breath. My heart, my lungs, everything inside me seemed to freeze in that instant. I strained to see the black shadow.

The moment I tried to focus on it, the shadow began to assume a definite shape, as if it had been waiting for me to notice it. Its outline became distinct, and began to be filled with substance, and then with details. It was a gaunt old man wearing a skintight black shirt. His hair was gray and short, his cheeks sunken. He stood at my feet, perfectly still. He said nothing, but his piercing eyes stared at me. They were huge eyes, and I could see the red network of veins in them. The old man's face wore no expression at all. It told me nothing. It was like an opening in the darkness.

This was no longer the dream, I knew. From that, I had already wakened. And not just by drifting awake but by having my eyes ripped open. No, this was no dream. This was reality. And in reality an old man I had never seen before was standing at the foot of my bed. I had to do something—turn on the light, wake my husband, scream. I tried to move. I fought to make my limbs work, but it did no good. I couldn't move a finger. When it became clear to me that I would never be able to move, I was filled with a hopeless terror, a primal fear such as I had never experienced before, like a chill that rises silently from the bottomless well of memory. I tried to scream, but I was incapable of producing a sound, or even moving my tongue. All I could do was look at the old man.

Now I saw that he was holding something—a tall, narrow, rounded thing that shone white. As I stared at this object, wondering what it could be, it began to take on a definite shape, just as the shadow had earlier. It was a pitcher, an old-fashioned porcelain pitcher. After some time, the man raised the pitcher and began pouring water from it onto my feet. I could not feel the water. I could see it and hear it splashing down on my feet, but I couldn't feel a thing.

The old man went on and on pouring water over my feet. Strange—no matter how much he poured, the pitcher never ran dry. I began to worry that my feet would eventually rot and melt away. Yes, of course they would rot. What else could they do with so much water pouring over them? When it occurred to me that my feet were going to rot and melt away, I couldn't take it any longer.

I closed my eyes and let out a scream so loud it took every ounce of strength I had. But it never left my body. It reverberated soundlessly inside, tearing through me, shutting down my heart. Everything inside my head turned white for a moment as the scream penetrated my every cell. Something inside me died. Something melted away, leaving only a shuddering vacuum. An explosive flash incinerated everything my existence depended on.

. . .

I got out of bed and went to the bathroom. I threw my sweat-soaked nightgown into the washing machine and took a shower. After putting on a fresh pair of pyjamas, I went to the living room, switched on the floor lamp beside the sofa, and sat there drinking a full glass of brandy. I almost never drink. Not that I have a physical incompatibility with alcohol, as my husband does. In fact, I used to drink quite a lot, but after marrying him I simply stopped. Sometimes when I had trouble sleeping I would take a sip of brandy but that night I felt I wanted a whole glass to quiet my overwrought nerves.

. . .

I closed my eyes and swallowed another mouthful of brandy. The warmth spread from my throat to my stomach. The sensation felt tremendously *real*.

With a start, I thought of my son. Again my heart began

pounding. I hurried from the sofa to his room. He was sound asleep, one hand across his mouth, the other thrust out to the side, looking just as secure and peaceful in sleep as my husband. I straightened his blanket. Whatever it was that had so violently shattered my sleep, it had attacked only me. Neither of them had felt a thing.

I returned to the living room and wandered about there. I was not the least bit sleepy.

I considered drinking another glass of brandy. In fact, I wanted to drink even more alcohol than that. I wanted to warm my body more, to calm my nerves down more, and to feel that strong, penetrating bouquet in my mouth again. After some hesitation, I decided against it. I didn't want to start the new day drunk. I put the brandy back in the sideboard, brought the glass to the kitchen sink, and washed it. I found some strawberries in the refrigerator and ate them.

I realised that the trembling in my skin was almost gone.

What was that old man in black? I asked myself. I had never seen him before in my life. That black clothing of his was so strange, like a tight-fitting sweatsuit, and yet, at the same, old-fashioned. I had never seen anything like it. And those eyes— bloodshot, and never blinking. Who was he? Why did he pour water on my feet? Why did he have to do such a thing?

I had only questions, no answers.

. . .

I thought I'd read a book until I got tired again. I went to the bedroom and picked a novel from the bookcase. My husband didn't even twitch when I turned on the light to hunt for it. I chose 'Anna Karenina'. I was in the mood for a long Russian novel, and I had only read 'Anna Karenina' once, long ago, probably in high school. I remembered just a few things about it: the first line, 'All happy families resemble one another, every unhappy family is unhappy in its own way', and the heroine's throwing herself under a train at the end. And that early on there was a hint of the final suicide. Wasn't there a scene at a racetrack? Or was that in another novel?

Whatever. I went back to the sofa and opened the book. How many years had it been since I sat down and relaxed like this with a book? True, I often spent half an hour or an hour of my private time in the afternoon with a book open. But you couldn't really call that reading. I'd always find myself thinking about other things—my son, or shopping, or the freezer's needing to be fixed, or my having to find something to wear to a relative's wedding, or the stomach operation my father had last month. That kind of stuff would drift into my mind, and then it would grow, and take off in a million different directions. After a while I'd notice that the only thing that had gone by was the time, and I had hardly turned any pages.

Without noticing it, I had become accustomed in this way to a life without books. How strange, now that I think of it. Reading had been the centre of my life when I was young. I had read every book in the grade-school library, and almost my entire allowance would go for books. I'd even scrimp on lunches to buy books I wanted to read. And this went on into junior high and high school. Nobody read as much as I did. I was the middle one of five children, and both my parents worked, so nobody paid much attention to me. I could read alone as much as I liked. I'd always enter the essay contests on books so I could win a gift certificate for more books. And I usually won. In college I majored in English literature and got good grades. My graduation thesis on Katherine Mansfield won top honours, and my thesis adviser urged me to apply to graduate school. I wanted to go out into the world, though, and I knew that I was no scholar. I just enjoyed reading books. And, even if I had wanted to go on studying, my family didn't have the financial where-withal to send me to graduate school. We weren't poor by any means, but there were two sisters coming along after me, so once I graduated from college I simply had to begin supporting myself.

When had I really read a book last? And what had it been? I couldn't recall anything. Why did a person's life have to change so completely? Where had the old me gone, the one who used to read a book as if possessed by it? What had those days—and that almost abnormally intense passion— meant to me.

That night, I found myself capable of reading 'Anna Karenina' with unbroken concentration. I went on turning pages without another thought in mind. In one sitting, I read as far as the scene where Anna and Vronsky first see each other in the Moscow train station. At that point, I stuck my bookmark in and poured myself another glass of brandy.

Though it hadn't occurred to me before, I couldn't help thinking what an odd novel this was. You don't see the heroine, Anna, until Chapter 18. I wondered if it didn't seem unusual to readers in Tolstoy's day. What did they do when the book went on and on with a detailed description of the life of a minor character named Oblonsky—just sit there, waiting for the beautiful heroine to appear? Maybe that was it. Maybe people in those days had lots of time to kill—at least the part of society that read novels.

Then I noticed how late it was. Three in the morning! And still I wasn't sleepy.

What should I do? I don't feel sleepy at all, I thought. I could just keep on reading. I'd love to find out what happens in the story. But I have to sleep.

I remembered my ordeal with insomnia and how I had gone through each day back then, wrapped in a cloud. No, never again. I was still a student in those days. It was still possible for me to get away with something like that. But not now, I thought. Now I'm a wife. A mother. I have responsibilities. I have to make my husband's lunches and take care of my son.

But even if I get into bed now, I know I won't be able to sleep a wink.

I shook my head.

Let's face it, I'm just not sleepy, I told myself. And I want to read the rest of the book.

I sighed and stole a glance at the big volume lying on the table. And that was that. I plunged into 'Anna Karenina' and kept reading until the sun came up. Anna and Vronsky stared at each other at the ball and fell into their doomed love. Anna went to pieces when Vronsky's horse fell at the racetrack (so there *was* a racetrack scene, after all!) and confessed her infidelity to her husband. I was there with Vronsky when he spurred his horse over the obstacles. I heard the crowd cheering him on. And I was there in the stands watching his horse go down. When the window brightened with the morning light, I laid the book down and went to the kitchen for a cup of coffee. My mind was filled with scenes from the novel and with a tremendous hunger, obliterating any other thoughts. I cut two slices of bread, spread them with butter and mustard, and had a cheese sandwich. My hunger pangs were almost unbearable. It was rare for me to feel that hungry. I had trouble breathing, I was so hungry. One sandwich did hardly anything for me, so I made another one and had another cup of coffee with it.

To my husband I said nothing about either my trance or my night without sleep. Not that I was hiding them from him. It just seemed to me that there was no point in telling him. What good would it have done? And besides, I had simply missed a night's sleep. That much happens to everyone now and then.

I made my husband his usual cup of coffee and gave my son a glass of warm milk. My husband ate toast and my son a bowl of cornflakes. My husband skimmed the morning paper and my son hummed a new song he had learned in school. The two of them got into the Sentra and left. 'Be careful,' I said to my husband. 'Don't worry,' he answered. The two of them waved. A typical morning.

After they were gone, I sat on the sofa and thought about how to spend the rest of the day. What should I do? What did I have to do? I went to the kitchen to inspect the contents of the refrigerator. I could get by without shopping. We had bread, milk and eggs, and there was meat in the freezer. Plenty of vegetables, too. Everything I'd need through tomorrow's lunch.

I had business at the bank, but it was nothing I absolutely had to take care of immediately. Letting it go a day longer wouldn't hurt.

I went back to the sofa and started reading the rest of 'Anna Karenina'. Until that reading, I hadn't realised how little I remembered of what goes on in the book. I recognised virtually nothing—the characters, the scenes, nothing. I might as well have been reading a whole new book. How strange. I must have been deeply moved at the time I first read it, but now there was nothing left. Without my noticing, the memories of all the shuddering, soaring emotions had slipped away and vanished.

. . .

At ten o'clock I got into my bed, pretending that I would be sleeping there near my husband. He fell asleep right away, practically the moment the light went out, as if there were some cord connecting the lamp with his brain.

Amazing. People like that are rare. There are far more people who have trouble falling asleep. My father was one of those. He'd always complain about how shallow his sleep was. Not only did he find it hard to get to sleep, but the slightest sound or movement would wake him up for the rest of the night.

Not my husband, though. Once he was asleep nothing could wake him until morning. We were still newlyweds when it struck me how odd this was. I even experimented to see what it would take to wake him. I sprinkled water on his face and tickled his nose with a brush and that kind of thing. I never once got him to wake up. If I kept at it, I could get him to groan once, but that was all. And he never dreamed. At least he never remembered what his dreams were about. Needless to say, he never went into any paralytic trances. He slept. He slept like a turtle buried in mud.

Amazing. But it helped with what quickly became my nightly routine.

After ten minutes of lying near him, I would get out of bed. I would go to the living room, turn on the floor lamp, and pour myself a glass of brandy. Then I would sit on the sofa and read my book, taking tiny sips of brandy and letting the smooth liquid glide over my tongue. Whenever I felt like it, I would eat a cookie or a piece of chocolate that I had hidden in the sideboard. After a while, morning would come. When that happened, I would close my book and make myself a cup of coffee. Then I would make a sandwich and eat it.

My days became just as regulated.

. . .

No one noticed that I had changed—that I had given up sleeping entirely, that I was spending all my time reading, that my mind was some place a hundred years—and hundreds of miles—from reality. No matter how mechanically I worked, no matter how little love or emotion I invested in my handling of reality, my husband and my son and my mother-in-law went on relating to me as they always had. If anything, they seemed more at ease with me than before.

And so a week went by.

Once my constant wakefulness entered its second week, though, it started to worry me. It was simply not normal. People are supposed to sleep. All people sleep. Once, some years ago, I had read about a form of torture in which the victim is prevented from sleeping. Something the Nazis did, I think. They'd lock the person in a tiny room, fasten his eyelids open, and keep shining lights in his face and making loud noises without a break. Eventually, the person would go mad and die.

I couldn't recall how long the article said it took for the madness to set in, but it couldn't have been much more than three days or four. In my case, a whole week had gone by. This was simply too much. Still, my health was not suffering. Far from it, I had more energy than ever.

One day, after showering, I stood naked in front of the mirror. I was amazed to discover that my body appeared to be almost bursting with vitality. I studied every inch of myself, head to toe, but I could find not the slightest hint of excess flesh, not one wrinkle. I no longer had the body of a young girl, of course, but my skin had far more glow, far more tautness than it had before. I took a pinch of flesh near my waist, and found it almost hard, with a wonderful elasticity.

It dawned on me that I was prettier than I had realised. I looked so much younger than before that it was almost shocking. I could probably pass for twenty-four. My skin was smooth. My eyes were bright, lips moist. The shadowed area beneath my protruding cheekbones (the one feature I really hated about myself) was no longer noticeable—at all. I sat down and looked at my face in the mirror for a good thirty minutes. I studied it from all angles, objectively. No, I had not been mistaken: it was really pretty.

What was happening to me?

I thought about seeing a doctor.

I had a doctor who had been taking care of me since I was

a child and to whom I felt close, but the more I thought about how he might react to my story the less inclined I felt to tell it to him. Would he take me at my word? He'd probably think I was crazy if I said I hadn't slept in a week. Or he might dismiss it as a kind of neurotic insomnia. But if he did believe I was telling the truth, he might send me to some big research hospital for testing.

And *then* what would happen?

I'd be locked up and sent from one lab to another to be experimented on. They'd do EEGs and EKGs and urinalyses and blood tests and psychological screening and who knows what else.

I couldn't take that. I just wanted to stay by myself and quietly read my book. I wanted to have my hour of swimming every day. I wanted my freedom: that's what I wanted more than anything. I didn't want to go to any hospitals. And, even if they *did* get me into a hospital, what would they find? they'd do a mountain of tests and formulate a mountain of hypotheses, and that would be the end of it. I didn't want to be locked up in a place like that.

. . .

Now my inability to sleep ceased to frighten me. What was there to be afraid of? Think of the advantages! Now the hours from ten at night to six in the morning belonged to me alone. Until now, a third of every day had been used up by sleep. But no more. No more. Now it was mine, just mine, nobody else's, all mine. I could use this time in any way I liked. No one would get in my way. No one would make demands on me. Yes, that was it. I had expanded my life. I had increased it by a third.

You are probably going to tell me that this is biologically abnormal. And you may be right. And maybe someday in the future I'll have to pay back the debt I'm building up by continuing to do this biologically abnormal thing. Maybe life will try to collect on the expanded part—this 'advance' it is paying me now. This is a groundless hypothesis, but there is no ground for negating it, and it feels right to me somehow.

Which means that in the end the balance sheet of borrowed time will even out.

Honestly, though, I didn't give a damn, even if I had to die young. The best thing to do with a hypothesis is to let it run any course it pleases. Now, at least, I was expanding my life, and it was wonderful. My hands weren't empty anymore. Here I was—alive, and I could feel it. It was real. I wasn't being consumed any longer. Or at least there was a part of me in existence that was not being consumed, and that was what gave me this intensely real feeling of being alive. A life without that feeling might go on forever, but it would have no meaning to all. I saw that with absolute clarity now.

After checking to see that my husband was asleep I would go sit on the living-room sofa, drinking brandy by myself, and open my book. I read 'Anna Karenina' three times. Each time, I made new discoveries. This enormous novel was full of relevations and riddles. Like a Chinese box, the world of the novel contained smaller worlds, and inside those were yet smaller worlds. Together, these worlds made up a single universe, and the universe waited there in the book to be discovered by the reader. The old me had been able to understand only the tiniest fragment of it, but the gaze of this new me could penetrate to the core with perfect understanding. I knew exactly what the great Tolstoy wanted to say, what he wanted the reader to get from his book; I could see how his message had organically crystallised as a novel, and what in that novel had surpassed the author himself.

No matter how hard I concentrated, I never tired. After reading 'Anna Karenina' as many times as I could, I read Dostoyevski. I could read book after book with utter concentration and never tire. I could understand the most difficult passages without effort. And I responded with deep emotion.

I felt that I had always been meant to be like this. By abandoning sleep I had expanded myself. The power to concentrate was the most important thing. Living without this power would be like opening one's eyes without seeing anything.

Eventually, my bottle of brandy ran out. I had drunk almost all of it by myself. I went to the gourmet department of a big store for another bottle of Remy Martin. As long as I was there,

I figured, I might as well buy a bottle of red wine, too. And a fine crystal brandy glass. And chocolate and cookies.

Sometimes while reading I would become overexcited. When that happened, I would put my book down and exercise—do callisthenics or just walk around the room. Depending on my mood, I might go out for a nighttime drive. I'd change clothes, get into my Civic, and drive aimlessly around the neighbourhood. Sometimes I'd drop into an all-night fast-food place for a cup of coffee, but it was such a bother to have to deal with other people that I'd usually stay in the car. I'd stop in some safe-looking spot and just let my mind wander. Or I'd go all the way to the harbour and watch the boats.

One time, though, I was questioned by a policeman. It was two-thirty in the morning, and I was parked under a street lamp near the pier, listening to the car stereo and watching the lights of the ships passing by. He knocked on my window. I lowered the glass. He was young and handsome, and very polite. I explained to him that I couldn't sleep. He asked for my licence and studied it for a while. 'There was a murder here last month,' he said. 'Three young men attacked a couple, killed the man, and raped the woman.' I remembered having read about the incident. I nodded. 'If you don't have any business here, Ma'am, you'd better not hang around here at night.' I thanked him and said I would leave. He gave my licence back. I drove away.

. . .

I shook my head.

I closed my eyes and kept them shut. Then I opened them and looked at my son's face again. And then it hit me. What bothered me about my son's sleeping face was that it looked exactly like my husband's. And exactly like my mother-in-law's. Stubborn. Self-satisfied. It was in their blood—a kind of arrogance I hated in my husband's family. True, my husband is good to me. He's sweet and gentle and he's careful to take my feelings into account. He's never fooled around with other women, and he works hard. He's serious, and he's kind to everybody. My friends all tell me how lucky I am to have him. And I can't fault him, either. Which is exactly what galls me sometimes. His very absence of faults makes for a strange rigidity that excludes imagination. That's what grates on me so.

And that was exactly the kind of expression my son had on his face as he slept.

I shook my head again. This little boy is a stranger to me, finally. Even after he grows up, he'll never be able to understand me, just as my husband can hardly understand what I feel now.

I love my son, no question. But I sensed that someday I would no longer be able to love this boy with the same intensity. Not a very maternal thought. Most mothers never have thoughts like that. But as I stood there looking at him asleep, I knew with absolute certainty that one day I would come to despise him.

The thought made me terribly sad. I closed his door and turned out the hall light. I went to the living-room sofa, sat down, and opened my book. After reading a few pages, I closed it again. I looked at the clock. A little before three.

I wondered how many days it had been since I stopped sleeping. The sleeplessness started the Tuesday before last. Which made this the seventeenth day. Not one wink of sleep in seventeen days. Seventeen days and seventeen nights. A long, long time. I couldn't even recall what sleep was like.

I closed my eyes and tried to recall the sensation of sleeping, but all that existed for me inside was a wakeful darkness. A wakeful darkness: what it called to mind was death.

Was I about to die?

And if I died now, what would my life have amounted to?

There was no way I could answer that.

All right, then, what *was* death?

Until now I had conceived of sleep as a kind of model for death. I had imagined death as an extension of sleep. A far deeper sleep than ordinary sleep. A sleep devoid of all consciousness. Eternal rest. A total blackout.

But now I wondered if I had been wrong. Perhaps death was a state entirely unlike sleep, something that belonged to a different category altogether—like the deep, endless wakeful darkness I was seeing now.

No, that would be too terrible. If the state of death was not to be a rest for us, then what was going to redeem this imperfect life of ours, so fraught with exhaustion? Finally, though, no one knows what death is. Who has ever truly seen it? No one. Except the ones who are dead. No one living knows what death is like. They can only guess. And the best guess is still a guess. Maybe death *is* a kind of rest, but reasoning can't tell us that. The only way to find out what death is is to die. *Death can be anything at all.*

An intense terror overwhelmed me at the thought. A stiffening chill ran down my spine. My eyes were still shut tight. I had lost the power to open them. I stared at the thick darkness that stood planted in front of me, a darkness as deep and hopeless as the universe itself. I was all alone. My mind was in deep concentration, and expanding. If I had wanted to, I could have seen into the uttermost depths of the universe. But I decided not to look. It was too soon for that.

If death was like this, if to die meant being eternally awake and staring into the darkness like this, what should I do?

At last, I managed to open my eyes. I gulped down the brandy that was left in my glass.

I'm taking off my pyjamas and putting on jeans, a T-shirt, and a windbreaker. I tie my hair back in a tight ponytail, tuck it under the windbreaker, and put on a baseball cap of my husband's. In the mirror I look like a boy. Good. I put on sneakers and go down to the garage.

I slip in behind the steering wheel, turn the key, and listen to the engine hum. It sounds normal. Hands on the wheel, I take a few deep breaths. Then I shift into gear and drive out of the building. The car is running better than usual. It seems to be gliding across a sheet of ice. I ease it into higher gear, move out of the neighbourhood, and enter the highway to Yokohama.

It's only three in the morning, but the number of cars on the road is by no means small. Huge semis roll past, shaking the ground as they head east. Those guys don't sleep at night. They sleep in the daytime and work at night for greater efficiency.

What a waste. I could work day *and* night. I don't have to sleep.

This is biologically unnatural, I suppose, but who really

knows what is natural? They just infer it inductively. I'm beyond that. *A priori*. An evolutionary leap. A woman who never sleeps. An expansion of consciousness.

I have to smile. *A priori*. An evolutionary leap.

Listening to the car radio, I drive to the harbour. I want classical music, but I can't find a station that broadcasts it at night. Stupid Japanese rock music. Love songs sweet enough to rot your teeth. I give up searching and listen to those. They make me feel I'm in a far-off place, far away from Mozart and Haydn.

I pull into one of the white-outlined spaces in the big parking lot at the waterfront park and cut my engine. This is the brightest area of the lot, under a lamp, and wide open all around. Only one other car is parked here—an old, white two-door coupé of the kind that young people like to drive. Probably a couple in there now, making love—no money for a hotel room. To avoid trouble, I pull my hat low, trying not to look like a woman. I check to see that my doors are locked.

Half consciously, I let my eyes wander through the surrounding darkness, when all of a sudden I remember a drive I took with my boyfriend the year I was a college freshman. We parked and got into some heavy petting. He couldn't stop, he said, and he begged me to let him put it in. But I refused. Hands on the steering wheel, listening to the music, I try to bring back the scene, but I can't recall his face. It all seems to have happened such an incredibly long time ago.

All the memories I have from the time before I stopped sleeping seem to be moving away with accelerating speed. It feels so strange, as if the me who used to go to sleep every night is not the real me, and the memories from back then are not really mine. This is how people change. But nobody realises it. Nobody notices. Only I know what happens. I could try to tell them, but they wouldn't understand. They wouldn't believe me. Or if they did believe me, they would have absolutely no idea what I'm feeling. They would only see me as a threat to their inductive world view.

I am changing, though. *Really* changing.

How long have I been sitting here? Hands on the wheel. Eyes closed. Staring into the sleepless darkness.

Suddenly I'm aware of a human presence, and I come to

myself again. There's somebody out there. I open my eyes and look around. Someone is outside the car. Trying to open the door. But the doors are locked. Dark shadows on either side of the car, one at each door. Can't see their faces. Can't make out their clothing. Just two dark shadows, standing there.

Sandwiched between them, my Civic feels tiny—like a little pastry box. It's being rocked from side to side. A fist is pounding on the right-hand window. I know it's not a policeman. A policeman would never pound on the glass like this and would never shake my car. I hold my breath. What should I do? I can't think straight. My underarms are soaked. I've got to get out of here. The key. Turn the key. I reach out for it and turn it to the right. The starter grinds.

The engine doesn't catch. My hand is shaking. I close my eyes and turn the key again. No good. A sound like fingernails clawing a giant wall. The motor turns and turns. The men— the dark shadows—keep shaking my car. The swings get bigger and bigger. They're going to tip me over!

There's something wrong. Just calm down and think, then everything will be OK. Think. Just think. Slowly. Carefully. Something is wrong.

Something is wrong.

But what? I can't tell. My mind is crammed full of thick darkness. It's not taking me anywhere. My hands are shaking. I try pulling out the key and putting it back in again. But my shaking hand can't find the hole. I try again and drop the key. I curl over and try to pick it up. But I can't get hold of it. The car is rocking back and forth. My forehead slams against the steering wheel.

I'll never get the key. I fall back against the seat, cover my face with my hands. I'm crying. All I can do is cry. The tears keep pouring out. Locked inside this little box, I can't go anywhere. It's the middle of the night. The men keep rocking the car back and forth. They're going to turn it over.

A Sense of Quickened Heartbeats

ANN RADCLIFFE

Our heroine, Emily St Aubert, is placed in the care of her aunt, Madam Cheron, after the death of her parents. The aunt soon marries Count Montoni, a gambler and the villain in the Gothic novel The Mysteries of Udolpho. *He takes the two women to his isolated Castle of Udolpho. There Emily lives in fear that the Count will sell her to one of his gambling friends to pay off his debts. Montoni torments Emily with the prospect of allowing her to be raped by one of his associates who is infatuated with her, the Count Morano. Trapped in the castle and with bedroom doors that cannot be properly locked, Emily dreads Morano's arrival. Fear dominates Emily's life, but it is not the ghosts that the servant Annette tells her haunt Montoni's castle that most threaten her (though they give her some sleepless nights too), but real men. Like Wollstonecraft, Radcliffe was concerned with the problems women experienced when not in control of their own bodies or property. The passages below come mid-way through the novel.*

Ann Radcliffe was born in London in 1764. In 1790 she published her first full length Gothic novel of terror and romance, A Sicilian Romance, *to a good deal of praise. It was then followed by* Romance of the Forest *and* Udolpho *in 1794. Radcliffe continued to write until a few years before her death in 1823.*

The Mysteries of Udolpho

Emily's mind had not yet sufficiently recovered from its late shock, to endure the loneliness of her chamber, and she remained upon the ramparts; for Madame Montoni had not invited her to her dressing-room, whither she had gone evidently in low spirits and Emily, from her late experience, had lost all wish to explore the gloomy and mysterious recesses of the castle. The ramparts, therefore, were almost her only retreat, and here she lingered, till the gray haze of evening was again spread over the scene.

The cavaliers supped by themselves, and Madam Montoni remained in her apartment, whither Emily went, before she retired to her own. She found her aunt weeping, and in much agitation. The tenderness of Emily was naturally so soothing, that it seldom failed to give comfort to the drooping heart: but Madam Montoni's was torn, and the softest accents of Emily's voice were lost upon it. With her usual delicacy, she did not appear to observe her aunt's distress, but it gave an involuntary gentleness to her manners, and an air of solicitude to her countenance, which Madam Montoni was vexed to perceive, who seemed to feel the pity of her niece to be an insult to her pride, and dismissed her as soon as she properly could. Emily did not venture to mention again the reluctance she felt to her gloomy chamber, but she requested that Annette might be permitted to remain with her till she retired to rest; and the request was somewhat reluctantly granted. Annette, however, was now with the servants, and Emily withdrew alone.

With light and hasty steps she passed through the long galleries, while the feeble glimmer of the lamp she carried only showed the gloom around her, and the passing air threatened to extinguish it. The lonely silence, that reigned in this part of the castle, awed her; now and then, indeed, she heard a faint peal of laughter rise from a remote part of the edifice, where the servants were assembled, but it was soon lost, and a kind of breathless stillness remained. As she passed the suite of rooms which she had visited in the morning, her eyes glanced fearfully on the door, and she almost fancied she heard murmuring sounds within, but she paused not a moment to enquire.

Having reached her own apartment, where no blazing wood on the hearth dissipated the gloom, she sat down with a book, to enliven her attention, till Annette should come, and a fire could be kindled. She continued to read till her light was nearly expired, but Annette did not appear, and the solitude and obscurity of her chamber again affected her spirits, the more, because of its nearness to the scene of horror, that she had witnessed in the morning. Gloomy and fantastic images came to her mind. She looked fearfully towards the door of the stair-case, and then, examining whether it was still fastened, found that it was so. Unable to conquer the uneasiness she felt at the prospect of sleeping again in this remote and insecure apartment, which some person seemed to have entered during the preceding night, her impatience to see Annette, whom she had bidden to enquire concerning this circumstance, became extremely painful. She wished also to question her, as to the object, which had excited so much horror in her own mind, and which Annette on the preceding evening had appeared to be in part acquainted with, though her words were very remote from the truth, and it appeared plainly to Emily, that the girl had been purposely misled by a false report: above all she was surprised, that the door of the chamber, which contained it, should be left unguarded. Such an instance of negligence almost surpassed belief. But her light was now expiring; the faint flashes it threw upon the walls called up all the terrors of fancy, and she rose to find her way to the habitable part of the castle, before it was quite extinguished.

As she opened the chamber door, she heard remote voices, and soon after, saw a light issue upon the further end of the corridor, which Annette and another servant approached. 'I am glad you are come,' said Emily: 'what has detained you so long? Pray light me a fire immediately.'

'My lady wanted me, ma'amselle,' replied Annette in some confusion; 'I will go and get the wood.'

'No,' said Caterina, 'that is my business,' and left the room instantly, while Annette would have followed; but, being called back, she began to talk very loud, and laugh, and seemed afraid to trust a pause of silence.

Caterina soon returned with the wood, and then, when the cheerful blaze once more animated the room, and this servant had withdrawn, Emily asked Annette whether she had made the enquiry she bade her. 'Yes, ma'amselle,' said Annette, 'but not a soul knows anything about the matter: and old Carlo—I watched him well, for they say he knows strange things—old Carlo looked so as I don't know how to tell, and he asked me again and again, if I was sure the door was ever unfastened.

Lord, says I—am I sure I am alive? And as for me, ma'am, I am all astounded, as one may say, and would no more sleep in this chamber, than I would on the great cannon at the end of the east rampart.'

'And what objection have you to that cannon, more than to any of the rest?' said Emily smiling: 'the best would be rather a hard bed.'

'Yes, ma'amselle, any of them would be hard enough for that matter; but they do say, that something has been seen in the dead of night, standing beside the great cannon, as if to guard it.'

'Well! my good Annette, the people who tell such stories, are happy in having you for an auditor, for I perceive you believe them all.'

'Dear ma'amselle! I will shew you the very cannon; you can see it from these windows!'

'Well,' said Emily, 'but that does not prove, that an apparition guards it.'

'What! not if I shew you the very cannon! Dear ma'am, you will believe nothing.'

'Nothing probably upon this subject, but what I see,' said Emily.—'Well, ma'am, but you shall see it, if you will only step this way to the casement.'—Emily could not forbear laughing, and Annette looked surprised. Perceiving her extreme aptitude to credit the marvellous, Emily forbore to mention the subject she had intended, lest it should overcome her with idle terrors, and she began to speak on a lively topic—the regattas of Venice.

'Aye, ma'amselle, those rowing matches,' said Annette, 'and the fine moon-light nights, are all, that are worth seeing in Venice. To be sure that moon is brighter than any I ever saw; and then to hear such sweet music, too, as Ludovico has often and often sung under the lattice by the west portico! Ma'amselle, it was Ludovico, that told me about that picture, which you wanted so to look at last night, and—'

'What picture?' said Emily, wishing Annette to explain herself.

'O! that terrible picture with the black veil over it.'

'You never saw it, then?' said Emily.

'Who, I!—No, ma'amselle, I never did. But this morning,' continued Annette, lowering her voice, and looking round the room, 'this morning as it was broad daylight, do you know, ma'am, I took a strange fancy to see it, as I had heard such odd hints about it, and I got as far as the door, and should have opened it, if it had not been locked!'

Emily, endeavouring to conceal the emotion this circumstance occasioned, enquired at what hour she went to the chamber, and found, that it was soon after herself had been there. She also asked further questions, and the answers convinced her, that Annette, and probably her informer, were ignorant of the terrible truth, though in Annette's account something very like the truth, now and then, mingled with the falsehood. Emily now began to fear, that her visit to the chamber had been observed, since the door had been closed, so immediately after her departure; and dreaded lest this should draw upon her the vengeance of Montoni. Her anxiety, also, was excited to know whence, and for what purpose, the delusive report, which had been imposed upon Annette, had originated since Montoni could only have wished for silence and secrecy; but she felt that the subject was too terrible for this lonely hour, and she compelled herself to leave it, to converse with Annette, whose chat, simple as it was, she preferred to the stillness of total solitude.

Thus they sat, till near midnight, but not without many hints from Annette, that she wished to go. The embers were now nearly burnt out; and Emily heard, at a distance, the thundering sound of the hall doors, as they were shut for the night. She, therefore, prepared for rest, but was still unwilling that Annette should leave her. At this instant, the great bell of the portal sounded. They listened in fearful expectation, when after a long pause of silence, it sounded again. Soon after, they heard the noise of carriage wheels in the court-yard. Emily sunk almost lifeless in her chair; 'It is the Count,' said she.

'What, at this time of night, ma'am!' said Annette: 'no, my dear lady. But, for that matter, it is a strange time of night for any body to come!'

'Nay, pr'ythee, good Annette, stay not talking,' said Emily in a voice of agony—'Go, pr'ythee, go, and see who it is.'

Annette left the room, and carried with her the light, leaving Emily in darkness, which a few moments before would have terrified her in this room, but was now scarcely observed by her. She listened and waited, in breathless expectation, and heard distant noises, but Annette did not return. Her patience, at length, exhausted, she tried to find her way to the corridor, but it was long before she could touch the door of the chamber, and, when she had opened it, the total darkness without made her fear to proceed. Voices were not heard, and Emily even thought she distinguished those of Count Morano, and Montoni. Soon after, she heard steps approaching, and then a ray of light streamed through the darkness, and Annette appeared, whom Emily went to meet.

'Yes, ma'amselle,' said she, 'you are right, it is the Count sure enough.'

'It is he!' exclaimed Emily, lifting her eyes towards heaven and supporting herself by Annette's arm.

'Good Lord! my dear lady, don't be in such a *fluster*, and look so pale, we shall soon hear more.'

'We shall, indeed!' said Emily, moving as fast as she was able towards her apartment. 'I am not well; give me air.' Annette opened a casement, and brought water. The faintness soon left Emily, but she desired Annette would not go till she heard from Montoni.

'Dear ma'amselle! he surely will not disturb you at this time of night; why he must think you are asleep.'

'Stay with me till I am so, then,' said Emily, who felt temporary relief from this suggestion, which appeared probable enough, though her fears had prevented its occurring to her. Annette, with secret reluctance, consented to stay, and Emily was now composed enough to ask her some questions; among others, whether she had seen the Count.

'Yes, ma'am, I saw him alight, for I went from hence to the grate in the north turret, that overlooks the inner court-yard, you know. There I saw the Count's carriage, and the Count in it, waiting at the great door,—for the porter was just gone to bed—with several men on horseback all by the light of the torches they carried.' Emily was compelled to smile. 'When the door was opened, the Count said something, that I could not make out, and then got out, and another gentleman with him.

I thought, to be sure, the Signor was gone to bed, and I hastened away to my lady's dressing-room, to see what I could hear. But in the way I met Ludovico, and he told me that the Signor was up, counselling with his master and the other Signors in the room at the end of the north gallery; and Ludovico held up his finger, and laid it on his lips, as much as to say—There is more going on, than you think of, Annette, but you must hold your tongue. And so I did hold my tongue, ma'amselle, and came away to tell you directly.'

Emily enquired who the cavalier was, that accompanied the Count, and how Montoni received them; but Annette could not inform her.

'Ludovico,' she added, 'had just been to call Signor Montoni's valet, that he might tell him they were arrived, when I met him.'

Emily sat musing, for some time, and then her anxiety was so much increased, that she desired Annette would go to the servants' hall, where it was possible she might hear something of the Count's intention, respecting his stay at the castle.

'Yes, ma'am,' said Annette with readiness; 'but how am I to find the way, if I leave the lamp with you?'

Emily said she would light her, and they immediately quitted the chamber. When they had reached the top of the great stair-case, Emily recollected, that she might be seen by the Count, and, to avoid the great hall, Annette conducted her through some private passages to a back stair-case, which led directly to that of the servants.

As she returned towards her chamber, Emily began to fear, that she might again lose herself in the intricacies of the castle, and again be shocked by some mysterious spectacle; and, though she was already perplexed by the numerous turnings, she feared to open one of the many doors that offered. While she stepped thoughtfully along, she fancied, that she heard a low moaning at no great distance, and, having paused a moment, she heard it again and distinctly. Several doors appeared on the right hand of the passage. She advanced, and listened. When she came to the second, she heard a voice, apparently in complaint, within, to which she continued to listen, afraid to open the door, and unwilling to leave it. Convulsive sobs followed, and then the piercing accents of an agonising spirit burst forth. Emily stood appalled, and looked through the gloom, that surrounded her, in fearful expectation. The lamentations continued. Pity now began to subdue terror; it was possible she might administer comfort to the sufferer, at least, by expressing sympathy, and she laid her hand on the door. While she hesitated she thought she knew this voice, disguised as it was by tones of grief. Having, therefore, set down the lamp in the passage, she gently opened the door, within which all was dark, except that from an inner apartment a partial light appeared; and she stepped softly on. Before she reached it, the appearance of Madame Montoni, leaning on her dressing-table, weeping, and with a handkerchief held to her eyes, struck her, and she paused.

Some person was seated in a chair by the fire, but who it was she could not distinguish. He spoke, now and then, in a low voice, that did not allow Emily to hear what was uttered, but she thought, that Madame Montoni, at those times, wept the more, who was too much occupied by her own distress, to observe Emily, while the latter, though anxious to know what occasioned this, and who was the person admitted at so late an hour to her aunt's dressing-room, forbore to add to her sufferings by surprising her, or to take advantage of her situation, by listening to a private discourse. She, therefore, stepped softly back, and, after some further difficulty, found the way to her own chamber, where nearer interests, at length, excluded the surprise and concern she had felt, respecting Madame Montoni.

Annette, however, returned without satisfactory intelligence, for the servants, among whom she had been, were either entirely ignorant, or affected to be so, concerning the Count's intended stay at the castle. They could talk only of the steep and broken road they had just passed, and of the numerous dangers they had escaped and express wonder how their lord could choose to encounter all these, in the darkness of night; for they scarcely allowed, that the torches had served for any other purpose but that of shewing the dreariness of the mountains. Annette, finding she could gain no information, left them, making noisy petitions, for more wood on the fire and more supper on the table.

'And now, ma'amselle,' added she, 'I am so sleepy!—I am

sure, if you was so sleepy, you would not desire me to sit up with you.'

Emily, indeed, began to think it was cruel to wish it; she had also waited so long, without receiving a summons from Montoni, that it appeared he did not mean to disturb her, at this late hour, and she determined to dismiss Annette. But, when she again looked round her gloomy chamber, and recollected certain circumstances, fear seized her spirits, and she hesitated.

'And yet it were cruel of me to ask you to stay, till I am asleep, Annette,' said she, 'for I fear it will be very long before I forget myself in sleep.'

'I dare say it will be very long, ma'amselle,' said Annette.

'But, before you go,' rejoined Emily, 'let me ask you—Had Signor Montoni left Count Morano, when you quitted the hall?'

'O no, ma'am, they were alone together.'

'Have you been in my aunt's dressing-room, since you left me?'

'No, ma'amselle, I called at the door as I passed, but it was fastened; so I thought my lady was gone to bed.'

'Who, then, was with your lady just now?' said Emily, forgetting, in surprise, her usual prudence.

'Nobody, I believe, ma'am,' replied Annette, 'nobody has been with her, I believe, since I left you.'

Emily took no further notice of the subject, and, after some struggle with imaginary fears, her good nature prevailed over them so far, that she dismissed Annette for the night. She then sat, musing upon her own circumstances and those of Madame Montoni, till her eye rested on the miniature picture, which she had found, after her father's death, among the papers he had enjoined her to destroy. It was open upon the table, before her, among some loose drawings, having, with them, been taken out of a little box by Emily, some hours before. The sight of it called up many interesting reflections, but the melancholy sweetness of the countenance soothed the emotions, which these had occasioned. It was the same style of countenance as that of her late father, and, while she gazed on it with fondness on this account, she even fancied a resemblance in the features. But this tranquillity was suddenly interrupted, when she recollected the words in the manuscript, that had been found with this picture, and which had formerly occasioned her so much doubt and horror. At length, she roused herself from the deep reverie, into which this remembrance had thrown her; but, when she rose to undress, the silence and solitude, to which she was left, at this midnight hour, for not even a distant sound was now heard, conspired with the impression the subject she had been considering had given to her mind, to appall her. Annette's hints, too, concerning this chamber, simple as they were, had not failed to affect her, since they followed a circumstance of peculiar horror, which she herself had witnessed, and since the scene of this was a chamber nearly adjoining her own.

The door of the stair-case was, perhaps, a subject of more reasonable alarm, and she now began to apprehend, such was the aptitude of her fears, that this stair-case had some private communication with the apartment, which she shuddered even to remember. Determined not to undress, she lay down to sleep in her clothes, with her late father's dog, the faithful *Manchon*, at the foot of the bed, whom she considered as a kind of guard.

Thus circumstanced, she tried to banish reflection, but her busy fancy would still hover over the subjects of her interest, and she heard the clock of the castle strike two, before she closed her eyes.

From the disturbed slumber, into which she then sunk, she was soon wakened by a noise, which seemed to arise within her chamber; but the silence, that prevailed, as she fearfully listened, inclined her to believe, that she had been alarmed by such sounds as sometimes occur in dreams, and she laid her head again upon the pillow.

A return of the noise again disturbed her; it seemed to come from that part of the room, which communicated with the private stair-case, and she instantly remembered the odd circumstance of the door having been fastened, during the preceding night, by some unknown hand. Her late alarming suspicion, concerning its communication, also occurred to her. Her heart became faint with terror. Half raising herself from the bed, and gently drawing aside the curtain, she looked towards the door of the stair-case, but the lamp, that burnt on the hearth, spread so feeble a light through the apartment, that the remote parts of it were lost in shadow. The noise, however, which, she was convinced, came from the door, continued. It seemed like that made by the undrawing of rusty bolts, and often ceased, and was then renewed more gently, as if that hand, that occasioned it, was restrained by a fear of discovery. While Emily kept her eyes fixed on the spot, she saw the door move, and then slowly open, and perceived something enter the room, but the extreme duskiness prevented her distinguishing what it was. Almost fainting with terror, she had yet sufficient command over herself, to check the shriek, that was escaping from her lips, and, letting the curtain drop from her hand, continued to observe in silence the motions of the mysterious form she saw. It seemed to glide along the remote obscurity of the apartment, then paused, and, as it approached the hearth, she perceived, in the stronger light, what appeared to be a human figure. Certain remembrances now struck upon her heart, and almost subdued the feeble remains of her spirits; she continued, however, to watch the figure, which remained for some time motionless, but then, advancing slowly towards the bed, stood silently at the feet, where the curtains, being a little open, allowed her still to see it; terror, however, had now deprived her of the power of discrimination, as well as of that of utterance.

Having continued there a moment, the form retreated towards the hearth, when it took the lamp, held it up, surveyed the chamber, for a few moments, and then again advanced towards the bed. The light at that instant awakening the dog, that had slept at Emily's feet, he barked loudly, and jumping to the floor, flew at the stranger, who struck the animal smartly with a sheathed sword, and, springing towards the bed, Emily discovered—Count Morano!

She gazed at him for a moment in speechless affright, while he, throwing himself on his knee at the bed-side, besought her to fear nothing, and, having thrown down his sword, would have taken her hand, when the faculties, that terror had suspended, suddenly returned, and she sprung from the bed, in the dress, which surely a kind of prophetic apprehension had prevented her, on this night, from throwing aside.

Morano rose, followed her to the door, through which he had entered, and caught her hand, as she reached the top of the stair-case, but not before she had discovered, by the gleam of a lamp, another man half-way down the steps. She now screamed in despair, and, believing herself given up by Montoni saw, indeed, no possibility of escape.

The Count, who still held her hand, led her back into the chamber.

'Why all this terror?' said he, in a tremulous voice. 'Hear me, Emily: I come not to alarm you; no, by Heaven! I love you too well—too well for my own peace.'

Emily looked at him for a moment, in fearful doubt.

'Then leave me, sir,' said she, 'leave me instantly.'

Morano continues to plead his love to Emily who does not cease to resist him. Before he can leave her chamber, Emily's uncle Count Montoni enters, furious that Morano and Emily have been courting without his intercession. A fight between the men ensues, with Morano seriously injured. Emily tends to his wounds and then is bid to Montoni's chamber where he rebukes her for lacking virtue. She is shocked by his words.

Emily, who had always endeavoured to regulate her conduct by the nicest laws, and whose mind was finely sensible, not only of what is just in morals, but of whatever is beautiful in the female character, was shocked by these words; yet, in the next moment, her heart swelled with the consciousness of having deserved praise, instead of censure, and she was proudly silent. Montoni, acquainted with the delicacy of her mind, knew how keenly she would feel his rebuke; but he was a stranger to the luxury of conscious worth, and, therefore, did not foresee the energy of that sentiment, which now repelled his satire. Turning to a servant who had lately entered the room, he asked whether Morano had quitted the castle. The man answered, that his servants were then removing him, on a couch, to a neighbouring cottage. Montoni seemed somewhat appeased, on hearing this; and, when Ludovico appeared, a few moments after, and said, that Morano was gone, he told Emily she might retire to her apartment.

She withdrew willingly from his presence; but the thought of passing the remainder of the night in a chamber, which the door from the stair-case made liable to the intrusion of any person, now alarmed her more than ever, and she determined to call at Madame Montoni's room, and request, that Annette might be permitted to be with her.

On reaching the great gallery, she heard voices seemingly in dispute, and, her spirits now apt to take alarm, she paused, but soon distinguished some words of Cavigni and Verezzi, and went towards them, in the hope of conciliating their difference. They were alone. Verezzi's face was still flushed with rage; and, as the first object of it was now removed from him, he appeared willing to transfer his resentment to Cavigni, who seemed to be expostulating, rather than disputing, with him.

Verezzi was protesting, that he would instantly inform Montoni of the insult, which Morano had thrown out against him, and above all, that, wherein he had accused him of murder.

'There is no answering,' said Cavigni, 'for the words of a man in a passion; little serious regard ought to be paid to them. If you persist in your resolution, the consequences may be fatal to both. We have now more serious interest to pursue, than those of a petty revenge.'

Emily joined her entreaties to Cavigni's arguments, and they, at length, prevailed so far, as that Verezzi consented to retire, without seeing Montoni.

On calling at her aunt's apartment, she found it fastened. In a few minutes, however, it was opened by Madame Montoni herself.

It may be remembered, that it was by a door leading into the bedroom from a back passage, that Emily had secretly entered a few hours preceding. She now conjectured, by the calmness of Madame Montoni's air, that she was not apprised of the accident, which had befallen her husband, and was beginning to inform her of it, in the tenderest manner she could, when her aunt interrupted her, by saying, she was acquainted with the whole affair.

Emily knew indeed, that she had little reason to love Montoni, but could scarcely have believed her capable of such perfect apathy, as she now discovered towards him; having obtained permission, however, for Annette to sleep in her chamber, she went thither immediately.

A track of blood appeared along the corridor, leading to it; and on the spot, where the Count and Montoni had fought, the whole floor was stained. Emily shuddered, and leaned on Annette, as she passed. When she reached her apartment, she instantly determined, since the door of the stair-case had been left open, and that Annette was now with her to explore whither it led,—a circumstance now materially connected with her own safety. Annette accordingly, half curious and half afraid, proposed to descend the stairs; but, on approaching the door, they perceived, that it was already fastened without, and their care was then directed to the securing it on the inside also, by placing against it as much of the heavy furniture of the room, as they could lift. Emily then retired to bed, and Annette continued on a chair by the hearth, where some feeble embers remained.

FRANK BIDART

Frank Bidart's 'translation' of a poem by John of the Cross gives to the work an eroticism not previously evoked by others. An American poet, Bidart has published a number of books of poetry including The Book of the Body, Golden State *and* In the Western Night: Collected Poems, 1965–1990. *This poem is taken from the 1990 group in* In the Western Night.

Dark Night
(John of the Cross)

In a dark night, when the light
    burning was the burning of love (*fortuitous*
    night, fated, free,—)
    as I stole from my dark house, dark
    house that was silent, grave, sleeping,—

by the staircase that was secret, hidden,
    safe: disguised by darkness (*fortuitous*
    night, fated, free,—)
    by darkness and by cunning, dark
    house that was silent, grave, sleeping—;

in that sweet night, secret, seen by
    no one and seeing
    nothing, my only light or
    guide
    the burning in my burning heart,

night was the guide
    to the place where he for whom I
    waited, whom I had long ago chosen,
    waits: night
    brighter than noon, in which none can see—;

night was the guide
   sweeter than the sun raw at
   dawn, for there the burning bridegroom is
   bride
   and he who chose at last is chosen.

As he lay sleeping on my sleepless
   breast, kept from the beginning for him
   alone, lying on the gift I gave
   as the restless
   fragrant cedars moved the restless winds,—

winds from the circling parapet circling
   us as I lay there touching and lifting his hair,—
   with his sovereign hand, he
   wounded my neck—
   and my senses, when they touched that, touched
   nothing . . .

In a dark night (*there where I
   lost myself.*—) as I learned to rest
   in his smooth white breast, everything
   ceased
   and left me forgotten in the grave of forgotten
   lilies.

GILLIAN MEARS

Here are two insomniacs, mother and daughter, both with yearnings not dissimilar to the girl's sexual longing in Christina Stead's For Love Alone. *Clementine is the middle daughter of Cairo, who planted the mint lawn in the garden of their large country-town house. While Clementine has inherited her mother's sensual nature, she is too naive to understand why Cairo looks to Dr Gummer, the man she will later have an affair with, from her bedroom window that night.*

Gillian Mears won the Australian/Vogel Literary *Award with this novel in 1990. Her other books include* Fineflour *and* The Grass Sister.

The Mint Lawn

One year the Young girls all grow warts. They spread in age order and are a small white type, prone to sprouting white hairs in the middle. They seem to shoot up fast. To prevent their spread Cairo rubs homemade salve with mint into the worst areas. The mint gives the surface of the warts a greeny tinge. Sky believes hers glow green in the dark, especially the crop beginning to bump her left knee.

To see if this is true of her own warts, Clementine stays awake one evening. She walks out from the kitchen, onto the veranda and into the garden, her fingers held aloft. Nothing close by glows, only the light from her parents' window. The curtains are not drawn. She puts her fingers up to the faint light that falls down to where she stands. It is as if she has actually called out to her mother. Cairo appears naked at the window, her breasts pointing downwards to the Gummers' garden. Clementine looks over to the Gummers but all the windows are dark and when she swings her head back, her mother has disappeared.

It is so late, the stock cars in the showgrounds have all but fallen quiet. Just every few moments one of the wrecked cars will roar reluctantly into life. Under the ring lights, the cars being towed away look like strange bashed-in insects.

Clementine wants to believe it is the stock-car night keeping her mother awake, though she is beginning to sense some far greater dissatisfaction rules her mother. Clementine wonders that her sisters are asleep. The violence of the stock cars, their violent night whine and the way the cars moan if they spin right over, always keeps Clementine from sleeping.

Clementine puts her arms over her head and stretches. The lights in the showground dim and darken except for those hanging over the caravan amenities block. Clementine glances back up at her parents' room. The light is still on and again Cairo appears at the window. Her skin looks so soft and white the smallest pinch could brighten it. She is using the sharp pair of surgical scissors Dr Gummer gave her to cut her nails. Clementine lets out a sigh. She picks up a lip-shaped leaf and places it over her mouth. The leaf is too small to cover it properly. As the overnight train to Brisbane goes rattling over the river, she catches sight of the new sliver of moon. A lucky four-day moon. Of course Michael Moon, his name, his body, the way he rosins his violin bow, slides into her mind. His hair is that colour of silver the real moon reflects onto the river. One day, she imagines, we will all of us be dead. Cairo, my sisters, Michael Moon, the dogs, my Dad . . . Her mouth opens with a puff of pain. The gum leaf falls from her mouth. Tonight, she despairs absolutely that any boy will ever kiss her, or any man ever love her. She will die like Miss Gee, the old woman in the poem, untouched until death.

Clementine begins to hum her mint song. It is more a chant really, monotonous but fond, of all the mint names known to Cairo, their common names. Black peppermint. African apple, Basil mint. Queen of mint. Curly tip. Cardinal. Camel mint. Water mint. Pot of mint. Spearmint and sea mint. Horse mint. Woolly mint. Black forest and white peppermint. Egyptian. Her parents' bedroom light blinks off.

Their middle daughter continues her creep through the garden, reciting mint names like a poem. Pennyroyal. Eau de cologne. Lemon. Menthol. Japanese. She reaches the old abandoned high-chair, deep in wet, sharp-smelling weeds by the messiest edge of the garden. Morning glories bound over it. When she strokes the old tray her thumb goes through the softened corner. Clementine moves a step closer to tearfulness, thinking of the babies she won't ever have if she doesn't find a boyfriend.

Labia, labiate mentha, labiate family, lips. The inner lips of mint flowers. How they are small and purply and slightly crinkled looking. Everything reminds Clementine of everything these days. No wonder it isn't easy any more to go to sleep. She yawns, trying to summon up other scientific-sounding names. She thinks of all the sex-maniacs locked away in the maximum security prison which, strangely enough, is sited bang in the middle of the other side of town. She wonders what all those sad, bad men are doing and thinking on their narrow cell beds. Are they really spitting up their dicks the way Beth says? A small smile drifts over her face when she remembers how she used to think the prison was some kind of castle. This was because of its fortress-like walls and gates, the gilt and crest around the main entrance; the turreted watch towers. It was the only building she had ever seen with the required density and presence to assume such a word as castle. But it was too sombre ever to work as a palace in her imagination. Bluebeards and princesses lived behind those heavy walls, she used to think, peopling the Fineflour Prison with characters from the fairytale volumes she used to borrow compulsively from the town library. Now, whenever she happens to ride or be driven past the gaol, she sees only the stalking uniforms of the watchmen, the tips of their rifles turning into silhouettes on sunset.

From around town comes the loneliest sound of the semi-trailers crashing gears into the darkness as they climb into the hills or, much closer by, slow for the long corners of the river bridge. A motorbike on the descent sounds suddenly crazed and out of control. Its rider would have no eyes behind a big black helmet and on his feet would be big boots called Lethal Weapons. Clementine feels shivery with the magnitude of her sadness. She hears the bike cross the bridge and lets her body flop, the way she used to years ago, playing at being ragdolls with Alex. Last year a boy died on the bridge. He was spinning his motorbike on its back wheels. A semitrailer mashed him up. Had he kissed anybody before he died? Had he? Had he? Clementine hopes he did.

Christina Stead

Stead was never afraid to write about passion, be it
for sex or politics. Born in 1902 in Rockdale, New
South Wales, Stead spent most of her years overseas,
publishing in America and Britain while being little
read in Australia. She wrote many novels and short
stories before returning to Australia where she died
in 1983. The short extract below is from *For Love
Alone*.

I Beg, I Beg . . .

The house was haunted by legends of sleep-walking. Every
relative who came there had something to say about it, the
men to the men, the women to the women. There were sleep-
walkers who had been seen on roofs, travelling on drain-pipes,
dancing on chimney-pots. They returned safely to their beds
unless spoken to, when they lost their balance, their wits or
their lives. It seemed that a woman having a sleep-walking
son placed a tub of water at the foot of the stairs and went to
bed, easy in mind. She heard a howl and rushed out to find
her son dead of his footbath. Leo might get into some trouble;
and so one of the watchwords of the house was, 'Last to bed,
get up Leo'. Hawkins had another, simpler theory about Leo's
weakness, that it was due to a small physical irritation and
the brother or sister waking him had to see that this was
attended to.

Lance was not fond of his brother and detested this duty,
though he was the one who usually came in late; and Kitty
had to rise early, so it was Teresa who went down to him as
a rule. Leo was hard to waken; he never really waked. Though
he would get up, do what he was told, walk, drink, go outside,
he did it all in his sleep. He got up rosy and tousled, muttering
and laughing. Sometimes he would hit out. Sometimes he
snapped and when scolded would answer, but however his
sentences started off, they always ended incoherently.

Teresa tonight helped the big boy up and led him flaring and staring wildly to the kitchen, to the yard, and back into bed, where he rolled suddenly over on his side, with his eyes shut. He often snored while standing up, loud, sudden, peremptory snorts, and snored at the moment of rolling into bed. Sometimes he fell sideways across the bed and seemed unable to move further, so that she had to drag him in, tugging at his heavy muscular limbs, fighting with him for the bedclothes in which he was entangled. Many times he fell into her arms, leaned on her neck, her shoulder, stood like an apple-cheeked country drunk with his head against her cheek while he slept. The fragrant moist heat of his brown body came to her nostrils in gusts from his open nightshirt, sliding off his smooth chest; in summer he slept naked. His nakedness was nothing to her; she did not even think of him as a man. He was only her brother, her own flesh. It was pleasant, friendly, to help the adorable boy, staggering with his eyes shut and often a silly smile on his mouth; or the brown eyes peering as if wickedly in the slits of the weighted lids, his hair ragged, a glimpse of the square white teeth as he answered with his comical mad babble. She remembered the funny things he said, to ask him afterwards:

'Last night, you said: "Oh, gemme, gemme, down on the Lawny"—what did that mean?'

'I never did,' he would grin at her sideways.

'And you said: "The lights were down at four o'clock."'

He grinned and shook his head. He was proud of her, he did not know why.

She was staggering about there with Leo for fully half an hour tonight. She heard the single bell ring from the ships while she was still in the lower passage. Presently she came up to bed. The house was shut and locked now, Leo could not get out, no one could get in. It was night, lingering, drowsy, real night.

She was in her room again with the door shut and suddenly she threw herself on her knees at the side of the bed, where the nets and sheets were tumbled. Into her hands she whispered: 'Let me find a lover soon, let me get a lover soon, I must, I must, I beg, I beg.' She was willing it, not praying. She believed firmly in the power of will to alter things and force things to an end. Cheerful, she got up and jumped into bed, as if she had heard a promise. She did not sleep yet; she was too tired for her legends but she tossed convulsively. She thought: 'Oh, I'll never be able to sleep.' The girls in the Botanic Gardens last Saturday had all given their remedies for sleeplessness; one said: 'Breathe deeply.' She tried that and it woke her up. Another said: 'Take hot milk.' There wasn't enough milk for everyone to be having glasses of milk. Teresa said: 'Read an abstruse page, it's infallible.' But the other girls, one a young doctor, one a social worker, said reading kept them awake. She tossed and turned. She listened to the sea, thought of it rolling in, and herself began to roll, like a ship at sea, moving quite ignorantly as women move with their lovers. 'A storm far out at sea, coming in,' she muttered. 'Love, learning, bread—myself—all three, I will get.'

ANGELA CARTER

*The extract from this 1979 short story is narrated
from the point of view of one of Dracula's young
wives.*

The Bloody Chamber

I had drowsed away that afternoon and now I could not sleep.
I lay tossing and turning in his ancestral bed until another
daybreak discoloured the dozen mirrors that were iridescent
with the reflections of the sea. The perfume of the lilies
weighed on my senses; when I thought that, henceforth, I
would always share these sheets with a man whose skin, as
theirs did, contained that toad-like, clammy hint of moisture,
I felt a vague desolation that within me, now my female wound
had healed, there had awoken a certain queasy craving like
the cravings of pregnant women for the taste of coal or chalk
or tainted food, for the renewal of his caresses. Had he not
hinted to me, in his flesh as in his speech and looks, of the
thousand, thousand baroque intersections of flesh upon flesh?
I lay in our wide bed accompanied by a sleepless companion,
my dark newborn curiosity.

I lay in bed alone. And I longed for him. And he disgusted me.

Were there jewels enough in all his safes to recompense me
for this predicament? Did all this castle hold enough riches to
recompense me for the company of the libertine with whom I
must share it? And what, precisely, was the nature of my
desirous dread for this mysterious being who, to show his
mastery over me, had abandoned me on my wedding night?

Then I sat straight up in bed, under the sardonic masks of
the gargoyles carved above me, riven by a wild surmise. Might
he have left me, not for Wall Street but for an importunate
mistress tucked away God knows where who knew how to
pleasure him far better than a girl whose fingers had been
exercised, hitherto, only by the practice of scales and arpeg-
gios? And, slowly, soothed, I sank back on to the heaping

pillows; I acknowledged that the jealous scare I'd just given myself was not unmixed with a little tincture of relief.

At last I drifted into slumber, as daylight filled the room and chased bad dreams away. But the last thing I remembered, before I slept, was the tall jar of lilies beside the bed, how the thick glass distorted their fat stems so they looked like arms, dismembered arms, drifting drowned in greenish water.

SHAKESPEARE

William Shakespeare

Shakespeare's Insomnia

In an eclectic handbook called The Complete Insomniac, *Hilary Rubinstein examines the possibility that Shakespeare was an insomniac. He suggests that because Shakespeare frequently wrote about the condition, he could indeed have been one, but counterargues that Shakespeare also wrote a good deal about paranoia and senility without being a sufferer of either.*

However, both these disorders are public ones that the dramatist could have observed in others, whereas insomnia is a private experience which, if we follow the autobiographies of writers such as those included in this anthology, enters the writer's writing only after the experience.

Born in 1564, William Shakespeare was an English playwright and poet. He died in 1616.

Macbeth

MACBETH
    Methought I heard a voice cry 'Sleep no more,
    Macbeth does murder sleep'—the innocent sleep,
    Sleep that knits up the ravelled sleave of care,
    The death of each day's life, sore labour's bath,
    Balm of hurt minds, great nature's second course,
    chief nourisher in life's feast—

LADY MACBETH   What do you mean?

MACBETH
    Still it cried 'Sleep no more' to all the house,
    'Glamis hath murdered sleep, and therefore Cawdor
    Shall sleep no more, Macbeth shall sleep no more.'

LADY MACBETH
> Who was it that thus cried? Why, worthy thane,
> You do unbend your noble strength to think
> So brain-sickly of things. Go get some water
> And wash this filthy witness from your hand.
> Why did you bring these daggers from the place?
> They must be there. Go, carry them, and smear
> The sleepy grooms with blood

MACBETH   I'll go no more.

Sonnet 61

Is it thy will, thy image should keep open
My heavy eyelids to the weary night?
Dost thou desire my slumbers should be broken,
While shadows like to thee do mock my sight?
Is it thy spirit that thou send'st from thee
So far from home into my deeds to pry.
To find out shames and idle hours in me,
The scope and tenure of thy jealousy?
O no, thy love though much, is not so great.
It is my love that keeps mine eye awake,
Mine own true love that doth my rest defeat,
To play the watchman ever for thy sake
  For thee watch I, whilst thou dost wake elsewhere
  From me far off, with others all too near.

Henry IV Part II

How many thousand of my poorest subjects
Are at this hour asleep! O sleep, O gentle sleep,
Nature's soft nurse, how have I frighted thee,
That thou no more wilt weigh my eyelids down,
And steep my senses in forgetfulness?
Why rather, sleep, liest thou in smoky cribs,
Upon uneasy pallets stretching thee,
And hush'd with buzzing night-flies to thy slumber,

Than in the perfumed chambers of the great,
Under the canopies of costly state,
And lull'd with sound of sweetest melody?
O thou dull god, why liest thou with the vile
In loathsome beds, and leavest the kingly couch
A watch-case or a common 'larum-bell?
Wilt thou upon the high and giddy mast
Seal up the ship-boy's eyes, and rock his brains
In cradle of the rude imperious surge,
And in the visitation of the winds,
Who take the ruffian billows by the top,
Curling their monstrous heads, and hanging them
With deafening clamour in the slippery clouds,
That, with the hurly, death itself awakes?
Canst thou, O partial sleep, give thy repose
To the wet sea-boy in an hour so rude;
And in the calmest and most stillest night,
With all appliances and means to boot,
Deny it to a king? Then happy low, lie down!
Uneasy lies the head that wears a crown.

Henry V

'Tis not the balm, the sceptre and the ball,
The sword, the mace, the crown imperial,
The intertissued robe of gold and pearl,
The farced title running 'fore the king,
The throne he sits on, nor the tide of pomp
That beats upon the high shore of this world,
No, not all these, thrice gorgeous ceremony,
Not all these, laid in bed majestical,
Can sleep so soundly as the wretched slave,
Who with a body fill'd and vacant mind
Gets him to rest cramm'd with distressful bread;
Never sees horrid night, the child of hell,
But, like a lackey, from the rise to set
Sweats in the eye of Phoebus, and all night
Sleeps in Elysium.

SILENCE

RAINER MARIA RILKE

Rilke's beginnings were unlikely. He was born in Prague in 1875, the son of an army officer and a very religious mother who had wanted a girl—hence his middle name 'Maria'. The Notebooks of Malte Laurids Brigge *took seven years to write, for Rilke found it 'a heavy, a difficult book'. Even so, the writing soars. He said of his character that 'Poor Malte starts so deep in misery, and in a strict sense, reaches to eternal bliss; he is a heart that strikes a whole octave; after him all songs are possible'. The first passage below is taken from an early page. It is a truly urban rendering of insomnia, drawing together the individual's insomnia and the city's wakeful, crowded streets in one movement. The second extract addresses Malte's mother, a powerful and loving figure in the* Notebooks.

Electric Streetcars

To think that I cannot give up sleeping with the window open. Electric street-cars rage ringing through my room. Automobiles run their way over me. A door slams. Somewhere a window-pane falls clattering; I hear its big splinters laugh, its little ones snicker. Then suddenly a dull, muffled noise from the other side, within the house. Someone is climbing the stairs. Coming, coming incessantly. Is there, there for a long time, then passes by. And again the street. A girl screams: Ah tais-toi, je ne veux plus. An electric car races up excitedly, then away, away over everything. Someone calls. People are running, overtake each other. A dog barks. What a relief: a dog. Toward morning a cock even crows, and that is boundless comfort. Then I suddenly fall asleep.

O night without objects. O obtuse window outward, o carefully closed doors; arrangements from long ago, taken over, accredited, never quite understood. O stillness in the staircase, stillness from adjoining rooms, stillness high up against the ceiling. O mother: o you only one, who shut out all this stillness, long ago in childhood. Who take it upon yourself, saying: Don't be afraid, it is I. Who has the courage all in the night yourself to be this stillness for that which is afraid and perishing with fear. You strike a light, and already the noise is you. And you hold the light before you and say: it is I; don't be afraid. And you put it down, slowly, and there is no doubt: It is you; you are the light around these familiar intimate things, that are there without afterthought, good, simple, unambiguous. And when there is restlessness somewhere in the wall, or a step on the floor: you only smile, smile, smile transparent against a light background into the fearsome face that looks searchingly at you, as if you were one and in the secret with every half-sound, in concert and agreement with it. Does any power equal your power among the rulers of the earth? See, kings lie and stare, and the teller of tales cannot distract them. On the blissful breasts of their favourite mistress terror creeps over them and makes them shaky and lifeless. But you, you come and hold the monstrous thing behind you, and are in front of it altogether; not like a curtain it can throw open here or there. No, as if you had overtaken it at the call that needed you. As if you had come far ahead of anything that may yet happen, and had behind you only your hasting hither, your eternal path, the flight of your love.

FYODOR DOSTOEVSKY

The monologue, Notes from Underground, *comprise the 'notes' of a forty-year-old retired clerk. It traces a consciousness constantly aware of itself, one that is entirely alone and opposed to the world and to itself. The narrator's consciousness is sleepless, just as the narrator often suffers from insomnia. The kind of omnipotent illumination that makes up the* Notes *has also been described as 'Dostoevsky's Epilepsy'. His epileptic condition began after his conviction in 1849 for involvement in a group which discussed social and political reform. Dostoevsky was sentenced to death, and on a December morning lined up with his fellow prisoners for execution. Just as the soldiers were about to shoot, a messenger arrived with a pardon from the czar. The reprieve had actually been secured months earlier, but withheld until the last minute to demonstrate the czar's benevolence.*

In the second extract the clerk shares his bed with a young woman.

Notes from Underground *was published in 1864. When Dostoevsky died in 1881, almost forty thousand people attended his funeral.*

Somewhere Behind a Partition a Clock Wheezed . . .

I have been living this way for a long time—twenty years or so. I'm forty now. I used to have a post in the civil service, but I don't any more. I was a nasty official. I was rude and took pleasure in it. After all, I never took a bribe, so that was the least I could do to compensate myself for it. (A poor joke, but I am not going to cross it out. I wrote it thinking that it would be very clever, but now that I myself see that I only wanted to show off abominably, I purposely won't cross it out!) When petitioners looking for information happened to come to the desk where I sat, I gnashed my teeth at them, and I felt an insatiable delight when I succeeded in upsetting someone. I almost always succeeded. For the most part they were timid people—you know, petitioners. But of the swaggerers I particularly despised a certain officer. He just wouldn't submit and clanged his sabre in an obnoxious way. For a year and a half I carried on a war with him over that sabre. In the end I prevailed. He stopped clanging. But then, that was back in my youth. But do you know, gentlemen, what the main point of my nastiness was? Well, what the whole thing consisted of, what made it such a vile mess, was that every moment, even at the moment of greatest rancour, I shamefully recognised inwardly that I was not only not a nasty man but not even a disgruntled one, that I was only needlessly frightening sparrows and satisfying my whims that way. I might be frothing at the mouth, but bring me some little trinket, give me a bit of tea with sugar, and I'd probably calm right down. I might even be touched to the heart, even though afterwards I'd surely gnash my teeth at myself, and suffer from insomnia, out of shame, for several months. That's the way I am.

. . . Somewhere behind the partition a clock wheezed, as if some sort of pressure were being applied to it, as if someone were strangling it. After an unnaturally long period of wheezing came high-pitched, repulsive, and somehow unexpectedly rapid chiming—exactly as if someone had suddenly rushed forward. The clock struck two. I came to, though I had not really been sleeping, just lying there half-conscious.

It was almost completely dark in the narrow, close, low-ceilinged room, encumbered by an enormous wardrobe and littered with cardboard boxes, rags, and all kinds of dress-making junk. An almost spent candle stub burned on a table at the end of the room, occasionally flaring up just a little. In a few moments it would be completely dark.

It didn't take me long to regain consciousness; all at once everything came back to me without any effort, as if it had been lying in wait to spring on me again. Actually, even during my unconscious state there had remained in my memory something like a point that stayed awake and around which my sleepy visions gloomily revolved. But it was odd: everything that had happened to me that day now seemed, as I awoke, like something long, long past, as if I had already left all that behind long, long ago.

There was chaos in my head. Something seemed to be hovering over me, provoking, agitating, and bothering me. Anguish and bile surged up in me again and sought a release. Suddenly I saw next to me two open eyes examining me curiously and insistently. The look was coolly indifferent, morose, and completely uninvolved; it made me feel depressed.

A gloomy thought arose in my brain and spread throughout my body like a vile sensation of some kind reminiscent of the one you get when you enter a damp and musty underground. It seemed somehow unnatural that these two eyes decided to scrutinise me precisely then and not before. I also remembered that during the course of two hours I had not exchanged a single word with this being and did not deem it at all necessary; in fact, for some reason I had liked it that way. Right then I suddenly grasped clearly the incongruous idea of depravity, repulsive as a spider, that, without love, crudely and shamelessly, begins directly with that which crowns true love. We looked at one another for a long time but she didn't lower her eyes before mine and did not alter her look, so that at last, for some reason, I felt terrified.

'What is your name?' I asked abruptly, to end it all as quickly as possible.

VIKRAM SETH

As well as All You Who Sleep Tonight *from which
this poem is taken, Seth has published other volumes
of poetry, a novel in verse, and more recently the
novel,* A Suitable Boy.

   *Seth was born in Calcutta in 1952 and lives in
India.*

Adagio

> *Fate is against me (though only in Vienna)*
> Wolfgang Amadeus Mozart, *Letters*

No need for *dolce*; once more, unemphasised,
The theme's slow clarity curves above the strings.
He does not awe us yet for while we listen
There is no more than this plain tapestry.
He never like the great Beethoven thunders,
'My stomach's aching and my heart is breaking
And you will hear me', yet to hear him is
To suffer all heartbreak, to assume all sorrow
And to survive. Where does his music cry,
'I could not sleep all night for pain. Dear friend,
Picture my situation—ill and full
Of grief and care. I am in want—could you
Assist me with a trifle? O God, here I am
With fresh entreaties instead of with thanks.'
                              . . . 'Death
When we think of it is the true goal of our life.'
'I could not write for very grief; black thoughts
(Which I must forcibly banish) . . .'
                              We listen to
The adagio of the Clarinet Quintet; if
We see the abyss, as who can not, who can
Resist the enveloping tranquillity
Drawn from the heart of 1789

In the clear supple lilt of one who like
The nightingale, his breast against the thorn,
Sang jubilantly in sorrow, who defied
The immobility of childhood fame
To work this web of tenderness between
The freedom of a child and a man's power
Two years before an endless requiem.

OVID

*Born Publius Ovidius Naso in 43 BC, Ovid was pop-
ular in Rome for his poems about love. He also wrote
serious works, and a definitive collection of ancient
mythology known variously as the* Metamorphoses
and the Stories of Changing Forms, *from which the
story of Argus is drawn.*

*Jove falls in love with Io, and fearing his wife Juno's
anger, hides Io by changing the young woman into a
pretty cow. However, Juno is suspicious and asks Jove
to give her the heifer as a gift. Of course, Jove can't
refuse—to do so would be to increase his wife's suspicions. Juno then gives the young cow Io to Argus: 'She
turned her over to the keeping of Argus Who had a
hundred eyes; two at a time, No more than two, would
ever close in slumber, The rest kept watch. No matter
how he stood, Which way he turned, he always looked
at Io, Always had Io in sight.' Unhappy Io finds a way
to ask her father for help.*

Argus

She would ask for help, and tell her name and sorrow,
But as it was, all she could do was furrow
The dust was the one forefoot, and make an I,
And then an O beside it, spelling her name,
Telling the story of her changed condition.
Her father knew her, cried, 'Alas for me!'
Clung to her horns and snowy neck, poor heifer,
Crying, 'Alas for me! I have sought you, daughter,
All over the world, and now that I have found you,
I have found a greater grief. You do not answer,
And what you think is sighing comes out mooing!
And all the while I, in my ignorance counted
On marriage for you, wanting, first a son,
Then, later, grandsons; now your mare must be
Selected from some herd, your son a bullock.
Not even death can end my heavy sorrow.

It hurts to be a god; the door of death,
Shut in my face, prolongs my grief forever.'
And both of them were weeping, but their guardian,
Argus the star-eyed, drove her from her father
To different pasture-land, and sat there, watching,
Perched on a mountain-top above the valley.
Jove could not bear her sorrows any longer;
He called his son, born of the shining Pleiad,
Told him *Kill Argus!* And Mercury came flying
On winged sandals, wearing the magic helmet,
Bearing the sleep-producing wand and lighted
On earth, and put aside the wings and helmet
Keeping the wand. With this he plays the shepherd
Across the pathless countryside, a driver
Of goats, collected somewhere, and he goes
Playing a little tune on a pipe of reeds,
And this new sound is wonderful to Argus.
'Whoever you are, come here and sit beside me,'
He says, 'This rock is in the shade; the grass
Is nowhere any better.' And Mercury joins him,
Whiling the time away with conversation
And soothing little melodies, and Argus
Has a hard fight with drowsiness; his eyes,
Some of them, close, but some of them stay open.
To keep himself awake by listening,
He asks about the pipe of reeds, how was it
This new invention came about?
                                        The god
Began the story: 'On the mountain slopes
Of cool Arcadia, a woodland nymph
Once lived, with many suitors . . .

                              . . . And Mercury
Might have told more, but all the eyes of Argus,
He saw, had closed, and he made the slumber deeper
With movements of the wand, and then he struck
The nodding head just where it joins the shoulder,
Severed it with the curving blade, and sent it
Bloody and rolling over the rocks. So Argus
Lay low, and all the light in all those eyes
Went out forever, a hundred eyes, one darkness.

And Juno took the eyes and fastened them
On the feathers of a bird of hers, the peacock,
So that the peacock's tail is spread with jewels . . .

Emily Brontë

Wuthering Heights *opens and closes with sleepless nights, the first when Mrs Dean begins the tale of Heathcliff's story to the new tenant Mr Lockwood, the last when after four sleepless nights, Heathcliff dies, wide awake, and is found by her. Moonlit and moonless nights texture the book; indeed some of the most important events happen in the sleeping hours.*

Born in 1818, Emily Brontë published Wuthering Heights *in 1847. She died the following year.*

Wuthering Heights—the last chapter

He solicited the society of no one more. At dusk, he went into his chamber. Through the whole night, and far into the morning, we heard him groaning, and murmuring to himself. Hareton was anxious to enter, but I bid him fetch Mr Kenneth, and he should go in and see him.

When he came, and I requested admittance and tried to open the door, I found it locked; and Heathcliff bid us be damned. He was better, and would be left alone; so the doctor went away.

The following evening was very wet; indeed it poured down, till day-dawn; and, as I took my morning walk round the house, I observed the master's window swinging open, and the rain driving straight in.

He cannot be in bed, I thought; those showers would drench him through! He must either be up, or out. But I'll make no more ado. I'll go boldly and look!

Having succeeded in obtaining entrance with another key, I ran to unclose the panels, for the chamber was vacant; quickly pushing them aside, I peeped in. Mr Heathcliff was there—laid on his back. His eyes met mine so keen and fierce, I started; and then he seemed to smile.

I could not think him dead, but his face and throat were washed with rain; the bedclothes dripped, and he was perfectly still. The lattice, flapping to and fro, had grazed one hand that rested on the sill; no blood trickled from the broken skin, and when I put my fingers to it, I could doubt no more—he was dead and stark!

I hasped the window; I combed his black long hair from his forehead; I tried to close his eyes—to extinguish, if possible, that frightful, life-like gaze of exultation, before any one else beheld it. They would not shut; they seemed to sneer at my attempts, and his parted lips and sharp, white teeth sneered too!

. . . We buried him, to the scandal of the whole neighbourhood, as he had wished. Earnshaw, and I, the sexton and six men to carry the coffin, comprehended the whole attendance.

The six men departed when they had let it down into the grave: we stayed to see it covered. Hareton, with a streaming face, dug green sods, and laid them over the brown mould himself. At present it is as smooth and verdant as its companion mounds—and I hope its tenant sleeps as soundly. But the country folks, if you asked them, would swear on their Bible that he *walks*. There are those who speak to having met him near the church, and on the moor, and even within this house. Idle tales, you'll say, and so say I. Yet that old man by the kitchen fire affirms he has seen two on 'em looking out of his chamber window, on every rainy night, since his death . . .

Virgilio Piñera

*This tale is as grim and succinct as can be, yet Piñera
tackles both the cure and the metaphysics of insomnia. Insomnia can bring on real despair when death
and sleep are interchangeable while insomnia reigns.*

*Piñera is a Cuban writer, born in 1912, though he
lived for some years in Buenos Aires where he knew
Jorge Luis Borges.*

Insomnia

The man goes to bed early but he cannot fall asleep. He turns
and tosses. He twists the sheets. He lights a cigarette. He
reads a bit. He puts out the light again. But he cannot sleep.
At three in the morning he gets up. He calls on his friend next
door and confides in him that he cannot sleep. He asks for
advice. The friend suggests he take a walk and maybe he will
tire himself out—then he should drink a cup of linden-tea and
turn out the light. He does all these things but he does not
manage to fall asleep. Again he gets up. This time he goes to
see the doctor. As usual the doctor talks a good deal but in
the end the man still cannot manage to sleep. At six in the
morning he loads a revolver and blows out his brains. The
man is dead but still he is unable to sleep. Insomnia is a very
persistent thing.